TEXTILE
CONSERVATION

Detail of rep curtain with embroidery in silk, silver and gold. From Queen Christina's trophy coach, for the coronation in 1650 (Reproduced by kind permission of Kungl. Livrustkammaren, Stockholm)

TEXTILE CONSERVATION

EDITED BY JENTINA E. LEENE, D.Sc.

Senior Reader, Laboratory for Textile Technology,
Delft University of Technology

The International Institute
for Conservation of
Historic and Artistic Works

SMITHSONIAN INSTITUTION
WASHINGTON, D.C.

Published in the United States by the
Smithsonian Institution Press

Distributed in the United States and Canada
by George Braziller, Inc., One Park Avenue,
New York, New York

First published in 1972 by
the Butterworth Group

Library of Congress Catalog Card Number 74-179287

Filmset by Photoprint Plates Ltd, Rayleigh, Essex

Printed in England by Fletcher & Son Ltd, Norwich

Preface

The editing of this book has taken much time and energy, but with the excellent cooperation of all the contributors it has also been a very satisfying task.

I should like to express my gratitude to the Council of the International Institute for Conservation of Historic and Artistic Works for the help and advice given to me, and in particular to Mr G. Thomson, General Editor of Technical Publications.

A generous grant by Courtaulds Limited has made it possible to illustrate the book with a large number of coloured plates.

Further, I am greatly indebted to Dr S. Müller-Christensen, of the Bavarian National Museum, Munich, for her help and criticism on the first outline of the book. The cooperation of the directors and staff of the Colonial Williamsburg Museum, Williamsburg, Virginia, and the Henry Francis Dupont Winterthur Museum, Winterthur, Delaware, who supplied much information on the methods of storage and display of their textile collections, has also been much appreciated.

Finally, I should like to thank the Head of the Laboratory for Textile Technology at the Delft University of Technology, Delft, The Netherlands, Prof. Dipl. Ing. J. Beyer, for providing the facilities which were needed in the preparation of this work.

1972   Jentina E. Leene

Contents

1
Introduction

JENTINA E. LEENE, D.Sc.
Senior Reader, Laboratory for Textile Technology, Delft University of Technology

The International Institute for Conservation of Artistic and Historic Works (I.I.C.) held a conference on Textile Conservation in 1964 at Delft, Netherlands.

From the attendance, it appeared that many curators and restorers were interested in this subject. Several topics of considerable importance, however, had not been discussed. The Council of the I.I.C., therefore, decided to publish a book on textile conservation, in which the different classes of objects in the field of textile conservation and restoration could be treated more fully. This volume is written not only for the restorers of textiles, but also for curators, who, because of their responsibility for the collections under their care, have to choose the methods of conservation and restoration. Because of this double purpose, a fundamental scientific discussion of the subjects had to be avoided, and it was imperative to write in a language which would be understood by the two categories of readers. Scientists who work in museum laboratories on problems connected with textiles and who are not acquainted with the typical characteristics of these materials, will also find this book useful.

Having surveyed current opinions regarding the preservation of textiles, it appears that, on the whole, the conservative attitude is still dominant over the so-called progressive attitude. The conservative approach advocates the use of natural materials for sewing yarns and supporting fabrics (silk, cotton and linen) and natural methods of bleaching (sunlight, moonlight, grass-bleach), whereas the progressive approach is not opposed to the application of yarns and fabrics consisting of man-made fibres (rayons, polyamides, such as Nylon 66 and Nylon 6, polyesters, such as Dacron and Terylene, and polyacrylonitriles, such as Dralon and Orlon) or synthetic adhesives, such as polyvinyl alcohol, polyvinyl acetate and its co-polymers, and poly-methacrylates.

Whichever approach is favoured, it is evident that in the preservation of culturally important textiles one has to avoid those methods which affect the appearance and the touch of the objects unfavourably, if there exists a

1

better alternative. Sometimes the best method will be to do nothing, especially in those cases where the fabrics are greatly weakened, and their aesthetic value is much greater than their historic value. In a few cases even the removal of dust by soft brushing or by careful rinsing in water will be sufficient. More often a mild washing in a solution of a detergent will give the desired result. However, when the objects are very damaged (and/or weakened), one of the reinforcing methods may be applied. Here the right choice is very difficult, because, in principle, every method has its advantages and disadvantages.

The method which has been accepted by prominent art historians is the sewing of the object on or between transparent silk fabrics. The aesthetic effect may be improved by using fabrics dyed in a matching colour. When this method is used, the appearance as well as the touch are more or less adversely affected, but the textile character of the object has been preserved (*see* Figures 10.6 and 10.7). In cases where this sewing technique would not be of any help or, for other reasons, would be inapplicable, and the curator still wants to preserve the object, methods of reinforcement by impregnation with resins and/or by adhesion to thin, transparent supporting fabrics may be tried. Here, it is not only the appearance and the touch which are affected, but, depending on the chosen chemicals and on their concentrations, the flexibility may also be altered. The change in the latter property may lie between nearly imperceptible and totally unacceptable. The curator will also have to consider the reversibility of the alternative treatments, assessing possible accelerating effects of the added fabrics and chemicals on the deterioration of the object, against preserving properties of some of the recommended chemicals. It is clear that these decisions must not be made by intuition, but must be accounted for by scientific arguments.

One point remains to be mentioned. Even when the best method for the given circumstances has been determined, by considering material, climate, capability of the restorer, and then applied, the restored object is still liable to deterioration and all the care, energy and money spent on it will have been wasted if it is not going to be kept in the right preserving environment. Serious attention has to be given, therefore, to the architecture and the equipment of the exhibition and store rooms.

Every decision requires a certain basic knowledge of the properties of the textiles and their behaviour under the conditions present in museums and in exhibition halls. Moreover, every type of textile collection has specific problems in addition to the general ones. The book has been divided into two parts based on these considerations.

In the first part (Chapters 2–9) information is given on the characteristics of textiles and dyes, the principles of cleaning and bleaching, the prevention of pests, the influence of museum climate on textiles and dyes, the architecture and equipment of store rooms, as well as exhibition rooms, and the requirements for conservation rooms. In the second part (Chapters 10–23) the practice of conservation and restoration, as it is exercised by curators and restorers· will be elucidated, with reference to different categories of textiles.

In textile collections there are the flat textiles, e.g. tapestries, carpets, flags and damasks (Chapters 11–14). This category of two-dimensional objects has several common problems such as storage and display. However, when the structures are more complicated, as in costumes (dresses and uniforms) the treatments used for flat structures, which for the greater part are the single elements of the costumes, are not applicable without further consideration. Moreover, here there is a much greater difference between the treatments for the specimens which will only be stored and those which have to be displayed. These three-dimensional objects will be discussed in Chapters 15 and 16.

Chapters 17–19 deal with the restoration of lace, beadwork and gloves. These objects are often made of textile materials and sometimes partly or totally made of other materials, such as metal, glass or leather.

A chapter on the restoration of ethnographical textiles (Chapter 20) has been added to stress a few problems which are presented when one has to restore objects of non-western origin, and this is followed by a chapter on the restoration of featherwork on ethnographical objects (Chapter 21), which contains a few remarks relevant to other objects made or partly made with feathers. A chapter on the restoration of archaeological textiles (Chapter 22) is also included, because it was thought that quite different considerations from those already mentioned are followed when working with some of these textiles, especially when they have little aesthetic value but nevertheless are very important witnesses of early cultures.

Finally, in Chapter 23, the conservation of leather is extensively discussed. Although leather is not a textile, it is often an integral part of costumes and uniforms (coats, shoes or bags) and of the surroundings when they are on exhibition.

2
Textiles

JENTINA E. LEENE, D.Sc.
Senior Reader, Laboratory for Textile Technology, Delft University of Technology

In this chapter textiles will be discussed briefly from the point of view of a curator of textiles. A scheme of analysis of textiles is given, and only those items which are considered basic to this subject are dealt with further. For the identification of fibres it is necessary to consult references[1-4]. Only those fibres which are most common in ancient textiles, and in the supporting fabrics used in cleaning and conservation, are mentioned. Finally, the drape and handle of fabrics are discussed because their physical properties are extremely important in the evaluation of conservation and restoration treatments.

2.1 DEFINITION

The word 'textile' has been derived from the Latin, *textere*, which means to weave. It is obvious, therefore, that textiles are understood to be those objects which have been fabricated by some kind of weaving, or have been made of woven fabrics. The term, however, is not limited to woven fabrics. It also applies to those materials which are products of other kinds of inter-lacing of yarns (or of comparable structures), such as braiding, looping, knitting, lace making and netting, and to such materials as felts and non-wovens, in which the fibres have gained coherence, not by spinning, but by some kind of mechanical treatment and/or chemical process. Moreover, the term 'textile' is used for the fibres themselves, and for yarns, twines, cords and ropes which are products of spinning, twining and the rope-making processes.

If the characteristics given by the manufacturing process alone were considered in defining a textile, all kinds of basketry and matting would have to be included, but the decision depends to a large extent on the presence of textile properties, such as handling, drape and suppleness. From this point of view the products of basketry should be excluded. It is still very difficult at times to decide if an object is to be classified as a textile and be included in textile collections. Perhaps, in this instance, the end use, e.g. as clothing, should give the answer.

In general, pelts and hides are not considered to be textiles, unless manufactured into coats or dresses, although they are fibrous structures and are flexible. Plastics sheets are not fibrous structures, but when they possess such textile characteristics as suppleness and drape, they can be used for raincoats, and therefore, be included in textile collections.

From the foregoing it should be clear that it is impossible to draw a strict dividing line between textiles on the one hand, and leather goods, plastics, paper, basketry and matting on the other.

2.2 ANALYSIS

Before starting a restoration or a conservation, an analysis of the object is recommended. In Section 2.2.1, the most important items of such an analysis are tabulated. It is outside the scope of this book to discuss all the different techniques of interlacing. In [31, 32] definitions are given for those techniques, which are applied in textiles manufactured by the textile industry. In [33, 34] classifications and descriptions of primary textile techniques are discussed; they are of special interest to the study of the evolution of textile techniques.

When a restorer has at least a basic knowledge of spinning, weaving and other textile techniques, and a more detailed knowledge of different embroidery techniques, the technical analysis of textiles will not be very difficult, even though it is very time consuming. In general, however, it will be impossible for him to analyse all items. In many cases, with sufficient experience, the restorer does without analytical information and proceeds directly to the restoration or conservation work. There are many cases, however, when it is absolutely necessary to ask for help from laboratories, which have experience in the field of chemical, micro-chemical, physical and microscopical analysis of fibres, dyestuffs, blood, dirt, glues, etc. Moreover, without reports on these details, much information, which would not only be necessary for the restoration work, but also for our knowledge of the ancient textiles and their ageing processes, would be lost.

2.2.1 SCHEME FOR ANALYSIS OF TEXTILES

1. *Classification of the techniques of interlacing*

   (*a*) Weaving
   (*b*) Braiding
   (*c*) Knitting
   (*d*) Knotting
   (*e*) Lace making
   (*f*) Embroidery
   (*g*) Other techniques

2. *Classification of finishing treatments*

  (*a*) Dyeing
  (*b*) Printing
  (*c*) Waxing
  (*d*) Fulling
  (*e*) Other treatments

3. *Analysis of the fabrics*

  (*a*) Kind of weave (binding system):
       (i) Design,
       (ii) Weaving unit: tabby, twill, satin, etc.
  (*b*) Thread count
  (*c*) Characteristics of the yarns:
       (i) Structure: single, folded, twined,
       (ii) Twist,
       (iii) Twist direction,
       (iv) Fineness (number)
  (*d*) Identification of fibres:
       (i) Warp,
       (ii) Weft,
  (*e*) Other particulars:
       Condition: mechanical damage, chemical and/or biological damage.
(Section 3 covers woven fabrics only; for the other classes of fabrics the items
3(*a*) and 3(*b*) have to be adapted.)

2.3   WEAVING[5]

In the simplest form of weaving, two sets of yarns (the warp and the weft),
are interlaced in such a way that the elements pass each other at right angles
with one set of elements parallel to the fabric axis. It is, however, possible
to weave with more than one warp and/or weft.

  The warp consists of parallel threads (sheet of warp threads) which can
be raised or lowered by means of shafts. In primitive weaving, as well as in
tapestry weaving, this can also be done with the fingers with or without the
help of a small lath. For the most simple weave, the sheet of warp threads is
divided into odd and even ends, which can be lifted alternately by means of
two shafts (Figure 2.1). When the odd ends, drawn through the eyes of the
needles of shaft 1 are raised, the even ends in shaft 2 may stay in the horizontal
position, or be pulled down. The shed, which is formed by this division in the
sheet, makes it possible for the weft to pass through, and a pick (weft thread) is
laid. When the two parts of the warp change their position, the next pick can
be laid.

  To keep the picks even and the textile compact they have to be beaten-up
and for this purpose one can use a sword (a flat bladelike stick used with
simple looms), a comb (as in tapestry-weaving) or a reed. The last also
keeps the warp ends evenly spaced and aligned.

  Because the weft always returns at the border of the sheet of warp threads,
a selvedge is formed here. This selvedge runs parallel to the warp. It can

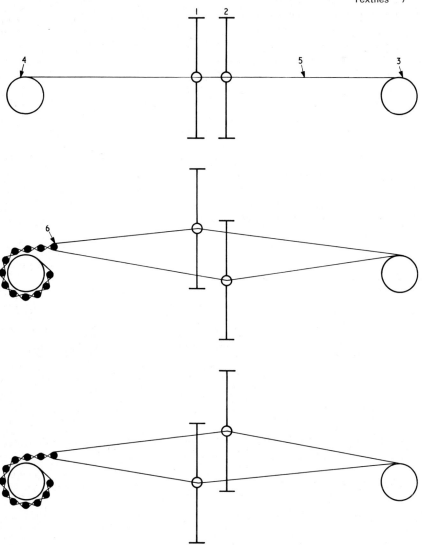

Figure 2.1. Weaving by means of two shafts: 1,2: Shafts; 3: Warp beam; 4: Cloth beam; 5: Sheet of warp threads; 6: Pick

sometimes be distinguished by warp ends differing from those in the body of the textile, and/or by another binding.

The ends and picks are bound at the points where they change their mutual position, and this system is called a binding system. It is determined by its weave unit, i.e. the smallest cycle of interlacement of the warp and weft that is constantly repeated in the weave (Figure 2.2).

When the repetition of the weave unit is side by side without variation, it is called a *straight repeat*. If the repetition is by inverting it about an axis parallel with the weft, it is an *inverse repeat*, and when about an axis parallel to the warp, a *reverse repeat*.

The design can be drawn on design paper with the spaces between the vertical lines representing the warp threads, and between the horizontal lines the weft threads. (It is also possible to draw the design more realistically, as is sometimes done in archaeological publications.) Another convention used is that the warp is indicated by black bars, and the weft by white. This means that where there is a black square, the warp passes over the weft, and vice versa. When more than one warp and/or weft is present the different warps (wefts) may be indicated by different colours.

The main binding systems are *tabby weave, twill weave* and *satin weave*. All other kinds are derived from these three.

Tabby weave is a binding system based on a unit of two ends and two picks, in which each end passes over and under one pick, the points of binding being set over one end on successive picks (see Figure 2.2). The arrows indicate the weave unit.

Twill weave is a binding system based on a unit of three or more ends and three or more picks, in which each end passes over two or more adjacent picks and under the next one or more. The points of binding are set over by one end, always in the same direction, on successive picks, forming diagonal lines (Figures 2.3 and 2.4). The repeat of a twill may be expressed as a

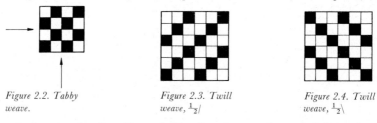

Figure 2.2. Tabby weave.   Figure 2.3. Twill weave, $\frac{1}{2}/$ Figure 2.4. Twill weave, $\frac{1}{2}\backslash$

numerical ratio, the first figure indicating the number of picks over which an end passes, and the second the number of picks under which it passes. Thus $\frac{1}{2}$ (or 1/2) twill indicates a binding system in which, on the right face the ends pass over one pick and under the next two picks. The diagonal bar (/ or \) between the figures is sometimes used to indicate the direction of the twill diagonal. It is also possible to place an extra diagonal bar after the formula to indicate the direction of the twill diagonal, e.g. $\frac{1}{2}/$ or $\frac{1}{2}\backslash$.

Figure 2.5. Chevron twill in the direction of the weft

There are different kinds of twill. Zig-zag twill is a twill in which the direction of the diagonal lines is reversed over groups of ends, or groups of picks. According to the direction of their axis there can be distinguished a chevron in the direction of the warp or in the direction of the weft (Figures 2.5 and 2.6). Another type is the herringbone twill, in which the floats oppose each other where the diagonal lines reverse (Figure 2.7). From the zig-zag and herringbone twills the diamond twill is derived. Here the direction of the diagonals formed by the points of binding is reversed over the group of ends, also over groups of picks (Figure 2.8).

Satin weave is based on a unit of five or more ends, and a number of picks equal to, or a multiple of, the number of ends. Each end either passes over four or more adjacent picks and under the next one, or passes under four

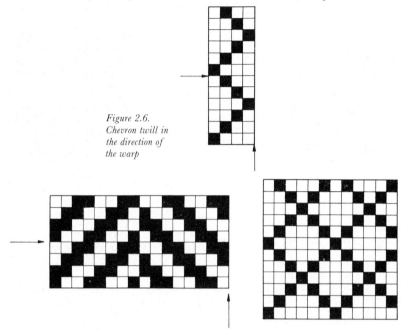

Figure 2.6.
Chevron twill in
the direction of
the warp

Figure 2.7. Herringbone twill

Figure 2.8. Diamond twill

or more adjacent picks and over the next one. The points of binding are set over two or more ends on successive picks, i.e. the step* (move, count) is two or more.[6] According to the regular or irregular spacing of the points of binding the satins are separated into regular and irregular satins.

Twills and satins can be warp-faced or weft-faced (Figures 2.9 and 2.10). In the first case the warp predominates on the right side of the fabric, and in the second case the weft. This can be more accentuated by a larger thread count of the ends or the picks per unit of length.

The pattern of a fabric is determined by repeating design units (straight, inverse or reverse). When the weave unit of one of the types of weave mentioned above is the only repeating unit of the fabric, then the weave unit is the same as the design unit, but when the fabric has a more complicated pattern, e.g. damasks, the design unit will be composed of different weave units. In a design unit each weave unit may repeat itself several times.

The number of warp threads and picks per unit of measure, called the *thread count*, is one of the factors which determine the compactness of a fabric. The other factors are the fineness of the yarns and the weave. When a fabric is tightly woven it is necessary to be extra careful when it is put in

*The nomenclature is rather confusing on this point. Here is chosen the term used by Watson.[6] It corresponds with the French *décochement* and the German *Fortschreitungszahl*.

water for cleaning, for when the fibres swell, there will be no room left for the increase in diameter, and the tensions in the fabric will increase considerably. The wet strength of yarns is more often than not much lower than the dry strength, and hence there is a risk that the fibres will break when wet.

Yarns are continuous strands of textile fibres (including filaments and other comparable materials) which are characterised by twist, direction of twist,

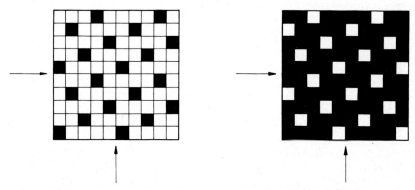

Figure 2.9. Satin weave, $\frac{1}{4}$, step 2, weft faced

Figure 2.10. Satin weave, $\frac{4}{1}$, step 2, warp faced

and fineness. To get a continuous strand of fibres, which is suitable for weaving (including knitting, braiding, etc.) it must be given a *twist*. (This does not apply to filaments, and similar strands.) Twist is the number of turns per unit of length. The product of twisting is called yarn. To make a thicker, stronger yarn, two or more yarns can be twisted together (twined yarn) or folded.

The number of turns per unit length does not give sufficient information on the tightness of the twisting, when not correlated with the diameter of the yarn. By twisting, the fibres make a helix angle with the yarn axis, which is dependent on the position of the fibre in the yarn. This angle in the outer layer is different from the angles in the inner layers. When measuring the helix angle (α) of the surface elements, and the yarn diameter (d) the turns per unit length (T) can approximately be calculated by the formulae:

$$T \text{ per meter} = \frac{1000 \, tg\alpha}{\pi d} \quad \text{or} \quad T \text{ per inch} = \frac{25 \cdot 4 \, tg\alpha}{\pi d}$$

where πd is the circumference of the cross-section of the yarn, at the point of measurement (Figure 2.11). Measuring at different points on a yarn,

Figure 2.11. Diagram of the position of a fibre in the outer layer of a yarn. h = height of one winding, α = helix angle, d = diameter of yarn, πd = circumference of the cross-section of the yarn

and on different yarns of the same category (warp ends or picks) an average diameter (mm) and an average α can be calculated.

From the formula it can be seen that when T is constant, and d varies, α

will also vary. When *d* increases, α also increases, and the twist spiral is less steep. By the same argument, it can be seen that when α is constant and *d* varies, the yarns with a small *d* need more turns per unit length than those with a larger *d*. In archaeological literature, it is often mentioned that yarns are 'tightly spun', without any indication of yarn diameter or twist. In many cases the *thread count* of the fabrics is given, but this gives no information on the yarn diameter.

Unfortunately, it is not easy to determine the diameter and helix angle of a given yarn, even when long lengths of yarn, as well as the right apparatus (goniometers, microscopes) are available. Moreover, from many measurements on yarns with known twist, it appears that the formula, which is valid for an ideal yarn, does not produce the right number, but only indicates the order of magnitude (*g*). This, however, is more satisfactory than such terms as 'very tight', 'tight', or 'loose'. The results of the measurements are further unfavourably influenced when the yarns are damaged, so that the surface elements are lacking.

The *direction of the twist* can be left-hand or right-hand. To avoid any misunderstanding, nowadays, these two directions are indicated by the capital letters S (= left-hand) and Z (= right-hand) (Figure 2.12). The

Figure 2.12. S- and Z-twist

appearance of a fabric is influenced by the correct use of these two directions in combination with the binding systems, and the predominance of weft or warp on the face. The directions may be the same for weft and warp, or different. A striped 'shadow' effect can be obtained in twills by alternating groups of warp threads with S- or Z-direction, because the light reflectance is different for the two groups.

The diameter of a yarn, as a measure of its fineness, can be expressed as a unit of length (mm, μ) but, because of the difficulty of measuring it exactly and because of a sometimes large variation in diameter within the yarn (thinner and thicker parts may be irregularly distributed over the length of the yarn), the *fineness of the yarn* is mostly indicated by the number which expresses either:

1. mass per unit length, or
2. length per unit mass.

The first system is called the direct numbering system, which means that the higher the number, the larger the diameter. Examples are:

Denier: the number of deniers (1 denier = 0·05 g) per 450 m or the number of grams per 9000 m (symbol Td).

This system originated in the French silk industry for net silk. Later it was applied to man-made filament yarns, filaments and staple fibres.

Tex: the number of grams per 1000 m (symbol Tt).

This system is now recommended for all kinds of yarns, filaments and fibres.

The second system is an indirect numbering system, which means that the higher the number, the smaller the diameter of the yarn. Examples are:

Cotton count: the number of 840 yd lengths per pound (lb)
Worsted count: the number of 560 yd lengths per pound (lb)
Metric count: the number of metres (or km) per gram (or kg).

There are many other direct and indirect numbering systems, often used only very locally, so when meeting yarn counts in historic descriptions (specifications, diaries, etc.), it is necessary to be aware that the numbering system can be quite different from the systems mentioned here.

2.4 FIBRES

In general, the basic elements of textiles are those fibres which can be spun into a yarn, or made into a fabric by some kind of interlacing. They are called *textile fibres* because by these characteristics (spinnability, weavability) they are distinct from paper fibres, as well as from brush and mat fibres. According to their origin they can be divided into natural and man-made fibres.

For a comprehensive survey of the various fibres see reference 7, which could be of special interest to cultural anthropologists because many less usual kinds, which may be present in ethnographical textiles, are mentioned.

Until the beginning of this century only natural fibres were used for textiles, although at the end of the nineteenth century large-scale experiments were being made on the production of synthetic fibres (at that time always based on natural polymers). In only a very few cases were these fibres used in clothing, so one can be sure that if any of these clothes have survived, they will have been labelled with the name of the product. The largest part of the textiles in museum collections, therefore, is made of natural fibres, but in those museums where recent textiles are also collected, the man-made fibres will enter in increasing measure.

The behaviour of fibres during cleaning in water, which is an important conservation treatment, depends on their chemical structure, their physical properties (e.g. swelling), their wet tensile strength and their position in the yarn. For the explanation of this behaviour, a few fibres which may be considered as good representatives, will be discussed.

2.4.1 COTTON[8]

The cotton fibre grows in large numbers on the seeds of the cotton plant (*Gossypium* sp.), which is cultivated in different species and varieties.

The fibres are single, long, narrow cells, about 1000–3000 or more times as long as wide. At the moment when the fruit (boll) opens, these cells are cylindrical with a high water content. After opening they lose water and collapse. Their shape is then flat and ribbon-like, and along their length, spiral twists (convolutions) originate in varying numbers, alternately in the S- and Z-directions (*see* Plate 2.1). The number of convolutions is dependent on the thickness of the cell wall.

These convolutions are so typical for cotton fibres that, in general, cotton can easily be identified by their presence. These characteristics still apply in cotton fibres degraded by ageing, as can be seen in Plate 2.2. The cell walls have become less homogeneous, however, a property which is very apparent when the cells are viewed in polarised light between crossed Nicol prisms.

The cylindrical shape cannot be restored by immersion in water. It is true that the fibres swell but not to such an extent that they get back to the cylindrical shape. In a concentrated solution of NaOH, however, they do, and after rinsing in water and drying this cylindrical shape appears to be stable. When this treatment *(mercerisation)* has been applied on yarn (or fabric) under tension, it gets a more or less silky gloss and a smooth touch. Seen under the microscope these cylindrical mercerised fibres still have traces of the convolutions left, where a complete swelling has been hampered by the twist of the yarn, and/or the crossing of yarns in the fabric.

The length and the width of the fibres are very important. Fine yarns can only be spun from long and fine fibres; the short and coarse fibres are used for the spinning of coarser yarns. Cotton fibres from different species and varieties differ in average length, diameter, number of convolutions and shape of the cross section.

The many kinds of cotton which are commercially important are generally divided into four main types. In Table 2.1 the ranges of the dimensions of length and width in these types have been compiled.[1] It appears that the longer cottons (Sea Island, Egyptian, long staple American) are also the finer, and the shorter (Indian) the coarser. It is also evident that the ranges of the different types partly overlap one another. The finest Indian cottons for example, have about the same dimensions as the coarsest Egyptian.

Table 2.1 RANGES OF DIMENSIONS OF COTTON FIBRES[1]

Type	Length (mm)		Diameter ($\mu = 0.001$ mm)
	Mean	Maximum	Mean
Indian	12–20	20–36	14·5–22
American	16–30	24–48	13·5–17
Egyptian	20–32	36–52	12·0–14·5
Sea Island	28–36	50–64	11·5–13·0

The variability of these dimensions is not only large within the types, but also within each variety and species belonging to them. To identify fibres by dimension, therefore, large samples drawn by an accurate sampling method and statistically analysed are necessary. For this reason the determination of the *origin* of ancient cotton fibres, even when standard samples from older cottons were present, would be extremely difficult, if not impossible.

The breaking strength of cotton fibres (yarn, fabric) depends on the relative humidity of the surroundings. When the relative humidity increases, this strength also increases. When wet, the strength of yarns and fabrics is about 10–30% higher than when kept in ambient air with a relative humidity of 65%. This is true for undegraded cottons and linens, but those which have undergone the damaging influence of chemicals, light or heat, have lost this property, and their wet strength will be lower than the dry strength. This means that they have to be handled very carefully when wet (Table 2.2).[9]

Table 2.2 WET AND DRY BREAKING STRENGTHS OF RAW AND DEGRADED COTTONS

Cotton yarn	Breaking strength (g)		Elongation at break (%)	
	dry	*wet*	*dry*	*wet*
Raw	216	324	7·1	11·3
Degraded by light	122	79	2·73	*Ca* 4

2.4.2   FLAX [2.10]

The flax fibre originates from the stem of the flax plant *(Linum usitatissimum L.)*, which is cultivated in several subspecies and varieties.[11]

The fibre, which is spun, is strictly speaking a compound fibre. It consists of a bundle of cells, transverse as well as longitudinal, of which each one has fibre properties. These cells (ultimates) have a round to polygonal cross section, and the ends are pointed. The thickness of the cell wall and the dimensions of the lumen vary according to the place of the cell in the stem. In the middle part of the stem the cell walls are thicker, and the lumens narrower than in the top or near the base. Length and diameter vary, depending on the cell location in the stem. The range of means of the length of ultimates is 27·4–36.1 mm, and of the diameter 17·8–21.6 μ.[1]

Under the microscope it can be seen that the flax cell shows transverse, faintly marked dislocations or nodes, often in the form of an X (Plate 2.3). They can be made more visible by staining the fibres with zinc chloriodide or another appropriate stain, or by use of polarised light (Plate 2.4). In ancient flax fibres, these dislocations can also be observed (Plate 2.5). In these fibres, which are often no longer complete, fibrillation—falling apart in smaller fibrous parts of the ultimates—may be present.

The question of whether the dislocations are caused by mechanical treatments, such as scutching etc., or have originated during the growth, has been discussed extensively. It is very probable that the latter is the case.[12] The number of dislocations, therefore, does not indicate whether the mechanical preparation has been done with the utmost care or very roughly. These dislocations are also characteristic of other bast fibres (hemp, jute, etc.). They can, therefore, only be used for distinguishing bast fibres from cotton.

The dimensions of the compound fibre—the spinnable fibre—are dependent on the variety of the flax plant, the length of the stem, the retting, and the scutching and hackling processes. Nowadays a good spinning length ranges from 0·6 to 0·8 m. These lengths probably occurred in former days too, because the machinery that was developed later must have been built according to the average naturally occurring lengths. Because of these large lengths, the twist in the yarns can be rather low compared with cotton yarns.

The ultimates adhere to one another by means of the middle lamella, the first very thin wall which during growth appears between two new cells, i.e. the two parts of a dividing cell. It contains a pectinous substance, which is affected by bleaching and repeated careless washing.[10] This may lead to the result that the compound fibres fall apart into smaller (finer and shorter) ones and/or into the ultimates. Therefore, when washing old linen fabrics, in which most if not all of the middle lamellae will certainly have vanished, one has to be very careful that no 'swimming' of the fibres occurs. The fibres are generally held in place by the twist in the yarns and the crossing of the yarns in the fabrics, but when the fibres are so weak (their wet strength having been reduced as a result of ageing) that they cannot oppose the swelling forces, irreparable damage may be done.

2.4.3   WOOL[3,4,13]

Wool is a textile fibre from the coat of a sheep, and depending on its place in the coat, also on the breed of sheep, it has different morphological, chemical and physical properties.

Wool fibre has a more or less apparent crimp, which correlates with its diameter and to a certain extent its length. A long fibre is often coarse and has little or no crimp; whereas fine fibres, which, in general, are also shorter, have more crimp. Wool fibres with more crimp tend to shrink easily when washed in a hot bath under some mechanical movement, which means that the dimensions may alter irreversibly (felting). Nowadays, many fabrics have undergone a finishing treatment, which makes them unshrinkable, but in general the textiles present in museum collections have not and, therefore, this unfavourable effect can only be avoided by washing in a cold or a luke-warm bath, with a minimum of rubbing. The wool fibres are weaker when wet, however, and handling of the fabrics (or garments) in the wet state has always to be done very carefully.

The morphological structure of the wool fibre is not yet clear, and is still being discussed by several outstanding scientists. It is outside the scope of this book to enter into these discussions and, therefore, only those characteristics which are of importance to the conservator will be mentioned.

The outer layer of the fibre, the cuticle, consists of scales, cells which overlap one another partly, and whose shape varies with the breed of sheep.[14] This layer of scales is characteristic for all kinds of hair, and, therefore, acts as a means to identify a textile fibre as a hair (Plate 2.6). In the case of greatly worn wool, reclaimed wool, or of archaeological wool textiles, the scales may have been rubbed off for the greater part, but the few which are left make identification as a hair not too difficult.

Under the cuticle lies the cortex, which may form a thin ring of spindle-shaped cells surrounding a large medulla (e.g. kemp fibres), a thicker ring when a less developed medulla is present, or it may take up the whole fibre, when the medulla is absent. Generally speaking, in the coarser wools a medulla may be present, but in the finer wools it is always absent. The shapes of the scales and of the medulla are characteristics which are used for identification of different kinds of wools, also of different types of hair.

2.4.4   SILK[15-18]

Silk is a protein fibre, which is obtained from the cocoons of caterpillars of the silk moth *(Bombyx mori)*. Shortly before the caterpillar (silk worm) transforms into a pupa, it makes a cocoon from threads (brins) which are produced by two spinning glands. These two brins are extruded together with silk gum, which surrounds them, so that they are fixed to one another, and form the cocoon thread (bave). The presence of the gum makes it possible to reel the silk, and to put it through the processes of twisting, weaving, etc. The bave is reeled together from several cocoons, the number of which depends on the end purpose, e.g. warp or weft yarn. This reeled silk, which has no twist, is also called net silk, raw silk or *grège*. The length of these silk fibre filaments is large (300–600 m). Shorter fibres can be gained from wastes which have arisen during cocoon spinning, reeling and subsequent processes. Depending on the quality of these wastes (e.g. fibre length) these can be processed into different kinds of spun silk, such as schappe and bourette. The difference between these two kinds is that schappe is spun from combed waste, and, therefore, has longer fibres, whereas bourette is spun from short brins recovered from the combing process. Consequently, the schappe is smoother, glossier and more regular than bourette.

The brins consist of fibroin, and the silk gum of sericin. Both are proteins but with different constitutions and chemical behaviour. The sericin makes the silk rather stiff and harsh to the touch; moreover, it hides the gloss which makes silk such a desired material for costly textiles. By removing the sericin *(degumming)* in a soap solution at a temperature of about 95°C the touch and gloss can be much improved. The removal of the gum causes a substantial decrease in weight, however, about 20% of the weight of the bave is sericin and this has an important influence on the drape of a fabric. To improve this property the silks can be weighted by some method. Often the tin–phosphate–silicate process is applied, but this unfortunately makes the silk extremely susceptible to light. Even storage in the dark may give appreciable decrease in strength. The opinions of different authors differ on this point, but there is reason to believe that the loss of strength depends to a considerable extent on the chemical nature of the weighting materials.

Examination of the cross section of a bave under the microscope shows the two triangular cross sections of the brins and a sheath of silk gum around as well as between the two brins (see reference 1, Figures 28–31). When a length of thread is examined it can be seen that the sericin is very unevenly distributed over the length. In degummed silk the brins have a very smooth surface with no or only small traces of gum left (Plate 2.7).

Although chiefly the silk of *Bombyx mori* is cultivated, different wild silks also have a wide use.[16, 19] Among them the tussah silks are very important. The wild silks differ from the cultivated silk in many respects (Plate 2.8). The composition of the fibroins and the sericins, the shape of the brins, the distribution of the silk gum, along as well as between the brins may all be different. In several species the cocoons cannot be reeled, and here the fibres can only be used for schappe spinning.

The cultivated silk, as well as the wild silks, swells in water by about 18%. Although the strength and extension for the different types are not the same, for all of them it is true that the wet strength is lower than the dry strength, and the wet extension higher than the dry extension.

Often the scroop of a silk fabric is considered as a very characteristic property, by which it can be distinguished from other silk-like materials

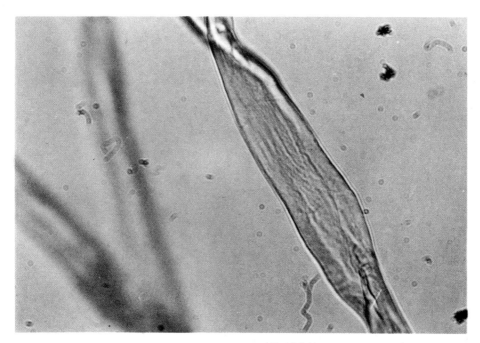

Plate 2.1. Cotton fibre (original magnification × 210 enlarged three and a half times on reproduction). New

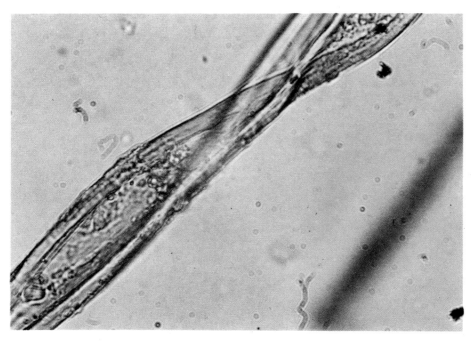

Plate 2.2. Cotton fibre (original magnification × 210 enlarged three and a half times on reproduction). End of eleventh century

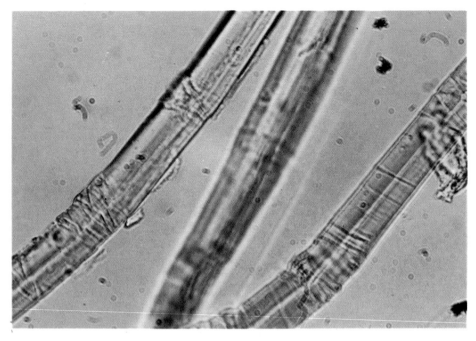

Plate 2.3. Flax fibre (original magnification × 210 enlarged three and a half times on reproduction). New

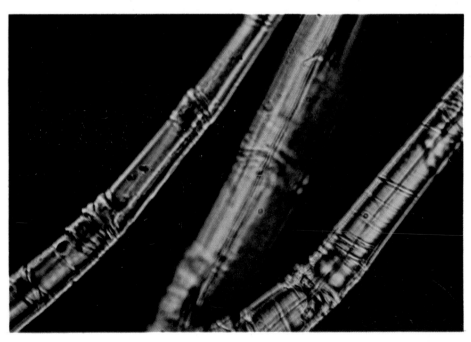

Plate 2.4. Flax fibre (original magnification × 210 enlarged three and a half times on reproduction). Between crossed nicols

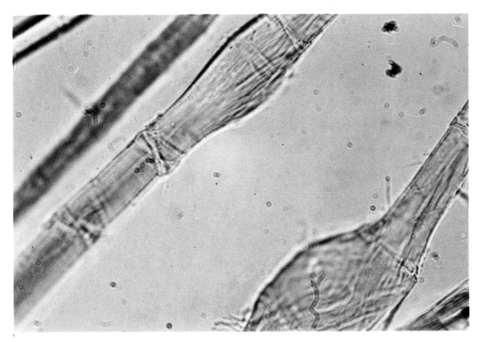

Plate 2.5. Flax fibre (original magnification × 210 enlarged three and a half times on reproduction). From seventeenth century damask

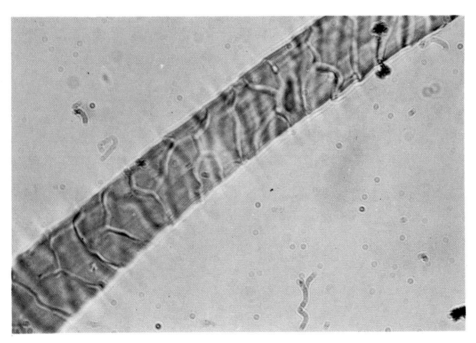

Plate 2.6. Wool (original magnification × 210 enlarged three and a half times on reproduction). New

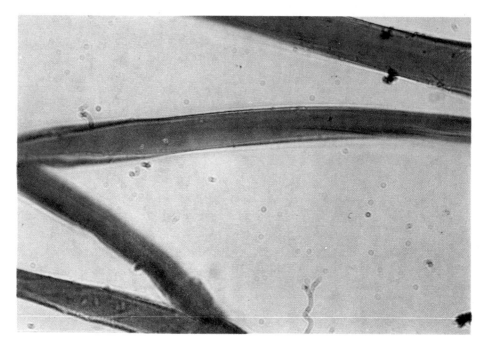

Plate 2.7. Red silk (original magnification × 210 enlarged three and a half times on reproduction). New

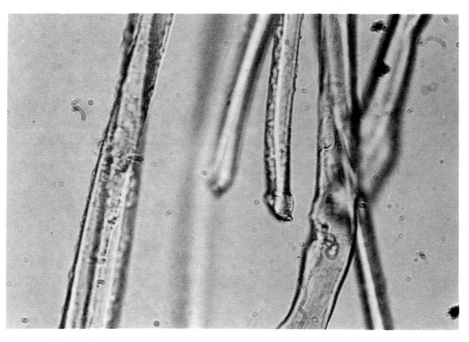

Plate 2.8. Silk (original magnification × 210 enlarged three and a half times on reproduction). First half of eighteenth century

(e.g. rayons, nylon). This property, however, is produced by an acid treatment, and is, therefore, not inherent in silk.

2.4.5 VISCOSE RAYON (See reference 7, pages 25–27, Figures 117–123.)

This fibre is manufactured from cellulose, which occurs in plant cell walls. After the cellulose has been dissolved, the solution is extruded in an appropriate spinning bath, where filaments are formed. The filament consists of a regenerated cellulose, whose chemical properties are quite similar to those of cotton and other natural cellulose fibres. The physical properties of these filaments largely depend on the method of preparation of the solution and the composition of the spinning bath.

When a filament is viewed under the microscope, morphological properties are also seen to depend on the factors mentioned above. Along the length of the filament continuous striations, running parallel to the longitudinal fibre axis, can be seen. On looking at the cross section the serrated margin is visible. With suitable optical or staining methods, a 'skin' and a 'core' can be distinguished. When the manufacturing process is performed on a more cotton-like fibre (polynosic fibre) the shape of the cross sections is quite different. For the last 10 years these polynosic fibres have been mixed with cotton fibres to improve the gloss and handle of cotton fabrics.

In museum collections containing items from the 1930s, fabrics or garments may be present which have been woven from viscose rayon staple yarns, which are yarns spun of short viscose rayon staple fibres. At that time, although the viscose rayon fibres had a lower quality than nowadays, textile technologists considered them to be as spinnable and weavable as cotton fibres, but did not take into consideration that they had larger swelling properties, and a wet strength which was much lower than the dry strength. The behaviour of the fabrics in water, therefore, was different from that of cotton. When they were woven with the usual number of warp and weft threads per unit of length—the yarn numbers being the same—as for cotton fabrics, the fabrics became very stiff in water, and often the threads broke down. Consequently, the utmost care has to be exercised when washing these densely woven viscose rayon fabrics from this particular period. These older types of viscose rayon fibres are also much more susceptible to damage by light.

2.4.6 ACETATE RAYON[20]

Another man-made fibre based on cellulose is the acetate rayon fibre. During processing, the natural cellulose is converted into the cellulose ester, acetylcellulose.

There are two types of fibre—the secondary cellulose acetates and the cellulose triacetates. The latter type has only been available commercially since 1960. These two acetate rayons differ distinctly from one another in their reaction to solvents and heat. Secondary acetate is soluble in acetone, and substantially insoluble in methylene chloride, whereas triacetate is soluble in methylene chloride and insoluble in acetone. The secondary acetate contracts at a temperature of 175–205°C and melts at 255°C, whereas triacetate contracts at 290°C and melts at 293°C. This means that at the mentioned temperatures these acetates deform irreversibly when pressed or stretched. Therefore, ironing can be done safely at a temperature of about 120°C, but at higher temperatures the surface tends to glaze. A wet fabric is more easily glazed than a dry one. Sticking is likely to occur at about 180°C.

Under the microscope the secondary acetate generally shows a longitudinal striation; the cross section has a lobed margin. The triacetate fibre is slightly different.[1]

Because the cellulose has been esterified for the greater part, the fibres take up much less water than, for example, viscose rayon. Therefore, they do not swell in water and in washing there is less danger of dimensional changes.

In the context of this book, man-made fibres based on synthetic polymers are only important as materials which could be considered as aids in conservation, e.g. as supports of fragile textiles during cleaning, or as linings on which these textiles can be sewn or glued. They are too modern to be found in the textile objects of most museum collections. Only when modern textiles are also collected will they be present in increasing quantity.

In the synthetic fibre industry, the development of new fibres is still taking place. It is, therefore, not possible to give a comprehensive general survey of all their physical, microscopical and chemical properties. Interested readers are advised to consult recent papers on these fibres. In the following, only those properties which may be of interest in the practice of restoration will be mentioned.

2.4.7 POLYAMIDE FIBRES   (See reference 1, pages 33, 34, Figures 95, 96.)

The polyamides are a group of synthetic polymers which are chemically related. The properties of polyamide fibres may differ considerably, according to the spinning processes and after treatments to which they may have been subjected.

In general, polyamide fibres are commercially available under trade names, which are very confusing because they show no connection with the chemical composition.[23] To this class belongs Nylon (Du Pont), a fibre which has been used for hosiery since October 1939, and which since World War II has found an increasing application in modern textiles.

These polyamide fibres have several advantages over natural fibres. They have a low moisture absorption, and so their moisture content changes only slightly with higher relative humidities. This is also the reason why they dry quickly. In water the swelling is distinctly less than that of the natural fibres, which is of importance particularly when polyamide fabrics are used as supports of fragile textiles during the cleaning process. They do not dissolve in solutions of soap or of synthetic detergents, and they do not change in drycleaning solvents. The melting points lie between 250 and 260°C, but they soften at about 180°C. For safety, ironing should be done at a temperature of about 130°C. Only in a few cases can this temperature be raised to 180°C, but then there is a risk of discoloration and glazing.

Polyamide filament yarns are often used for sewing thread. Unlike cotton and silk sewing thread, they have a large extensibility, and therefore care must be taken to sew with a low yarn tension, otherwise there will be an increase in length, which after a lapse of time is undone by relaxation. This shrinkage of the yarn will result in rumpling of the fabric around the stitches.

The polyamide fabrics may also have a large extensibility, which is partly irreversible, if during the manufacturing process they have not been stabilised. In conservation, this property could create difficulties, when the old textiles and the polyamide support do not have the same behaviour under the stresses exercised when they are tensioned on a frame, or when hung from one of their borders.

2.4.8 POLYESTER FIBRES (See reference 1, pages 31, 32, Figures 89, 90.)

The polyesters are another group of synthetic polymers which are more or less chemically related.[21, 23] The term does not imply that the different kinds of polyester fibre (Dacron, Terylene, Kodel, etc.) are chemically identical, nor that their physical properties are the same. Their trade names are, as with polyamide fibres, very confusing, and give no indication about their composition.

The fibres of this class absorb hardly any water, even when immersed in water. They do not swell, therefore, in higher relative humidities or in washing processes, and they dry very quickly. They are inert in water, soap, detergents and drycleaning solvents. Ironing should be done at a temperature of about 130°C. The fibres are less extensible than Nylon. Nevertheless, sewing threads of polyester filaments have a larger extensibility than cotton and linen sewing threads. In yarns of polyester staple fibre, when processed on the cotton spinning system, the extensibility is about the same as cotton and linen.

The light resistance is better than that of polyamide fibres. The properties already mentioned make polyester yarns and fabrics appropriate for use in conservation (see Chapter 10).

2.4.9 POLYOLEFINE FIBRES[23]

One of the best known representatives of this class of fibres is polyethylene fibre. It has its main application in technical devices, e.g. screens. Since it is inert towards soaps and synthetic detergents, and possesses hydrophobic properties, polyethylene gauze can be used for supports in the washing process of fragile textiles (see Chapter 13), but its stability is attacked at a temperature of about 70°C. Moreover, it dissolves in different drycleaning solvents.

2.5 DRAPE AND HANDLE

The *textile* character of textiles is mainly determined by their handle and drape. This is probably also the reason why visitors to textile collections are always tempted to touch the exhibits.

These properties of textiles are definitely influenced by the degree of suppleness, also called flexibility, which can be defined in two ways; first, as the ease of bending, which means that when a fabric is supple, it offers less resistance to bending than when it is stiff;[24] secondly, as that property of a material by virtue of which it may be flexed or bowed *repeatedly* without undergoing rupture.[25] It would be very satisfying for restorers if they could restore to an object the original flexibility in the latter sense. It could then be exposed to its normal use. More often than not the ancient textiles are so brittle and fragile that one cannot hope to revive them. The only aim is to improve their condition and to restore part of their original ease of bending (first definition).

The flexibility, in both senses, is dependent on the structure of the fabric and the elements from which this is made. This means that technique of interlacement, weight per unit of area, thread count, yarn number, twist, stiffness of the fibres, movability of the elements in respect of one another (yarns in the fabric, fibres in the yarns) as well as finish, all play an important role. From experience, it is already known that flexibility is unfavourably influenced by fixing warp and weft yarns at their binding points by stitches or adhesives. The same effect is to be seen when textiles have been washed in hard water. The different salts which stay behind between yarns and fibres, even when in very small quantities, cause the fabrics to be rather stiff when they are dried stretched on glass plates. In sizing, this movability is decreased on purpose. Crusts of soil and dirt also have a detrimental effect on flexibility. On the other hand, when a rather stiff old linen fabric is put into water, it may lose its stiffness and become very supple. Here the ease of bending has been improved by the action of water as a lubricant. Hence it will be clear that flexibility is a very complex characteristic of textiles, and that even small changes in one of the factors influencing flexibility may be perceptible.

To evaluate the influence of restoration and conservation treatments on flexibility it is necessary to have a method to measure it. The most perceptive measuring instrument is, perhaps, the human hand. It evaluates, however, only subjectively and qualitatively, and cannot measure exactly changes which have taken place over a period of time. Scientists have developed several apparatuses, therefore, for making and recording quantitative measurements, which can be objectively discussed.

Abbott has investigated these different apparatuses in order to establish those which give results that have a good correlation with the evaluation by hand.[26] He has shown that the cantilever-method of Peirce is one of the best.[27] Moreover, it is fairly simple, and, therefore, very appropriate for use in museum laboratories.

With this instrument two quantities can be measured, the bending length and the flexural rigidity. Of these two, the bending length is one of the factors which determine the manner in which a fabric drapes. It is related to the quality of stiffness that is appreciated by *visual examination* of the draped material, in that clothes having a high bending length tend to drape stiffly. The flexural rigidity is related to the quality of stiffness that is appreciated when a fabric is *handled*, in that cloth having a high flexural rigidity tends to feel stiff.[28] With this apparatus the effect of different common conservation methods on the flexibility has been measured.

In Table 2.3 the effects of laying two or three layers of cloth on top of each other, and of stitching them together have been compiled. From this table, it appears that merely the fact of laying the strips on top of one another does increase the bending length and the flexural rigidity, the latter increasing much more than would be expected from the number of layers. The

Table 2.3 EFFECT OF NUMBER OF STRIPS ON BENDING LENGTH AND FLEXURAL RIGIDITY

Number of strips (125 × 25 mm)	Stitches (zig-zag)	Cotton		Wool		Silk crepeline		Polyester crepeline	
		C	G	C	G	C	G	C	G
1	—	1·9	47	2·0	177	3·2	25	1·5	5
2	—	2·0	139	2·3	502	3·4	58	1·7	14
3	—	—	—	—	—	3·3	—	—	—
2	two rows, uninterrupted	2·3	451	3·9	2 552	—	—	—	—
2	three rows, uninterrupted	3·8	1 045	4·4	3 697	—	—	—	—
2	very short rows, randomly distributed	2·6	302	3·8	2 222	—	—	—	—

C—bending length   G—flexural rigidity

flexural rigidity of a double strip is distinctly more than twice that of one strip. The friction between the two strips undoubtedly plays a stiffening role. When two identical strips are sewn together the flexural rigidity increases much more. This increase is dependent on the number of stitches, on the number of rows of stitches, and on the tension in the sewing thread. This is entirely in accordance with the experience of centuries that for

Table 2.4 AGEING OF MOWITAL B 60 HH IN ABSENCE OF LIGHT AT 20°C ± 1°C, RELATIVE HUMIDITY 65 ± 2%

Fabric	Mowital B 60 HH %	Bending length (cm)		Flexural rigidity (mg × cm)	
		Oct. 1966	June 1969	Oct. 1966	June 1969
Cotton	0	2·2	—	129	—
(plain weave)	0·10	2·3	2·2	152	134
Polyester	0	1·7	—	14	—
mousseline	0·10	1·8	1·9	18	19
Polyester	0	1·6	—	6	—
crepeline	0·10	1·7	1·8	7	8
Silk	0	3·2	—	25	—
crepeline	0·10	3·4	3·5	30	33

making, for example, stiff collars, several rows of stitches have to be applied.[29, 30]

When adhesives need to be applied for conservation, it is necessary to investigate how far they influence the flexibility and how stable they are in the course of time. To illustrate this point, a few results of ageing experiments with the adhesive Mowital B 60 HH, a polyvinyl butyral, are given in

Table 2.4. From this data it can be concluded that this adhesive has proved to be very stable for more than $2\frac{1}{2}$ years.[30]

It also seems important to use, as supports, those fabrics which for the given circumstances have the lowest flexural rigidity.

REFERENCES

1. *Identification of Textile Materials*, 5th edn, The Textile Institute, Manchester, 116 (1965)
2. MAUERSBERGER, H. R., *Matthew's Textile Fibers*, 6th edn, John Wiley & Sons, New York, 281–298 (1954)
3. WILDMAN, A. B., *The Microscopy of Animal Textile Fibres*, Wool Industries Research Association, Leeds 6 (1954)
4. APPLEYARD, H. M., *Guide to the Identification of Animal Fibres*, Wool Industries Research Association, Leeds 6 (1960)
5. With kind permission of the President of the Centre International d'Études des Textiles Anciens at Lyon (France), I have made ample use of the multilingualistic *Vocabulaire Technique des Tissus* (in preparation)
6. WATSON, W., *Textile Design and Colour*, 5th edn, Longmans, Green and Co., London, 17 (1946)
7. ASTM Standard D2368–65 in 1968 *Book of ASTM Standards*, part 25, 509–521 (1968)
8. ROLLINS, M. L., 'The Cotton Fibre' in D. S. HAMBY's, *The American Cotton Handbook*, Vol. 1, 3rd edn, Interscience Publishers, New York, 44–81 (1965)
9. PARISOT, A., 'Méthodes de controle et de prévision du comportement à l'utilisation des tissus de coton et de lin', *Bull. I.T.F.*, No. 130, 379–400 (1967)
10. LAMBRINOU, I., 'Die Faserstruktur in Leinengarnen. II. Die Veränderung der Faserstruktur in Leinengarnen während ihrer Veredlung und Beanspruchung (Bleichen, Färben, Waschen)', *Melliand TextBer.*, **49**, 251–254, 373–381 (1968)
11. KIRBY, R. H., *Vegetable Fibres*, Leonard Hill Ltd., New York, 3 (1963)
12. NETTELNSTROTH, K. M., 'Zur Morphologie der Leinenfaser', *Melliand TextBer.*, **49**, 565–572 (1968)
13. BERGEN, W. VON, *Wool Handbook*, Vol. 1, 3rd edn, Interscience Publishers, New York (1963)
14. MORTON, W. E., and HEARLE, J. W. S., *Physical Properties of Textile Fibres*, Butterworths, London, 54–55, Figure 1.36 (1962)
15. HOWITT, F. O., *Bibliography of the Technical Literature on Silk*, Hutchinson's Scientific and Technical Publications, London (1946)
16. BRICK, C. J., 'The silk fibers and yarns' in H. E. MAUERSBERGER's *Matthews Textile Fibers*, 6th edn, John Wiley & Sons, New York, 749–812 (1954)
17. *Vocabulaire technique des Tissus*, in preparation by the Centre International d'Études des Textiles Anciens (CIETA), Lyon (different languages)
18. HANDSCHIN, E., 'Der Seidenspinner, Bombyx mori Linné', *Ciba-Rdsch.*, **67**, 2444–2456 (1946)
19. HANDSCHIN, E., 'Wilde Seidenspinner', *Ciba-Rdsch.*, **67**, 2458–2466 (1946)
20. SMITH, H. DE W., and CHILDS, H. R., 'Acetate fibers and yarns' in H. R. MAUERSBERGER's *Matthew's Textile Fibers*, 6th edn, John Wiley & Sons, New York, 859–924 (1954)
21. MAUERSBERGER, H. R., *Matthew's Textile Fibers*, 6th edn, John Wiley & Sons, New York, 934–971 (1954)
22. MONCRIEFF, R. W., *Man-made fibres*, 5th Ed., Butterworths, London, (1970)
23. FOURNÉ, F., *Synthetische Fasern*, Wissenschaftliche Verlagsgesellschaft M.B.H., Stuttgart (1964)
24. ASTM Designation: D123–68a, Appendix III in *1968 Book of ASTM Standards*, part 25, 50 (1968)
25. ASTM Designation: D123–68a, Appendix I in *1968 Book of ASTM Standards*, part 25, 45 (1968)
26. ABBOTT, N. J., 'The measurement of stiffness in textile fabrics', *Text. Res. J.*, **21**, 435–444 (1951)
27. PEIRCE, F. T., 'The handle of cloth as a measurable quantity', *J. Text. Inst.*, **21**, T377 (1930)
28. British Standard 3356: 1961. *Method for the determination of stiffness of cloth*. British Standards Institution, London
29. LEENE, J. E., *Flexibility of fabrics*. Report to I.C.O.M. Committee for Museum Laboratories, Brussels (1967)
30. LEENE, J. E., *Flexibility of fabrics II. Ageing of adhesives, used in textile conservation*. Report to ICOM Committee for Conservation, Amsterdam (1969)

3
Natural Dyestuffs

JOHANNA M. DIEHL
Workshop for Restoration of Ancient Textiles, Haarlem

Until about a century ago natural dyestuffs were used for the dyeing of fibrous materials, but since the development of synthetic dyestuffs their use has gradually decreased, and nowadays they are rarely used. However, because of the importance of the natural dyestuffs in connection with ancient textiles, their origin and properties are dealt with in this chapter.

The large number of colours in nature must have tempted man to use them for the dyeing of textiles, but only a few proved to have reasonable dyeing properties.[1, 2, 3] This means that, if applied in the right way, they are taken up by the fibres, and have a reasonable light and washing fastness. Dyeing properties are not only dependent on the dyestuff, but also on the chemical and physicochemical properties of the fibres. Accordingly, protein fibres take different dyes from those used for cellulose fibres, wool being more easily dyed than silk, and cotton than linen.

The choice of natural dyestuffs in different parts of the world was determined originally by the possibility of cultivating them in that place, which in turn depended on the prevailing climate. A number of dyes, however, have been used almost universally. The expansion of navigation and trade with Asia at the end of the Middle Ages added considerably to the number of dyestuffs in Europe; imported products sometimes supplanted indigenous ones. Perhaps best known throughout the world is the blue dyestuff, indigo.[2, 4, 5-7, 8, 9] It is obtained from the leaves of several plants containing a chemical compound, which has as a base the indole derivative indoxyl, bound as a glycoside (i.e. bound to a sugar—mostly rhamnose or glucose).[10] By fermentation of the picked leaves and a reaction in alkaline surroundings, mostly brought about by means of decomposing urine, the sugar is split off and the indoxyl is changed into the actual dyestuff, indigotin. This is a dark blue, kneadable mass, insoluble in water.

Although indigotin can be extracted from the leaves of several different botanical species, the main source was the species *Indigofera tinctoria L.*, which grows in the tropical regions of Asia. From here the indigotin was shipped to other parts of the world. In Western Europe, it totally ousted the indigenous indigotin, called woad, obtained from *Isatis tinctoria L.*, despite protective measures taken by some monarchs and unfounded remarks on its harmful effects on the fibres.[11] In the 1870s indigotin was successfully synthetised. This synthetic product, being totally comparable to the natural indigotin, and much cheaper, brought the *Indigofera* cultivation to ruin within a few decades.

Indigotin is a vat dye.[12] Being insoluble in water, it has to be changed into a water soluble compound. This can be achieved by dissolving it in an alkaline bath ('vatting'). The result is a pale yellow solution of the sodium salt of the leuco-compound indigo-white, in which the textile can be dyed. It leaves the bath almost colourless, but when exposed to the air it becomes blue, the indigo-white being oxidised into indigotin. To obtain dark shades the dyeing with indigo-white and the oxidation have to be repeated several times. It must be understood that experience and care are required to obtain a good result.

The indigo-dyed textiles have a good light fastness. They also have a good washing fastness, which could be expected as indigotin is insoluble in water. Because of these properties, indigo dyeing is still used today. The only disadvantage is its poor rubbing fastness. This may be the reason why, at one time, textiles were often dyed with the dyestuff orchil before the proper indigo dyeing, or in other cases were treated afterwards with tanning materials to make the rubbing off less annoying.

Closely related to indigotin is dibrome indigotin, the 'purple' of antiquity. It is a product of *Murex brandaris L.* and other species of *Murex*, a type of shellfish found on subtropical coasts.[13-16, 17] Textiles dyed with purple were extremely expensive, and their use was reserved for leading personalities and for special purposes only.

Another group of very important dyestuffs is formed by anthraquinone derivatives, also bound as glycosides, of which 'madder' is perhaps most widely known.[18-24] In the root of the madder plant *(Rubia tinctoria L.)* a mixture of several anthraquinone derivatives is found, including alizarin, purpurin, rubiatin, and munjistin, of which alizarin is the most important.

The dyestuff is prepared by drying and heating the roots, which are then ground and heated with sulphuric acid. The sugar is split off, and some noxious matter removed. After washing and drying, madder is ready for use in the form of a chocolate brown powder. Other *Rubia* species contain the same derivatives, but in different proportions, so that dyeing with them results in correspondingly different shades. In India, munjet which comes from *Rubia cordifolia L.*, in which purpurin is the predominant derivative, is generally used. *Oldenlandia umbellata L.*, also from India, provides 'chaya-root', in which purpurin is totally absent. This dyestuff produces a more violet hue than madder or munjet. Morindon which comes from several species of the genus *Morinda*, is closely related to alizarin, and is used for the duller red colours of batiks.[25-30]

Except for madder, the above mentioned plants are confined to tropical areas. In northern regions, roots of several species of the genus *Galium*, closely related to the genus *Rubia*, were used as an alternative source of alizarin. Madder, however, grows in temperate regions, and has, in the past, been cultivated in large quantities everywhere in Europe. It underwent the same fate as *Indigofera*, however, when in the nineteenth century alizarin and its relatives were produced synthetically.

Alizarin and its derivatives, being soluble in water, have a very poor washing fastness, but by putting metal salts (mordants) in the dyeing bath, insoluble compounds, which have a very good washing and light fastness, may be formed. Aluminium and tin mordants produce bright red shades such as Turkey red; chromium and iron mordants give more violet and dull hues.

In very early times, the very fine and fast red dye kermes had already been made from the scale insect *(Coccus ilicus L.)* which lives on the subtropical species of oak, *Quercus ilex L.* and *Q. coccifera L.* These insects were gathered, killed with vinegar, and then dried. The resulting material gives brilliant colours with mordants, and, especially with tin mordant, produces a very fine scarlet colour. Kermes has accordingly often been used to imitate *Murex* purple.[31, 32]

The same kind of dye is also produced by the insect *Margarodes polonensis L.*, which lives on the roots of *Scleranthus perennis L.*, growing in a more temperate climate. The dyestuff is known as root-kermes, German kermes or Polish kermes. After the discovery of America, *Coccus cacti L.* was found living on *Opuntia* species and other Cactaneae. This insect was used by the Indians for dyeing red, and as it was a better dyestuff than kermes, it was exported to Europe in large quantities under the name of cochineal.

The dyeing agents of the kermes and cochineal group differ only slightly from one another; they are carminic and kermesic acid, distant relatives of anthraquinone. Somewhat different is laccain acid, the colouring agent of lac-dye, a resinous fluid which is produced by the branches of some *Ficus* species, where *Coccus laccae L.* has attacked them. This dyestuff is inferior to cochineal.

Spread over the whole higher flora, derivatives of flavone can be found, also in the form of glycosides. Flavone is a white stuff that in its pure form can be seen as the mealy fur on leaves and stalks of several species of *Primula*. A number of its derivatives, the flavones and flavonols, are used as mordant dyes, and give yellow and brown colours.[1, 2, 33, 34] In Europe, an extract of the dried plant *Reseda luteola L.* (weld) was once much used for dyeing. The whole herb contains the flavone luteolin. *Genista tinctoria L.*, also contains luteolin. Both species maintained their position for a considerable period alongside imported yellow dyestuffs.

The flavonol quercitin is found in the bark of the dyers' oak *(Quercus tinctoria L.)* (Quercitron bark) from South America, and is also present in Chinese yellow berries, i.e. the flower-buds of *Sophora japonica L.*, with which the yellow clothing of the mandarins was dyed. Fisetin is the flavonol colouring element of the wood of the South American *Rhus cotinus L.*, the fiset wood. Morin was prepared from yellow wood of the South American *Chlorophora tinctoria Gaud.*

All these materials were imported in large quantities into Europe as were the unripe berries from different species of *Rhamnus* from Persia, especially *Rhamnus saxatiles Jacq.* Textiles dyed with these dyestuffs had a good washing fastness, but a low light fastness, those containing luteolin giving the best results in this respect. This low light fastness becomes evident in the fading of green colours, which were always the result of a blue and a yellow dyeing process. In ancient textiles one can often see that the original green colour, for example, of leaves, has got a blue hue, because the yellow dye has faded in the mixture.

The trade names under which the different kinds of wood which produce yellow colours were known, are extremely confusing. For the wood of *Rhus cotinus L.*, one finds besides the name of fiset wood, also those of fustic, young fustic, fustelwood, bois jaune, bois d'Hongrie. The name of fustic wood is also used for the wood of *Chlorophora*, which is also called old fustic and Cubawood.[34, 35]

Distantly related to flavone, but closely related to one another are brazilein and haematein, from the genera of *Caesalpinia* and *Haematoxylon* respectively. Both dyestuffs are present in the wood in a colourless form, but oxidation and solution in boiling water give rise to a red or blue colour.

Some species of *Caesalpinia* were already known and imported into Europe in the Middle Ages. Afterwards the same and other species of the genus were found in South America, and exported in large quantities to Europe under various names. Brazilwood (the word was derived from *braza*, i.e. fire blaze, because of the red colour it produced) comes from *Caesalpinia braziliensis Sw.*, which grows in Brazil in very large quantities. The finest qualities of red wood were *Caesalpinia sappan L.* and 'pernambucowood' of *Caesalpinia crista L.*[2, 35, 36] Inferior qualities were sandalwood, barwood, and caliaturwood from various species of *Pterocarpus*, and camwood from *Baphia nitida Lodd.*

Haematein is the dyestuff from logwood, the wood of *Haematoxylon campechianum L.* This tree was found for the first time in South America, but afterwards it was also cultivated in tropical Asia.[37-39] Brazilein was used, with a tin mordant and the addition of tanning materials, to yield fine red colours. Subtle differences of shade could be produced by adding yellow dyes. They were not very fast, however, the washing fastness being especially bad.

With the addition of mordants, haematein gives grey and violet hues, and was often used to dye silk in very dark colours or black. These very dark shades could, however, only be obtained by adding very large quantities of iron mordant to the dyeing bath. Haematein was also used, in addition to other dyes, in order to get darker shades. In connection with obtaining dark tones, it is useful to note a category of substances—the tanning materials—which were used as dyestuffs to get very dark colours, i.e. dark brown, dark grey, and black. These materials give very dark coloured compounds (e.g. ordinary writing ink), when combined with iron salts, the nuance and intensity of the colour produced on the fibre depending on the kind of tanning material and the concentration of iron salts in the dyebath.[40-43]

A dyestuff of great importance was orchil, or archil, the dried *Roccella tinctoria DC.*, which at first was only gathered on the coasts of Italy and used there with much secrecy. Later it was also found on the coasts of Africa and taken to other countries. Species of lichen growing in the mountains of Europe as the genera *Variolaria* and *Lecanora* also contain, like *Roccella*, compounds such as atranoic acid and lecanoric acid, derivatives of resorcin, from which the dyeing agent, orcein, is set free on oxidation in an ammoniacal solution.[2, 35, 40, 44]

Safflower is a dyestuff from *Carthamus tinctoria L.*[2, 33, 45] The dried flower-heads of this thistle have been used from earliest times to get a very bright orange-red colour. The dyeing agent is the chalkone derivative of carthamin, with which cotton and silk can be dyed with or without mordants. It was already used in the Middle East at the time of the Pharaohs, and afterwards was cultivated in the tropics. The colour is fine but not very fast, this being the reason why safflower was one of the first dyestuffs to disappear at the rise of the synthetic dyes.

Finally, two natural dyestuffs which are widely known, but which have not been of great economical importance in textile dyeing, must be mentioned. The first is henna, the naphthaquinone derivative lawsone, present in all parts of the henna shrub *(Lawsonia inermis L.)*.[2, 33] Today, the plant has a widespread reputation as a cosmetic, but formerly, leaves and roots were used in dyeing silk azure or black. The roots were imported from the Middle East into Europe under the name of 'real alkanna root'. This name is rather confusing, for the roots of various species of the genera *Alkanna* and *Anchusa* were also used for dyeing, and although they only had a local importance in the Mediterranean area, carried names such as alcanet, alkanna or false alkanna. The second is a flower dyestuff, saffron, dried stigmata of the saffron crocus *(Crocus sativa L.)*.[2, 33] The stigmata contain a carotinoid crocetin, from which the dyeing agent crocin can be obtained. A few other plants also contain crocin, and like saffron were used locally for the dyeing of silk, wool and cotton. The light fastness of these colours, however, is poor.

The dyeing processes with natural dyestuffs took a long time, if acceptable results were to be obtained. Moreover, these dyestuffs, except for indigo and madder, had a low light fastness. It will be clear that these factors almost naturally led to the disappearance of these dyestuffs with the rise of the synthetic ones. The latter were preferred because they were cheaper to make and the dyeing process was quicker, even if at the beginning their light and washing fastnesses were as bad, or worse.

At the end of the nineteenth century, industrial dyeing was at a very low level. Both natural and synthetic dyes were used and the results were equally bad. This fact gave the synthetic dyestuffs a bad reputation, which even nowadays has not been overcome. This is unjustified, because the dyer of today has a very large assortment of dyes in all kinds of shades and in all grades of light, washing and rubbing fastnesses at his disposal.

There is another advantage in the use of synthetic dyes. As mentioned before, it was necessary to add large quantities of iron salts to the dyeing bath with natural dyestuffs when very dark or black colours were required. Iron, however, is disastrous to the fibre material. When the fabric is exposed to light it can be seen that the dark coloured fibres are badly damaged, while the iron-free dyed fibres survive much longer (tapestries, embroideries, batiks, etc.). This danger is eliminated with synthetic dyestuffs.

When restoring textiles, it is often necessary to use yarns and fabrics which exactly match the surrounding materials. When using natural dyestuffs it will be very difficult, if not impossible, to get the right shade, and even if this could be obtained, the light fastness of the newly dyed material would rarely match that of the surrounding material. It is almost certainly necessary to use synthetic dyes, which can be chosen to the required fastness. To obtain the exact shade, it is necessary to blend the colours in the dyeing bath. For this reason only acid and direct dyes, or dyes with built-in mordants can be used. Indanthrene dyeing is not appropriate for this purpose.

In general, the museum-conservator will be in contact with objects dyed with natural dyes, but he may also meet some modern dyes. They may occur in nineteenth century objects and are common in twentieth century ones. He may even find them in older materials, for often in ancient objects, restorations are made with materials dyed with synthetic dyestuffs. It will, however, often be necessary to clean the objects before displaying them and then the question of the washing fastness comes to the fore.

The colours of ancient textiles have, in general, a rather good washing fastness, but there are exceptions. At any rate, one must be very careful if repairs are present, as they may date from the nineteenth or the early twentieth centuries, when the washing fastness of the synthetic dyes was bad. Even if the ancient material itself could be washed in water, the possibility remains that the repairs will not stand such treatment.[46, 47]

In cleaning the objects, it is of course not necessary to know exactly what kind of dyestuff has been used; if, for example, a red colour originates from madder, cochineal or another dye. It may, however, sometimes be desirable to know something more about the origin of the colours. It might, for example, be desirable to know if a repair was recently made with materials dyed with modern dyestuffs, or whether it dates from older times and was made with materials dyed with natural ones.

It is possible to learn quite a lot about the dyestuffs used. Experience shows that even if time has done much damage to the object, and to the colouring matter, the chemical foundation of the dyestuff is still preserved. Chemical analysis enables the kinds of colouring matter on the object to be determined, whether synthetic or natural. This technique requires a small piece of material to be used, but recently research has started on analysing dyestuffs by infra-red spectrographic methods.[22, 32, 48−52]

If the object originates from one of the great centres of culture, there is a good chance that the dyes used for it are among those named in this chapter, but in archaeological and ethnological collections, there must be many objects coloured by dyestuffs of unknown origin. The chemical class to which these dyestuffs belong can be determined in the same way, but it will nearly always be impossible to guess which plant or animal was used. Data about dyeing materials in prehistoric times, and dyeing by non-western peoples is very scarce, but fairly reliable references are often found in information of a totally different kind, such as in reports of missionaries or colonial officials. Larger compilations of data are extremely rare,[25−30, 45, 53−67] but an exception is formed by the publications of Jasper and Pirngadie, in which numerous dyeing recipes are summarised, with the Latin botanical names of the plants used.[45]

It would be very interesting to know more about the chemical compounds that form the basis of dyestuffs, in particular if there was any correlation between the relations of the chemical compounds and the botanical relations of the plants from which they come. An attempt in this direction has been made by W. Endrei and L. Hafnal.[49]

REFERENCES

1. ONSLOV-WHELDALE, M., *The Anthocyanine Pigments of Plants*, 2nd edn, Cambridge University Press (1925)
2. PERKINS, A. G. and EVEREST, A. E., *The Natural Colouring Matters*, London (1918)
3. ZECHMEISTER, L., *Die Karetinoide*, Berlin (1932)
4. BÜHLER, A., 'Die Indigofärbung bei den Naturvölkern.' *Ciba-Rdsch.*, **93**, 3438–3441 (1950)
5. HALLER, R., 'Die Gewinnung des Indigos', *Ciba-Rdsch.*, **93**, 3422–3425 (1950)
6. HALLER, R., 'Zur Geschichte der Indigofärberei', *Ciba-Rdsch.*, **93**, 3427–3431 (1950)

7. HALLER, R., 'Der Indigo in der Zeugdruckerei', *Ciba-Rdsch.*, **93**, 3433–3437 (1950)
8. MARTINET, J., *Matières Colorantes, L'Indigo et ses Dérivés*, Paris (1926)
9. VETTERLI, A., 'Zur Geschichte des Indigos', *Ciba-Rdsch.*, **93**, 3416–3421 (1950)
10. RYN, J. J. L. V., and DIETERLE, H., *Die Glykoside*, Berlin (1930)
11. LAUTERBACH, F., *Geschichte der in Deutschland bei der Färberei angewandten Farbstoffe mit besonderer Berücksichtigung des mittelalterlichen Waidbaues*, Leipzig (1905)
12. FOX, M. R., *Vat-Dyestuffs and Vat-Dyeing*, London (1946)
13. BORN, W., 'Die Purpurschnecke', *Ciba-Rdsch.*, **4**, 110–114 (1936)
14. BORN, W., 'Purpur im klassischen Altertum', *Ciba-Rdsch.*, **4**, 115–122 (1936)
15. BORN, W., 'Purpur im Mittelalter', *Ciba-Rdsch.*, **4**, 124–128 (1936)
16. BORN, W., 'Purpur bei den Indianern Mittelamerikas—ein Erbe der Antiken', *Ciba-Rdsch.*, **4**, 130–134 (1936)
17. DEDEKIND, A., *Einleitung zur Purpurkunde*, Berlin (1898)
18. BÜHLER, A., 'Türkischrot–Färberei in Süd- und Südostasien', *Ciba-Rdsch.*, **47**, 1739–1741 (1940)
19. COATES, H., *Weaving for Amateurs*, The Studio Publications, London, New York (1950)
20. HALLER, R., 'Vom Türkischrot zum Alizarinrot', *Melliand Textilber.*, **19**, 448–452, 504–506, 595–596, 731–734, 796–799 (1938)
21. HALLER, R., 'Zum Chemismus und zur Technik der Türkischrot–Färberei', *Ciba-Rdsch.*, **47**, 1733–1737 (1940)
22. MASSCHELEIN-KLEINER, L., and HEYLEN, J. B., 'Analyse des Lacques rouges anciennes', *Stud. Conserv.*, **13**, 87–97 (1968)
23. SCHAEFER, G., 'Der Anbau und die Veredlung der Krappwurzel', *Ciba-Rdsch.*, **47**, 1714–1722 (1940)
24. SCHAEFER, G., 'Zur Geschichte der Türkisschrotfärberei', *Ciba-Rdsch.*, **47**, 1723–1732 (1940)
25. BÜHLER, A., 'Farbstoffe und Färbemethoden für Ikat-garne', *Ciba-Rdsch.*, **51**, 1861–1867 (1941)
26. BÜHLER, A., 'Färberei der Naturvölker', *Ciba-Rdsch.*, **75**, 2764–2796, 2799–2801 (1948)
27. BÜHLER, A., 'Die Plangiverfahren', *Ciba-Rdsch.*, **111**, 4062–4070 (1953)
28. LOEBÈR, J. A., *Das Batikken*, Oldernburg/O (1925)
29. STEINMANN, A., 'Dic Technik des Batikens', *Ciba-Rdsch.*, **69**, 2528–2539 (1947)
30. TONOMURA, K., 'Reserveverfahren in Japan, Farbstoffe und Pigmente', *Ciba-Rdsch.*, **4**, 30–32 (1967)
31. BORN, W., 'Der Scharlach', *Ciba-Rdsch.*, **7**, 218–240 (1936)
32. OVEREEM, J. C., and KERK, G. J. M., V.D., 'Revised structure for cochenillic acid and for the insect pigments, carminic and kermesic acids'. Part IV of: Mollisin, a naturally occurring chlorine containing quinone, *Rec. Trav. chim. Pays-Bas*, **83**, 1023–1035 (1964)
33. KARSTENS, W. R. H., *Plantaardige Kleurstoffen*, Gorinchem (1943)
34. SCHAEFER, G., 'Fisettholz, Gelbholz und Quercitron', *Ciba-Rdsch.*, **10**, 351–352 (1937)
35. LEGGET, W. E., *Ancient and Mediaeval Dyes*, Brooklyn, New York (1944)
36. SCHAEFER, G., 'Die Rothölzer', *Ciba-Rdsch.*, **10**, 341–348 (1937)
37. SCHAEFER, G., 'Das Blauholz', *Ciba-Rdsch.*, **10**, 326–330 (1937)
38. SCHAEFER, G., 'Zur Geschichte der Blauholzverwendung', *Ciba-Rdsch.*, **10**, 331–335 (1937)
39. SCHAEFER, G., 'Der Blauholzhandel', *Ciba-Rdsch.*, **10**, 336–339 (1937)
40. GANSWINDT, A., *Die Farb- und Gerbekstrakte*, Wien-Leipzig (1916)
41. HARVEY, A., *The Tanning Materials*, London (1921)
42. HOWES, F. N., *Vegetable Tanning Materials*, London (1953)
43. ROTHSIEFER, E. H. W., *Vegetable Tannins*, St. Albans (1941)
44. BRIEGER, R., 'Flechtenstoffe', *in Klein's Handb. der Pflanzenanalyse*, III, No. 2, le H., 413–429 (1932)
45. JASPER, J. E. and PIRNGADIE, RADEN MAS, *De Inlandsche Kunstnijverheid in Nederlandsch-Indie*, I Vlechtwerk, 64–79 (1912), II Weefkunst, 61–82 (1912), III Batikkunst, 31–50 (1916), 's-Gravenhage (1916)
46. BEEK, H. C. A. van and HEERTJES, P. H., 'Fading by Light of Organic Dyes on Textiles and Other Materials', *Stud. Conserv.*, **11**, 123–132 (1966)
47. PADFIELD, T., and LANDI, S., 'The Lightfastness of Natural Dyes', *Stud. Conserv.*, **11**, 181–196 (1966)
48. AGSTER, A., *Färberei- und textilchemische Untersuchungen*, 10th edn, Springer-Verlag, Berlin/ Heidelberg/New York (1967)
49. ENDREI, W. and HAFNAL, L., 'Analyse des colorants pour textiles', *Bull. de Liais. du CIETA*, **13**, 27–40 (1961)

50. FLIEDER, F., 'Mise au point des techniques d'identification des pigments et des liants inclus dans la couche picturale des enluminures de manuscrits', *Stud. Conserv.*, **13**, No. 2, 49–86 (1968)

51. GREEN, A. G., *Analysis of Dyestuffs* (With schedules for the determination of dyestuffs on the fibre), London (1949)

52. KNECHT, E., RAWSON CH. and LOEWENTHAL, R., *A Manual of Dyeing*, 8th edn, 2 Vols., (with schedules for determination of dyestuffs on the fibre), London (1933)

53. BÜHLER, A., *Materialien zur Kenntnis der Ikattechnik*, Leiden (1943)

54. GALLOTI, J., 'Weben, Wirken und Färben in Nordafrika', *Ciba-Rdsch.*, **18**, 630–654 (1937)

55. HARCOURT, R. D., 'Textilrohstoffe, Spinnen, Färben, Werkzeuge' (der Peruanischen Textiltechnik), *Ciba-Rdsch.*, **148**, 6–10 (1960)

56. HEMNETER, E., 'Die Kasten der indischen Färber', *Ciba-Rdsch.*, **2**, 53–57 (1936)

57. JAMES, G. W., *Indian Blankets and their Makers*, Chicago (1934)

58. JUVET-MICHEL, A., 'Vom Färben und Knüpfen des Orientteppichs', *Ciba-Rdsch.*, **15**, 524–528 (1937)

59. KLEIN, O., 'Das textile Handwerk der Araukaner', *Ciba-Rdsch.*, **6**, 7–18 (1961)

60. KRÄMER, A., *Die Samoa-Inseln*, **2**, Ethnographie, Stuttgart 272–313 (1903)

61. LATOUR, A., 'Textile Künste der nordamerikanischen Indianer', *Ciba-Rdsch.*, **87**, 3241–3248 (1949)

62. LEIX, A., 'Indische Textilien, ihre Herstellung und ihre Muster im 19. Jahrhundert und in der Gegenwart', *Ciba-Rdsch.*, **46**, 1695–1705 (1940)

63. LEIX, A., 'Trachten der sesshaften Bevölkerung Turkestans', *Ciba-Rdsch.*, **54**, 1977–1985 (1942)

64. LERNER, F., Die Entwicklung des Farbstoffhandels (auf den Frankfurter Messen), *Ciba-Rdsch.*, **109**, 4007–4009 (1953)

65. NIEUWENHUYS, A. A. W., Figuur knopen: Ikat-verven en -weven in Oost-Indie. Nederlands Indië, Oud en Nieuw 5–16, 49–62 (1916–1917)

66. ROUFFAER, G. F., and JUYNBOLL, H. H., *De Batikkunst in Nederlandsch Indië en haar geschiedenis*, Utrecht (1914)

67. UNDERHILL, R., *Pueblo Crafts*, Publication of the Educational Division, United States Indian Service (1944)

FURTHER READING

CHATEAU, TH., 'Etudes historiques et chimiques pour servir à l'histoire de la fabrication de Rouge Turc ou d'Adrianople et à la théorie de cette teinture', *Monitor Scientific*, **18** (1876)

DUNBAR, J. TELFER, 'Wollverarbeitung und Färben (in Schottland)' *Ciba-Rdsch.*, **98**, 3605–3608 (1951)

FABER, G. A., 'Die Färberei in Griechenland', *Ciba-Rdsch.*, **20**, 704–711 (1937)

FABER, G. A., 'Die Färberei bei den Römern', *Ciba-Rdsch.*, **20**, 713–723 (1937)

FISCHEL, W. G., 'Färbemethoden der Maori', *Ciba-Rdsch.*, **90**, 3343–3345 (1950)

FURRY, M. S. and VIEMONT, B. M., *Home Dyeing with Natural Dyes*, U.S. Department of Agriculture (1935)

GARÇON, J., *La Pratique du Teinturier*, Paris, 3 Vols. (1893–1897)

GUTMAN, A. L., 'Technische Besonderheiten der flandrischen Tuchmacherei und Färberei', *Ciba-Rdsch.*, **14**, 496–500 (1937)

HENSCHEL, K., *Pflanzenfarben auf Wolle*, Berlin (1937)

HENSCHEN, I., 'Rohstoffe und Geräte in "Schwedische Bauerntextilien"', *Ciba-Rdsch.*, **95**, 3501–3505 (1951)

HORN, P., 'Textilien in biblischer Zeit, Die Färberei', *Ciba-Rdsch.*, **2**, 17–24 (1968)

LAMBERT, A., 'Färbemittel in der bäuerlichen Textilkunst', *Ciba-Rdsch.*, **37**, 1392 (1939)

LAWRIE, L. G., *A Bibliography of Dyeing and Textile Printing*, Chapman and Hall Ltd, London (1949)

LEIX, A., 'Färberei und Färberzünfte im mittelalterlichen Handwerk', *Ciba-Rdsch.*, **1**, 10–16 (1936)

LEIX, A., 'Die Farbstoffe des Mittelalters', *Ciba-Rdsch.*, **1**, 18–22 (1936)

LEIX, A., 'Die Farbenmärkte des Abendlandes im Mittelalter', *Ciba-Rdsch.*, **9**, 300–306 (1937)

LEIX, A., 'Mittelalterliche Farbenmärkte des Orients', *Ciba-Rdsch.*, **9**, 307–311 (1937)

LEIX, A., 'Die Färbigkeit des antiken Orients', *Ciba-Rdsch.*, **12**, 426–432 (1937)

MACQUER, M., *L'Art de la Teinture de Soie*, Paris (1763)

MAIRET, E., *Vegetable Dyes*, London s.a.

NEUBERGER, M. C., 'Färbeverfahren im Mittelalter', *Ciba-Rdsch.*, **9**, 313–316 (1937)

PLOSS, E. E., *Ein Buch von alten Farben*, Heidelberg-Berlin (1962)

REININGER, W., 'Die Florentiner Textilindustrie im Mittelalter', *Ciba-Rdsch.*, **38,** 1405–1414 (1939)

REINKING, K., 'Über die Färberei der Pflanzenfasern im Mittelalter', *Melliand TextBer.*, **19,** 198–200 (1938)

REINKING, K., and DRIESSEN, L., 'Die Quellenschrifte über die Färberei im Mittelalter', *Bull. Féd. Int. Ass. Chim. Text.*, 1–12 (1937)

VARRON, A., 'Seidenzucht, Seidenweberei und Färberei im alten Orient und in der Antike', *Ciba-Rdsch.*, **11,** 383–389 (1937)

WESCHER, H., 'Wege der Färbekunst in Frankreich bis zur Colbert', *Ciba-Rdsch.*, **22,** 774–781 (1938)

WESCHER, H., 'Grosse Lehrer der Färbekunst im Frankreich des 18. Jahrhundert', *Ciba-Rdsch.*, **22,** 783–799 (1938)

WESCHER, H., 'Der Stand der Färberei in Frankreich nach der Colbertschen Reglementierung', *Ciba-Rdsch.*, **22,** 801–804 (1938)

WESCHER, H., 'Alte Rezepte der Garnfärberei mit Pflanzenstoffen (in Rumänien)', *Ciba-Rdsch.*, **70,** 2605–2606 (1947)

4
Principles of Fragile Textile Cleaning

JAMES W. RICE
Consultant in Textile Chemistry and Engineering, Textile Museum, Washington, D.C.

4.1 INTRODUCTION

In the conservation of artistic and historic textiles, cleaning to some degree is almost always necessary. This work should not be attempted, however, without a plan based on an examination of the individual specimen and a knowledge of the risks involved in all the possible treatments. This chapter points out these risks and suggests various ways of overcoming them.

Some of the questions to be investigated when planning a job of fragile textile cleaning are indicated below and explained in greater detail later (but not necessarily in the same order).

What is the chemical composition of the textile?
What are the physical characteristics of the fibre, the yarns and the fabric?
What colourants are to be found on the specimen and how will they affect the cleaning task?
Are there any finishing agents, special treatments or surface effects which must be preserved?
What kinds of soils are encountered in the textile?
Which cleansing medium is safest and most effective?
What additives and cleaning aids are required?
What working temperatures will be best, considering the soils and fabric condition?
What sort of mechanical action may be used safely?
How long may the specimen remain exposed to the cleansing medium?

4.2 HOW THE FIBRE COMPOSITION AFFECTS THE CLEANING DECISION

From the point of view of cleaning and handling, merely knowing the chemical classification of the fibres is very helpful. Because the four principal groups into which all the individual fibres may be classified behave with characteristic differences towards the various cleansing mediums, additives, dyes and soils, we can make many fundamental decisions on this basis. These four classes are the *vegetable fibres* which are composed chiefly of the chemical cellulose, the *animal fibres* formed from proteins, the *mineral fibres* which differ from both of the first two, and finally the *synthetic or man-made fibres*, which not only differ from the first three, but vary greatly among themselves in individual properties. Except for very modern museum specimens and for special reinforcement and protective uses, this last group is of little interest at this time.

The most commonly encountered vegetable or cellulosic fibres are cotton, flax or linen, hemp, jute and rayon or regenerated cellulose; more rare is ramie or china grass. All of these, except jute, are principally cellulose and similar in most properties of interest to the cleaner. They are destroyed chemically by strong acids at a pH level of about 2·5 or below. They are not damaged by strong alkalies, but pick up moisture readily and will swell in water. Drycleaning fluids have no effect in this respect. They can be bleached by chlorine bleaches, but oxidation materially weakens them. They can be dyed with 'direct cotton' or substantive dyes, also vat dyes such as indigo and developed types, but will not accept acid or basic dyes unless mordanted. When ignited, all cellulosic fibres have a characteristic odour, that of burning paper. When they have been extinguished, they continue to glow with a travelling ember leaving behind a soft grey ash. A burning test wherein these several properties are observed is a common way to identify the cellulosics. Although disapproved of by many museum personalities, the burning test is a property of the class and is widely used by professional cleaners.

Jute, although possessing most of the common characteristics of the true cellulosics, differs in its chemical composition in that its molecule contains groups or radicals resembling slightly acidic phenol, which will accept basic dyes. Jute is also more easily decomposed and damaged by oxidation; hence, old jute fabrics are usually very brittle and weak.

The animal or protein fibres consist of wools, various hairs, feathers, leathers and silk, and differ from the vegetable class in cleaning behaviour in a number of ways. All with the exception of silk, and possibly leather, resemble one another in chemical composition in that they contain sulphur in a form that makes them more readily attacked by certain scavenger insects. Unlike the cellulosics, they are not damaged by acidic action at moderately low pH values. However, nitric acid at room temperature, 20°C, will destroy all of them and hydrochloric acid or a chloride ion will attack silk, especially if it is weighted.[1] This warns us to beware of common salt as a dye-setting agent in silk cleaning. While new wool and silk will withstand moderately alkaline conditions, below pH 11, any more active hydroxyl ion concentration should be considered as dangerous. If the protein fibre has been oxidised by bleaching, ageing or sunburn, it may not withstand higher alkalinity than pH 10. Alkalinity has been accused of fostering wool shrinkage, especially at medium and higher hydroxyl ion concentration.[2]

Protein fibres accept moisture and, like the cellulosics, will swell and become plasticised when wetted thoroughly with water. Drycleaning fluids do not have this effect. Because the protein molecular structure contains both acidic and basic sites that can combine chemically with basic or acidic dyes, these fibres have little or no affinity for 'direct cotton dyes'. They may be dyed satisfactorily with vat or developed and mordanted dyes, however, to a high degree of washing fastness. When ignited, protein fibres have a characteristic acrid odour resembling that of burning feathers. On being extinguished, the ember does not continue glowing and exhibits a friable charred bead. This test is a useful way of identifying the class quickly if a small sample of yarn can be spared.

For positive identification of individual fibres within classes, it is customary to study them by transmitted light with a microscope, using a magnification of at least 150. The characteristic appearance of each individual fibre class can then be established by reference to a set of comparison standard slides or to an atlas of the fibres.[3]

Mineral fibres are not uncommon in historic textiles and when encountered, are usually finely drawn metallic wires or strips of metal foil wound around a central core of some other fibre. The metals are usually alloys of various combinations of gold, silver, and copper and occasionally other base metals. Corrosion is the principal problem and each case represents an individual cleaning task. Other minerals such as asbestos and glass fibre are chemically inactive and are so rare in museum fabrics that we may disregard them.

The individual synthetic fibres are generally more uniform in chemical composition than the natural fibres. Most of them are not affected or easily penetrated by moisture. Some can be penetrated by drycleaning or special solvents. As a class, they are hard to colour and must be dyed by special techniques which take advantage of the above penetration information. They are inert to most chemicals. However, some, for example, cellulose acetate, may be damaged by acetone or strong alkalies, and nylon is dissolved by strong acids at 5% or more concentration. Many synthetic fibres are heat sensitive, tending to melt rather than burn. A few have a characteristic fibre appearance under microscopic examination. Others will dissolve in special solvents or react to various chemical tests, some of which are complicated. Official tests may be obtained from publications of the American Society for Testing Materials.[4]

4.3   THE IMPORTANCE OF STRUCTURE

The physical structure of the fibre profoundly affects its cleanability. For example, natural fibres are built up by the living plant or animal from very long molecules partially oriented into micelles which, in turn, are oriented into fibrils and thence into the finished fibre. There are definite spaces between the molecules and between the subdivisions of the fibres just listed which form pores and channels through the interior and present a pitted outer surface. These pores enable the fibre to absorb moisture, dyes and other chemicals within its structure, while the outside pits and crannies foster adherence of dye and attract soils to the surface.[5]

Most of the man-made and mineral fibres are of uniform chemical composition oriented in dense compact form which is not porous and they have a comparatively smooth outer surface. For these reasons synthetic fibres do not absorb water or dyes readily nor do they soil easily.

4.4   THE EFFECT OF COLOURANTS ON TEXTILE CLEANING

Colourants, as a whole, may be classified into four main groups—dyes, lakes, stains and soils. The dyes and lakes are of most interest to us at this moment because they are a part of the problem of conservation, in that they must not be lost. The stains resemble dyes in action and may be defined as accidental soluble colourants which should be removed, if possible. The soils are also accidental colourants, resembling the lakes because they are usually insoluble substances adhering to the fibre surfaces. These unwanted colourants will be discussed at greater length when dealing with soils.

Dyes are coloured substances that are soluble, at least at some stage when applied to the fibres. They owe their tinctorial power to certain chemical groups called chromophores which cause the dyestuff molecules to reflect specific light wavelengths. The dyestuff molecules also contain other chemical groups called auxochromes which govern the solubility of the molecule and help to fix it to the fibre. The lakes are insoluble coloured compounds which, if not formed as a result of a chemical reaction in place on the fibre, are pulverised, mixed with an adhesive and painted or printed on to the fabric. When this is done, they are called pigments.

Our principal interest is in the washing fastness of the colourants. This depends on the strength of the attraction between the fibres and the colourant, which is called the affinity. If the affinity is strong, the fibre does not release the dye and its dyeing is 'fast'. If it dissolves or is easily removed, the dye is said to 'bleed'. A lake pigment which fails to adhere properly is said to 'crock'.

From the cleaner's point of view, these colours fall into three different classes, according to the mechanisms by which they become 'washfast'. These classes are:

Those that depend on combining chemically with the fibre molecules;
Those whose solubility must be decreased and particle size increased after they have penetrated into the pores and crevasses of the fibre;
Those that depend on subsequent development of insoluble compounds within the pores and intermolecular spacings by first introducing a soluble colour component followed by a substance that will combine chemically with it to form a precipitate.

The first group is found principally in the protein fibres, wool and silk. These proteins are amphoteric, and, according to their structures, have some free basic and some free acidic radicals located at intervals along the molecular chain.[6] These sites permit acceptance of organic or other acids and organic or other bases. Thus, if the colourant or dye is acidic, it will unite with the basic site or if the dye is basic it will combine at the acid site. This gives rise to two subclasses within the first group.

4.4.1   THE ACID DYES

The acid dyes form most of the natural vegetable colourants and have been popular for dyeing wool in the past. They are found in many plants and come in many hues; perhaps the most common are browns, tans, and yellows. Their chemical composition is usually complex, but they will generally react in a similar way to tannic acid, which has high affinity for proteins and a powerful colouring effect. Each individual dyestuff, however, requires careful processing to force it to react satisfactorily with the fibre.

First the fibre must be wetted and swelled to a condition where the pores and interior molecular spacings are opened enough to permit penetration of the dye molecules. This is done by raising the temperature of the dyebath and by stirring and agitating the fabric in it. When this penetration begins to look satisfactory to the dyer, a setting agent such as a stronger acid is added. In the setting operation, the acid causes the weaker acid dye to collect into groups of molecules or micelles within the pores. If the colour is unevenly distributed or is not to the required depth value, a little detergent to assist penetration and levelling may be added instead. When the dyeing is satisfactory according to a test swatch or fragment that has been dried, and the setting agent has been added, the dye batch is drained quickly and rinsed in cooler water. The purpose of this is to shrink the swollen fibres and hold the dye particles more firmly in place. During this phase, acid rinse waters may be employed to maintain setting conditions. This brief description may be altered according to the individual dye and the whim or experience of the dyer, but it does suggest principles of cleaning and procedures for handling an acid dye problem.

The test for an acid dye should be made on all the hues in the specimen to be cleaned and is made as follows. To test for bleeding, a small area of each individual hue is wetted with a few drops of plain water. It is kept wet for a short time, about one minute, and then a white blotter or folded absorbent tissue paper is applied to the area and pressed in contact for a short time. It is then removed and examined for signs of colour transfers which, if present, warn the cleaner against wet cleaning. Next, a similar small area of the particular colour is wetted with a small amount of acetic acid solution (about 2% CH_3COOH) and the examination with a blotter is repeated. If the colour is not apparent at this point, the cause of the original colour transfer may be due to over dyeing and failure to rinse the original dye job properly.

To confirm a suspicion that the dyestuff is of an acid class, another area is wetted with a solution of ammonium hydroxide (about 2% NH_4OH) which is applied as before and examined. If bleeding occurs, the area is rewetted with the ammonium hydroxide, and acetic acid solution is applied generously and blotted again. If signs of colour are absent, the dye class has been established. At this point, the effect of detergent solution (about 0·4–0·5%) with an equal amount of the acid should be tried in the same way. If no bleeding occurs, the colour may be wet cleaned. If bleeding is apparent, the colour must be tested with drycleaning fluid in the same way to establish a method of cleaning it safely.

Sometimes, in case of doubt, it may be wise to try with hot wet cleaning solutions (60 to 70°C). Drycleaning fluids should not be used hot for several reasons that will be discussed later.

As a summary, acid dyes may bleed to alkalies, or detergents, especially if alkaline (soaps) and if above 60°C. They may be set by mild acids or sours.

4.4.2. BASIC DYES

The basic dyes are less common among the natural dyestuffs but are apt to be found as synthetic colours on fabrics dating from the last half of the nineteenth century. Usually, when fairly new, they will be brilliant, but, because they are light sensitive, fading is likely. They are also reputed to be less washfast as a class than the acid dyes. These basic dyes have an affinity for the occasional free acid sites on some of the amino-acids forming wool and silk, examples of which are aspartic and glutamic acids.[6] For this reason, they may be applied after an original dyeing with acid dyes to enhance the brightness of a particular hue. This is called top dyeing and, when encountered, will add to the cleaner's problems because although alkalies will set basic dyes, acids will cause them to bleed. In this case, neutral washing conditions may fail and the only way to remove soil may be by drycleaning.

Basic dyes will also combine chemically with ligno-cellulose found in jute, bark, and wood products. This is because the lignins are made up of some phenolic type radicals which are faintly acidic in action and can combine chemically with bases. These colours are used on jute cloth, and may be found on basketry, bark cloth, and curiously, for disguising browned grass lawns which are sometimes dyed with 'malachite green', a basic dye. These dyeings are not very washfast and bleed readily to detergent action.

The practical identification tests for the basic dyes follow a similar procedural pattern to that recommended for acid dyes. In this case, after seeing whether the test area has been over dyed or not rinsed thoroughly, one may establish the class by testing with 2% acetic acid solution. At this point, excessive colour transfer on blotting indicates presence of the basic dye. Confirmation is made by rewetting the spot with the acetic acid and applying a slight excess of 2% ammonium hydroxide or solution of some mildly alkaline salt. If the bleeding or transfer signs disappear on pressure blotting, the dye may be presumed to be a basic type. This test is not completely trustworthy because if the fabric or particular embroidered area has ever been top dyed, a considerable excess of the ammonium hydroxide may cause bleeding of the original acid dyeing.

Because many basic dyes are sensitive to acid–basic changes or the reverse, in a similar way to the familiar pH indicators, a decided colour change, as in the case of litmus, may confuse the observer. This pH colour change phenomenon is also a weakness in some acid dyes. Another danger about testing with ammonium hydroxide is that the vegetable fibres, especially those containing ligno-cellulose, may develop a distinctly brownish colour when it is used.

As a summary, in cleaning, basic dyes may solubilise or bleed in mild acids, probably will be solubilised by neutral detergents and be set by mild alkalies.

4.4.3 DIRECT COTTON DYES

The second principal dyeing mechanism grouping, that of the 'direct cotton' or substantive class, is composed of coloured substances that are appreciably non-ionisable, but soluble to a considerable degree. Many of these are salts of the acid dyes or related compounds. Colouring of the fibre depends on how well the molecules can penetrate into the fibre pores and eventually into the molecular spaces. This is one of the reasons why these dyes work quite well with cotton fibres, are less successful as a rule with flax, and may merely stain wool on the outside of the fibre with colour that is readily dissolved.

For a fast dye job, the fibre is wetted, its pores and finer spaces expanded in the hot or boiling dye bath and the dye solution forced in by working or stirring the fabric or fibre until a uniform acceptance occurs. This is assisted by solubilising and lubricating agents similar to detergents. (These will be treated later in detail when considering the properties of surface active agents.) As soon as satisfactory penetration is reached, the particle size is increased by addition of metallic salts usually either sodium chloride (NaCl or common table salt) or sodium sulphate (Na_2SO_4 or Glauber's salt). The effect of these is to cause the single molecules of dye to collect into micelles of a large number of molecules forming particles of considerable size. By cooling the solution, draining, and rinsing in salt brine followed by clear cold water, the fibre shrinks and entraps the dye particles. On drying, this seizure is reasonably secure. Like all dyeing procedures, this general scheme is subject to the whim of the dyer and the peculiarities of the dye.

A practical test for cleaning hazards, after learning whether or not the test area is over dyed and affected by plain water alone, is to resaturate the spot with water first and blot. If this is negative follow with a detergent solution, about $\frac{1}{4}\%$ concentration, and after a few seconds, try blotting under pressure. Traces of colour indicate a dye of this class. If the spot is resaturated with detergent, a salt brine solution of about 5% concentration is applied and the area is blotted again, a lack of colour transfer confirms the dye class. If this does not work, a more concentrated and colder solution may be required. Occasionally, on very heavily dyed goods, cleaning is only possible by drycleaning and before doing this, the colour should be tested in a similar way with the several drycleaning liquids.

4.4.4 MORDANTED AND DEVELOPED DYES

The third, or developed class of dyeings in which the soluble component of the dye penetrates the fibre and is fixed in place by a chemical reaction may be expected to produce the best washing fastness. There are a number of modern ways of doing this dyeing, but perhaps a description of the two oldest methods will prove our point adequately.

The first method uses the mordanted dyes and, in theory, depends on setting up an anchor between the fibre chemical and the dyestuff molecule which otherwise would not be accepted. The mordanting or anchoring agent must be able to attach itself to the fibre either by a chemical reaction with an active acid, or basic site, or a strong adhesive attraction to the fibre surface. The mordant must also be capable of developing active basic or acidic sites that are not attached to fibres, but which will react with an acid or basic dye to form the insoluble junction. By this mechanism, cotton or cellulosic fibres may be coloured more or less permanently with acid or basic dyes which would otherwise only stain.

There are two types of mordants. The first type is made up of those used for setting an acid dye on cellulose, the best of which are the trivalent metallic hydroxides of aluminium, iron, or chromium. In general, the fabric is impregnated with a solution of a soluble salt of any one of these and then steamed or boiled to hydrolyse the salt to the hydroxide which, in this condition, is usually gelatinous and sticky. The acid dye is then introduced and, as a result of chemical reaction, forms an insoluble coloured mass. Chromium was not discovered until relatively recently so we would not expect it to be found in older textiles. Aluminium has been known and used for centuries as alum and it produces excellent results. Iron mordanted dyes are common and are deep and dull in hue, mainly blacks and browns. The trivalent iron, unfortunately, is a catalyst for eventual oxidation and these colours oxidise sooner than other hues. The salts of tin are also used, the four valence metal being used to give rise to the so-called red or scarlet 'bow' dyes.[6] (An old English dyer's term for colours developed from dyeing in block tin vessels. Probably taken from the French *beau*.)

Tannic acid, a multivalent organic acid which may be hydrolysed in place, is a useful mordanting agent for the basic dyes. In application, vegetable tannins from barks, fruits, or roots are extracted, and the solution impregnated into the fibres. These are steamed to produce a gelatinous acidic plating on, or within, the fibre pores. The basic dye is then precipitated on this bridge which, on drying, becomes quite insoluble. This dyeing technique produces dark but lightfast shades that also resist wash fading.

The vat dyes constitute the second class of developed dyes. The two best-known examples in historic textiles are indigo and Tyrian purple. When applied, these must be in the reduced or leuco state at which time they are soluble under alkaline conditions. At this time, they are straw or pale yellow in colour. After penetration of the dyestuff, the fabric is exposed to the air for oxidation. As the oxidation develops, the hues change through green to blue for indigo, or through orange to red to deep crimson and purple for the Tyrian purple. As the colour compounds oxidise, they become more and more insoluble and washfast. Likewise, the shades deepen as oxidation progresses.

There are no simple recognition tests for either the mordanted dyes or the vat dyes, nor are any necessary in cleaning since they ordinarily do not constitute a cleaning hazard, and the simple solubility tests for other types would reveal these colourants as safe.

4.4.5   PAINTS AND PRINTS

A final test for painted, printed, or very deeply dyed fabrics is recommended. This is called a 'crocking' test and is made by rubbing the colour under examination first with a dry white cloth or tissue, followed by rubbing with a damp one. If the white cloth or tissue shows a pick-up of colour, crocking is indicated. It may be due to over dyeing or deterioration of the adhesive in the case of pigments. In this case, a similar test is made by rubbing the questionable colour with a cloth dampened with dry solvent to ascertain whether drycleaning is feasible.

4.5   HOW VARIOUS SOILS AFFECT CLEANING

We may oversimplify what we mean by soil by defining it simply as matter out of place, but this depends on one's point of view. For example, egg on a plate is food, but on a garment, it is soil.

There may be many ways, therefore, of classifying soils. For example, we might do so according to origin, or to the way they are deposited. Thus, they may be airborne, water deposited, contact smeared, accidental, or the results of oxidation or chemical degradation of any of the components of a textile such as fibres, dyes, textile finishing agents, adhesives, preservatives and other treatments. Alternatively, they may be fragments from wear, abrasion and bacterial, fungal or insect damage. A more practical way of grouping them from the cleaner's standpoint is to divide them into types that will yield, in general, to the three main cleansing mediums; air, water and organic liquids.

4.5.1   AIR REMOVABLE SOILS

These are usually loosely attached deposits of sand, dust, other earthy matter, lint or fibre fragments and finely divided foreign trash. They may be airborne, contact smeared, or, less often, water deposited. To get rid of them, we depend mainly on an air blast accompanied by shaking, agitation, scraping, brushing or other more or less violent mechanical actions to break up and dislodge the foreign substance. The air has very little actual cleansing power, other than its ability to pick up and carry away particles or droplets of the soil either by vacuum or direct air blast, both of which are fundamentally jet power. With an air blast, it is possible to add scouring materials such as sand in sand blasting, or sawdust in fur cleaning. Collection of the spent scouring substances and dust in this case becomes a problem, whereas a vacuum nozzle not only produces a jet action on the soil but takes care of dust collection also.

Vacuum cleaning, where possible, is a valuable first step in most cleaning processes, because often loosely encrusted soil matter will disintegrate on wetting, either by water or other solvents, and redeposit as finely divided particles which subsequently may become much harder to remove.

4.5.2   WETCLEANABLE SOILS

Soils that respond to cleaning in water are designated wetcleanable. There are eight categories which differ chiefly in the cleaning aids that may be needed for the job. These are:

  Soils that are soluble in water alone;
  Those that require alkaline conditions for removal;
  Those that may be released best by acids;
  Substances that will require digestion by enzymes;
  Stains that can be bleached or oxidised;
  Stains that can be decoloured by reduction;

Substances that may be dissolved by sequestrants or chelating agents;
Insoluble deposits that may be emulsified or solubilised by detergents.

Soils That May Dissolve in Water Alone

Although plain water is a most versatile solvent and will dissolve very many
different substances, its action is sometimes so slow and limited that it must
be helped. There are a number of things it will dissolve readily. Some
notable classes are: simple inorganic salts, especially those of the alkali
metals, potassium, sodium and ammonium; a number of salts of other metals;
the hydroxides of the alkali metals and a few hydroxides of other metals;
many oxygen containing organics of low molecular weights, among them
alcohols, organic acids, sugars and numerous crystalline compounds.

The amount of any substance that water will hold in solution in most
cases depends on the temperature. The speed of dissolving also depends on
how near it is to saturation with respect to the particular solute. The temperature rule of greater solubility in hot water does not hold for gases, and
a very few other substances, notably calcium sulphate $(CaSO_4)$ which is
more soluble in cold water.

Soils That Respond to Alkaline Cleaning Agents

Most soils encountered are those that require alkaline additives to the water
for best cleaning. Many of the natural products of oxidation are acidic and
often these are not soluble until they are changed by neutralisation into
salts or soaps or other compounds of the alkali metals that compose most of
the basic substances used. Experience with, and studies of, detergency have
shown, also, that cleaning and emulsification are usually faster and more
efficient under alkaline conditions.[7]

Some of the more common acidic soils are such substances as edible oils
and fatty foods, perspiration and body contact smears, matter condensed
from smoke and air fumes, fruit and plant juices, many vegetable and
synthetic dyestuffs, and products of decay of vegetable and animal matter.
Protein matter such as glues and blood stains, while they may not be acidic,
may be attacked and depolymerised by alkalies or strongly basic chemical
agents.

The ionic activity of the usual wetcleaning solution has much to do with
its effectiveness. As a rule, cleaning is best above pH 10 and decreases
markedly as the pH drops to neutrality or below. This high pH may have no
serious damaging influence on cellulosic fibres, but, with protein fibres,
degradation is likely. For this reason, control of the pH within reasonable
limits is advisable and a buffering system necessary. At the same time there
must be a source of strong positive ions that will form soluble products on
reaction with otherwise insoluble acidic soils. This is the reason why the
alkali metals are chosen. The hydroxides of these metals are so completely
ionised that pH control is not practical when they are used alone, so alkaline

Table 4.1 PH VALUES OF SOME COMMON ACIDS AND ALKALIES*

Name	Formula	pH at 0·1% concentration	pH at 1·0% concentration	
Sodium hydroxide	NaOH	12·3	13·3	
Sodium orthosilicate		12·1		
Sodium sesquisilicate		11·6		
Sodium metasilicate	Na_2SiO_3	11·4		
Sodium carbonate	Na_2CO_3	11·2	12·1	
Trisodium phosphate	$Na_3PO_4.12HOH$	11·1	11·9	
Ammonium hydroxide	NH_4OH	8·6	9·1	11·5 (26°Be.)
Modified soda	$\begin{cases} Na_2CO_3 \\ NaHCO_3 \end{cases}$	10·3	10·3	
Neutral soap		10·0	10·0	
Borax	$Na_2B_4O_7$	9·2	9·2	
Phenolphthalein changes				8·4
Sodium bicarbonate	$NaHCO_3$	8·3	8·3	
Boric acid	H_3BO_4	5·5	5·0	
Carbonic acid	H_2CO_3	4·1	3·6	
Acetic acid	CH_3COOH	3·3	2·8	2·0 (28%)
Methyl orange changes				3·3
Formic acid	HCOOH	2·7	2·2	
Hydrofluoric acid	HF	2·2	1·7	
Oxalic acid	$(COOH)_2$	1·6	1·0	
Hydrochloric acid	HCl	1·6	0·7	

*pH determinations above 10 are somewhat approximate in the first decimal place, due mainly to the effect of sodium ions on glass electrode measurements. The above pH values, with the exception of those of the silicates and of soap, have been calculated from data found in chemical literature.

Table 4.2 A pH CHART

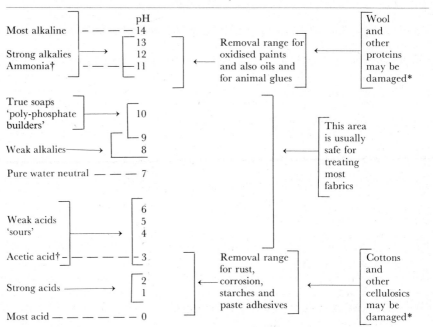

*The extent and seriousness of the damage will depend on the condition and age of the fibres, the time of contact and the temperature of the solution.
†These pH values are for concentrations of about 0·1% or less. Both ammonia and acetic acid are volatile and will disappear in a short time, usually before the fabric is damaged.

salts are used to bring about a buffering or alkalinity control action.[8]

These alkaline salts are salts of a weak acid and a strong base, such as sodium hydroxide (NaOH) or potassium hydroxide (KOH). When dissolved in water, these dissociate completely, i.e. $NaOH \rightarrow Na^+ + {}^-OH$ and the only way that the number of destructive hydroxyl ions (${}^-OH$) can be controlled is by drastic dilution. At 0·1% concentration this alkali has been reported to have a pH of about 12·3, far above the protein danger point.[9]

Ammonium hydroxide (NH_4OH) is a weak alkali that ionises incompletely, thus: $NH_4OH \rightarrow NH_4^+ + {}^-OH + (NH_4OH)$ (dissolved molecules) and at 0·1% concentration has a pH of about 8·6 and at 1·0% about pH 9·1, but at high concentration, about 28%, does not exceed pH 11·5. This alkali is volatile and often escapes long before damaging effects are noticed.

An alkaline salt such as borax produces a pH of 9·2 at both 0·1% and 1% concentrations. The control is based on the theory that water is ionisable to an extremely limited extent and that when a salt of a strong alkali and a weak acid is dissolved, a series of reactions takes place producing a limited number of free metal ions and free hydroxyl ions. The following is an example of this process:

$$Na(CH_3COO) + HOH \rightarrow Na^+ \quad + {}^-OH + HCH_3COO + [Na(CH_3COO)]*$$

| sodium
acetate | water | sodium
ions | hydroxyl
ions | acetic
acid
un-ionized | sodium
acetate
un-ionized
molecules | 4.1 |

Since many of the weak acids do not ionise to the same extent, it is possible to choose an alkaline salt that will produce a reasonably limited pH range even though the concentration is not adjusted precisely.

These alkaline salts are sometimes called 'soap builders' because they are frequently added to soaps or washing mixtures to increase the cleaning powers, especially for very heavily soiled cotton fabrics, e.g. industrial garments. Compounds such as trisodium phosphate (Na_3PO_4) sodium metasilicate (Na_2SiO_3) and sodium carbonate (Na_2CO_3) are representatives of builders. At a recommended concentration of 0·1% they produce pH values of 11–12 and are too active for safe wool cleaning work, especially under hot water conditions.

'Neutral' soaps, which will be defined later in a discussion of detergents and soaps, at concentrations of 0·2% give a pH of about 10. The best cleaning is achieved at about pH 10·5 so the soap is usually built with a 'builder' to prevent the formation of fatty acids which interfere with its work.

Synthetic detergents, on the other hand, are said to work best at about pH 9·5 and for these a class of complex phosphate ion compounds called polyphosphates are reputed to be valuable additives. Two of these, tetrasodium pyrophosphate ($Na_4P_2O_7$), and tripolyphosphate ($Na_3P_3O_{10}$), may be encountered in heavy duty home washing powders. Although unlikely to attack wool proteins chemically, they may cause some shrinkage and give rise to dye bleeding in high concentrations. For these reasons they should not be used without testing.

Other very weak alkaline salts which have very little neutralising power but may have special uses are borax ($Na_2B_4O_7$) and sodium bicarbonate

*These reaction equations are only illustrative for the composition of the solutions, and are not quantitative.

($NaHCO_3$). The borax is used for scouring soap curd deposits from utensils, and heavy greases and oils from workmen's hands. The sodium bicarbonate or baking soda is sometimes mixed with sodium carbonate or washing soda, half of each by weight, to make 'modified soda', which has a buffered pH of about 10 which does not vary appreciably on increasing the concentration.

Characteristics of Soils That Respond to Acids

As a general definition, a strong acid is one that ionises completely. There are three of these, hydrochloric acid (HCl), nitric acid (HNO_3) and sulphuric acid (H_2SO_4). All others are considered weak although they vary greatly in strength or completeness of ionisation.

Metal corrosion products such as iron rust, copper, and other metallic oxides are examples of soil substances that may yield to acid treatments. Direct chemical union with the oxide to form a soluble salt of the metal will require a particular acid, e.g. hydrochloric acid (HCl) would be suitable for dissolving iron rust on wool, but would not dissolve silver. Since it is one of the three strong acids, it would damage cotton if so soiled, and would not be suitable for silk. Earthy matter such as lime, chalk or cement may be dissolved by acids but again a specific acid must be chosen.

A few colours, notably the basic dyestuff class, and some organic chemicals are soluble in acidic solutions. Nylon fibre is an example and is affected by the strong acids at about 5% concentration. It is also dissolved by concentrated formic acid, but this is probably an individual property of that particular chemical. As another example, concentrated acetic acid (above 30%) will dissolve cellulose acetate.

Acids are quite often necessary for setting acid type dyes and for neutralising residual alkalinity in the washing process; to avoid damage to cotton fibres, either mild acids or buffering salts which will produce a pH level of 2·5 or above are recommended.

Acetic acid (CH_3COOH), the sour principle of vinegar, is the most widely used of the true acids. At concentrations of approximately 1% its pH is about 2·8. At 28% concentration, its pH is 2·0, but because it is volatile, it will usually evaporate before damaging cellulose. Formic acid (HCOOH) found in bee and ant venom, is sometimes substituted for acetic acid where a slightly stronger acid is needed, and is also volatile. Hydrofluoric acid (HF) is a third volatile acid which is even stronger. It is a valuable rust remover but will attack glass and metals, so it must be used in wooden or plastic basins.

For permanent setting of acid dyes, and prevention of development of brown discolourations in cotton or linen goods when dried slowly, the cleaner can use acid producing salts known as laundry sours. The safest of these are sodium and zinc silicofluorides (Na_2SiF_6, $ZnSiF_6$) sometimes known as fluosilicates. When dissolved in water, they produce a limited number of free hydrogen ions (H^+) (cf. hydrolysis equation 4.1). They produce a buffered pH of 3 to 4 even when quite concentrated and are not apt to damage cellulose. Of the two laundry sours mentioned, the zinc compound is preferred because it is more soluble than the sodium compound. If not rinsed away, it provides protection against moth damage in wool.

Soils That Are Affected by Sequestrants

Certain special soils, e.g. soap curds, which are formed by hard water, are dissolved readily by polyphosphate sequestrants such as tetrasodium pyrophosphate and tripolyphosphate which were mentioned previously in the discussion of alkali builders for synthetic detergents. A near relative of these, sodium hexametaphosphate $(Na_6(PO_3)_6)$ is an exceptionally efficient reagent for this purpose and is practically neutral. These substances are known as complex ion compounds and have the peculiar property of substituting sodium from the complex ion for calcium, magnesium, ferrous iron and other bivalent metals. The following equation illustrates this mechanism:

$$Na_2[Na_4(PO_3)_6] + 2\,Ca^{++} \rightarrow Na_2[Ca_2(PO_3)_6] + 4\,Na^+$$
Complex ion   calcium sequestered

It is probable that hydrofluoric acid acts in a similar way when removing rust. Oxalic acid $(H_2C_2O_4)$, which is substituted for the hydrofluoric acid in cases where a fabric contains metallic or glass yarns, probably owes its ability to remove rust to sequestering or chelating action.

Other examples of complex ion formation are to be found in the use of potassium cyanide for silver stain removal. This cyanide is a violently poisonous substance, and fortunately it is seldom necessary to use it, since silver stains may be removed by first treating them with iodine and then dissolving the silver iodide in sodium thiosulphate. This substitute treatment may bleach some dyes so it must be done with care and excess iodine removed at once. Copper corrosion may be removed by ammonia and certain amines. The principle in this case is again formation of complex ions.

Soils That May Require Digestion by Enzymes

Substances such as protein deposits, including blood stains, body stains, body decomposition matter, gelatin, food stuffs of many sorts, starches, sugars and other soils can be degraded or hydrolysed by enzymatic action. Such organic catalysts are quite effective for removal of glues, sizings, pastes and natural adhesives that may have hardened and become objectionable from ageing processes.

These enzymes or digesters are effective in action but require neutral pH conditions and tepid temperatures, not exceeding about 45°C. Below about 30°C the conversion becomes very slow. In digesting, the soils must remain in contact with the solution and the temperature maintained constant for about half an hour. The timing is left to the operator's discretion and his experience.

Although digestion is a very gentle process, it has been known to weaken and attack wool that has been damaged previously by repeated oxidation and other drastic chemical action.[10] From this one may suppose that both old wool and old cotton might possibly be affected to some degree by this soil removal method.

Coloured Stains That May Respond to Reduction

Bleaching is often considered to be the removal or the changing of an objectionable foreign colour in a textile to an acceptable hue. This general definition would include oxidation, reduction and hue change phenomena such as blueing or brightness changes with modern fluorescent dyes. Specifically, however, bleaching is destruction of the colour by oxidation, which may be defined simply as adding oxygen to a compound. Cleaners prefer to think of bleaching as controlled oxidation.

Reduction is the opposite of oxidation and may be defined as the removal of oxygen. In the language of cleaning this is called stripping and denotes controlled reduction.

There are two main classes of objectionable coloured soil substances. One of these is metal corrosion which is sometimes intensely coloured and insoluble. These corrosion soils are the result of oxidation, and as a rule they will respond to reduction upon which the colours change to a lighter and different hue and often become soluble. Iron and manganese are two examples of metals that will corrode in this way.

The second stain class is made up of organic substances that are either true dyes or natural colour substances that are related to them, in that each contains certain chemical groupings in its molecular structure, called chromophores, which are arranged in regularly repeating sequences. Chromophores have in common more or less unstable double or triple bonds between carbon or nitrogen atoms, which are readily attacked and changed by oxidation or reduction. Reduction of a chromophore is considered less drastic than oxidation because it is not likely to completely sever chromophoric double bonds such as $-C{=}C-$ or $-N{=}N-$, but may

change them to $-\overset{|}{C}-\overset{|}{C}-$ or $-\overset{|}{N}-\overset{|}{N}-$ which cease to be colour forming but

by mild oxidation may return to a double bond formation later.

Reduction is endothermic and requires continued application of heat. Since it is opposite to oxidation, we may consider it as an unnatural process, but one which may be useful in inhibiting or repairing oxidation. For these reasons we find many practical uses for strippers or reducing agents. First, they are useful in stopping oxidation after bleaching, for if not stopped at a precise stage, bleaching may go too far and damage the fibre. Secondly, many dyes and stains will respond to reduction but may not be removed by oxidation. The vat dyes are of this nature.

The professional cleaner has three types of reducing agents at his command. First, for bleaching control, sodium bisulphite ($NaHSO_3$) is a popular agent. It is not a powerful dye stripper, however, and for that purpose, most professionals prefer either sodium hydrosulphite ($Na_2S_2O_4$) or formaldehyde sulphoxalate ($NaHSO_2 \cdot CH_2O \cdot 2H_2O$). When stripping a garment, for example, a solution of approximately 2% is heated to about 50°C and the garment immersed. The temperature is maintained for about half an hour. If at that time the colour intensity has not been lowered, a fresh solution is made up, the garment is entered, the temperature raised about 10°C and the reducing action continued. This sequence may be repeated if not at first successful.

Spot bleaching with hydrosulphite stripper is sometimes done, by wetting the spot in question with detergent and then sifting on some of the powdered chemical. A little 5% solution of acetic acid applied to the spot and worked in with a wooden or bone spatula hastens the chemical action. Steam will also help. This is also a way of testing a dyed area to see if it may be reduced by the reagent.

The hydrosulphite strippers should not be used in steel or metal vessels. Stoneware, unscarred enamelware, glass or wooden vessels are preferred. Articles containing silver, copper, iron, or other embroidery and buttons will be tarnished by the hydrosulphites and in this case black stains may develop. However, these will usually yield to dilute hydrofluoric acid.

The titanium strippers constitute another type of reducing agent that is popular with professional cleaners. These are titanous chlorides or sulphates ($TiCl_3$ or $Ti_2(SO_4)_3$) and are purple liquids. In action, they are oxidised to four-valent substances. One of these is titanium oxide (TiO_2) a white but insoluble residue. This will respond to dilute hydrofluoric acid (HF) as will titanous hydroxide ($Ti(OH)_3$) a yellow precipitate sometimes formed by accident when ammonium hydroxide is applied. These insoluble compounds may be rendered colourless and soluble by dilute hydrofluoric acid but when using this fabrics should be rinsed thoroughly and the use of glass or enamel utensils or table tops avoided. The titanium strippers are more efficient if hot.

Coloured Stains That May Respond to Oxidation

Stains that respond to oxidation are common but this type of bleaching of historic textiles should always be considered as a last resort treatment. Two general classes of oxidisable stains may be mentioned. First, there are those that are the result of displacement of dyes within the textile itself, or perhaps of accidental contact with another coloured specimen at some stage of cleaning or wetting. These are called bleeding or smear stains. Sometimes they will respond to soaking without a bleach being used. In this event, the solution temperature, the time of treatment and the additives, such as alkalies or acids, the detergents and perhaps special dyesetting agents are important, and in each case present a unique problem. All of these items have to be determined by tests and observation. Often, however, the soaking technique will not remove all traces of the stain and bleaching becomes necessary.

The second main type of bleachable stains covers those that are either the result of accidents or develop within the textile itself from oxidation or ageing processes. The accidental stains may be from spills of various foods or beverages, or contacts with wet vegetation. Those that develop from within the textile itself may come from the breakdown of the fibre, perhaps from oxidation of a colourant, or a finishing agent such as starch. As a rule many of these, regardless of source, appear as tan or browned rings or spots and if the history of the specimen were known exactly, the original cause might be traced to wetting with a natural sugar or starch that had not been removed completely at the time of the accident. As these carbohydrates age, they oxidise through various stages to develop into compounds resembling acid dyes, which have no particular affinity for cellulose unless mordanted, but combine with proteins to make a very 'fast' staining job at the place of the original neglected spot. This theory will account for the gradual yellowing of cottons or linens over the years.

If hot, slightly alkaline solutions (pH 10, 60°C) do not remove the stain substance from cellulosic fibres, bleaching with a 'chlorine bleach' such as described below will often restore satisfactory whiteness. This does not guarantee that the brown colour will not return. The protein fibres are damaged or destroyed by chlorine bleaches. Sugar oxidation products form very insoluble substances with these proteins, so other types of bleaches have not proved to be satisfactory, mainly because drastic oxidation is necessary and the other bleaches may not have the specific whitening action attributed to the chlorine type.

There are two general classes of bleach widely used in the cleaning industry. The chlorine bleaches are commonly used in laundering cotton and linen goods because they are cheap and do a good job. The peroxides which will be discussed later are used principally for wool and silk but, occasionally, they may be chosen for delicate cotton specimens.

The chlorine bleaches are actually hypochlorites (^-OCl) which in contact with the fibre surfaces decompose to produce nascent oxygen (O) which is very reactive. If not in contact with the fibre, the nascent oxygen forms molecular oxygen (O_2) which is less efficient for oxidation purposes.

The hypochlorite radical is obtainable in three different widely marketed chemical compounds: sodium hypochlorite ($NaOCl$) a liquid of about $5\frac{1}{4}\%$ concentration for household use; calcium hypochlorite or H.T.H. ($Ca(OCl)_2$) a crystalline powder, only slightly soluble; and calcium oxychloride or bleaching powder ($CaOCl_2$) still less soluble. In most cases these last two are converted to soluble $NaOCl$ before use, by reacting them with sodium carbonate (Na_2CO_3) thus:

$$Ca(OCl)_2 + Na_2CO_3 \rightarrow 2NaOCl + CaCO_3\downarrow$$

The $CaCO_3$ precipitates and settles and the liquid is decanted off. When used in a bath, the concentration should be diluted to about $\frac{1}{10}\%$ or even $\frac{1}{50}\%$ for very old specimens. Best bleaching conditions are slightly alkaline—pH 10—in warm water. Thorough rinsing followed by a mild acid to neutralise the alkali is advisable.

Spot bleaching for small areas may be done with $\frac{1}{2}\%$ or lower concentrations in warm water. In this case, a cotton-tipped wooden applicator is saturated with the bleach and applied to the stain. The stain is observed, and when the colour is lessened to the desired degree, a reducing agent such as sodium bisulphite ($NaHSO_3$) is applied at about 2% concentration, using another wooden cotton-tipped applicator. This is followed by rinsing and absorbing the excess moisture by blotters.

The peroxide bleaches are suitable for bleaching on wool or silk because they are not so likely to cause yellow discolourations and fibre damage as the chlorine types. Two different substances that fall into this class are widely used and recommended. These are hydrogen peroxide (H_2O_2) and sodium perborate, chemical formula either $NaBO_23H_2O \cdot H_2O_2$ or $NaBO_3 \cdot 4H_2O$. Of these, the first is probably correct.

Hydrogen peroxide is supposed to break down on contact with the fibre surface, according to the chemical equation: $H_2O_2 \rightarrow H_2O + O$ (nascent oxygen). It is a very weak acid and is stable only when kept under acid conditions. When made alkaline, as with ammonium hydroxide, it decomposes rapidly according to the above equation. Exposure to light or heating will also cause decomposition of the acidified hydrogen peroxide. All these chemical properties provide us with several ways of controlling it in bleaching. Besides these, we may also stop its action by antioxidants such as sodium bisulphite. Immediate decomposition is also catalysed by metals, especially iron, and for this reason, metal vessels or table tops should be avoided when bleaching with it. Because of this property, it may be used as a rough qualitative test for blood spots. If the unknown dark spot foams rapidly when a drop of hydrogen peroxide is applied, it is probably blood.

Although peroxide can be purchased in several concentrations, 3%, 10%, 30% or even higher, the 3% or drug grade is preferred because it is considered safer from a fire hazard standpoint in storage or handling. In bath bleaching, it is usually diluted down to 0·2–0·5% concentration depending on the problem. For spot bleaching where it is under visual observation, about 1% may be tried. The bleach is applied first and often followed by dilute ammonium hydroxide to speed up the action.

Sodium perborate is the second member of the peroxide bleaches that is widely used for protein fibre bleaching. When dissolved in water, the crystal molecule is supposed to undergo a chemical change thus: $NaBO_2 \cdot 3H_2O \cdot H_2O_2 \xrightarrow[\text{solution}]{\text{in}} NaBO_2 + H_2O_2$, producing sodium metaborate and hydrogen peroxide. This reaction is probably surface catalysed on contact with the fabric and fibres. Since granular sodium perborate is of only slight solubility, about $3\frac{1}{2}$% at 20–30°C, this limits the maximum concentration of H_2O_2 to less than 0·7%. Thus, there is little or no danger of getting too high a concentration even though a mistake is made in mixing. At temperatures above 50°C, approximately, the solution or moist granules decomposes spontaneously, producing mainly molecular oxygen gas, so that temperatures of use must be moderate. This decomposition effect, however, is sometimes employed by professional cleaners in spot bleaching, wherein the small area is covered by perborate granules and heat and moisture are applied by a gentle steam jet. This is a rapid but wasteful method and might be too drastic for use on old weak fibres.

4.5.3   SOILS THAT MAY YIELD TO ORGANIC SOLVENTS

There are many soils that do not dissolve or soften appreciably in water but are attacked by non-aqueous liquids. Familiar soils of this type are oils, greases, waxes, tars, resins, some adhesives, rubbers, certain gums and lacs, varnishes, paints and modern polymers, and plastics. Many of the natural fats and oils can be saponified by alkalies in water solutions, or emulsified by soaps and detergents, but it is often more efficient, and safer from several points of view, to clean them in one of the modern drycleaning solvents.

There are some substances mentioned above that may not dissolve in the special drycleaning fluids but can be attacked by special solvents. These will be described later.

Petroleum Solvents

Two different classes of special drycleaning liquids have been developed and are in widespread use for commercial cleaning. One of these is composed of selected fractions obtained in distillation and cracking of crude mineral oils or petroleum. A great deal of care is taken to obtain a solvent that does not volatilise appreciably at temperatures below 60°C (140°F) so that explosive mixtures of the vapours and air cannot occur except at extreme and unbearable temperatures. This particular grade is known as 140°F flash solvent. Flash point solvent has been approved for use in homes by many states and municipalities in the U.S.A. as a safe drycleaning solvent. Another similar product, having a flash point of 38°C (100°F) and known as Stoddard solvent, was a forerunner but is not as widely approved as the 60°C (140°F) type.

Both of these are excellent cleaners for most textiles. They will remove many common soils, especially greasy, sooty matter and about the only dyes that are dissolved by them are oil mordanted colours similar to wax crayons. Soils resembling sugars, salt, and other water soluble deposits may be removed by emulsifying a little more water into the solvent than ordinarily present. The emulsifying agent is a special type of detergent called a drycleaning soap and is used in small quantities, no more than 4% at most. The mixture of water–drycleaning soap–drycleaning solvent is called a 'charged' system and its use has improved drycleaning performance greatly.

These petroleum solvents are cheap, of low toxicity and have no damaging effects on most textiles, so they are very widely used by cleaners in the U.S.A. They will swell and weaken rubbers, many paints and some plastic substances and should not be used on printed goods or paintings without testing. Although they are flammable and will burn if temperatures exceed the flash point, they are very much safer than automobile gasolines or commercial naphthas.

Synthetic Solvents

The synthetic or man-made solvents constitute the second main group of the drycleaning liquids. Most of these are chlorinated hydrocarbons, although in recent years, fluorinated hydrocarbon solvents have been developed for coin operated cleaning machines. The chlorinated solvents are used for professional cleaning, in locations where fire regulations will not permit the petroleum types, because they are non-flammable. In general, they are more rapid in cleaning action than the petroleum solvents and will attack some soils and substances that do not yield to that group.

These chlorinated hydrocarbons are rated as poisonous but toxicity varies greatly from one compound to another in degree and effect. Likewise, some persons are more resistant to the toxicity than others. To support these statements, the poisonous effects of two similar solvents, carbon tetrachloride (CCl_4) and perchlorethylene (C_2Cl_4) are quite different.

Carbon tetrachloride is a dangerous and violent poison. When its vapours are breathed, not only does it act as an anaesthetic, but the vapours may also damage various body organs. This last effect is cumulative and each succeeding dose renders the victim less able to withstand further damage. The liquid may also be absorbed through the skin with similar results.

In comparison, perchlorethylene is rated according to industrial safety codes variously as about $\frac{1}{20}$ to $\frac{1}{2}$ as toxic as carbon tetrachloride.[11] Its effect is said to be intoxicating chiefly, and the dangers of accumulating serious organic damage much less. Because there have been many deaths attributed to carbon tetrachloride, it is seldom used or approved for garment cleaning nowadays. Instead, perchlorethylene is very widely used in the U.S.A. for the purpose, and although thousands of people are exposed to its fumes daily, authentic reports of serious poisoning from it are very rare.

In Europe, a near relative, trichlorethylene (C_2HCl_3) has been more widely used because it was more readily available and less expensive than C_2Cl_4. Recent advances in chemical engineering technology, however, have lowered costs of the latter and it is becoming more widely used. Trichlorethylene is rated as slightly more toxic than perchlorethylene and has the additional drawback of being more likely to bleed some modern dyes, especially when it is warm as may happen during the cleaning process. Losses from evaporation are also slightly greater.

These two chlorinated solvents are efficient cleaners, both from the point of view of special solvent action and of insoluble soil particle removal. This last property may be due to their high specific gravities, approximately $1\frac{1}{2}$ times that of water or nearly twice that of the petroleum solvents. This makes them more buoyant and the greater weight of fluid produces a more concentrated mechanical action in stirring or tumbling, for disintegrating soil masses.

Like the petroleum solvents, these synthetics require a drycleaning–detergent–water 'charge' for salt and sweet stain removal. They are about five times as costly as petroleum solvents and the fumes are toxic, so they must be contained in closed machines, their vapours condensed wherever possible, and the condensate returned to the system for re-use.

Fire and explosion hazards are nil. In case of fire on the premises, however, the hot vapours may decompose into noxious products, one of which is phosgene ($COCl_2$) a very poisonous gas. Water in contact with some of the chlorinated types, especially in the light, cause them to break down into hydrochloric acid (HCl) and other products. The acid is not soluble in the solvent and may be separated by filtering through cotton or woollen rags. This is the usual practice in conventional drycleaning procedures. The acid may also be neutralised by an alkali. Again, decantation or treatment by rag filters may be needed for removing the moisture.

In addition to the drycleaning fluids discussed previously, there are a number of organic liquids that have special solvent power for particular substances, especially soils that do not yield to wetcleaning or ordinary drycleaning. Among these we find soils that are the result of either accidental or intended polymerisation of certain more or less readily combined molecules. Chemical actions such as oxidation, reduction, hydration, dehydration, heating or cooling may cause single molecules to form giant molecules. As a rule, these very large molecules are less soluble in ordinary solvents than smaller molecules. Occasionally, certain solvents are compatible with and can penetrate the polymer. The original soil substance molecule will be an unsaturated compound to begin with so that cross linking can take place. In many cases, the degree of setting or polymerisation increases with time; thus, an aged deposit is often harder to break down and remove. Vulcanised natural rubber is an exception because continued oxidation contributes to its depolymerisation and breakdown.

There are three major groups of soils that may yield to special solvents but not to water or ordinary drycleaning solvents. First, there are the unsaturated oils occurring in paints, foods, atmospheric smogs and soots and various other greasy deposits. The saturated oils are readily soluble in drycleaning solvents but if ignited or heated, may crack into unsaturated fractions. These, in turn, are susceptible to repolymerisation or 'drying', as in paint film development. The natural unsaturated oils such as linseed and soya bean oils are notorious in this respect. When relatively fresh, these paint films can be liquefied and removed by drycleaning solvents, but as they absorb oxygen from the air they become hardened and less easily penetrated. At this stage, aromatic hydrocarbon solvents such as benzene (C_6H_6) toluene $(C_6H_5CH_3)$ or xylene $(C_6H_4(CH_3)_2)$ may attack the film. All three are toxic and flammable and readily form explosive mixtures with the air. Benzene is reputed to have the highest solvent power, toxicity and flammability. Toluene is less and xylene least in these three characteristics. None of the three is likely to damage natural textiles or dyes, but any prints or painted specimens must be regarded as hazards and the solvents tested carefully on them before use.

Adhesives used for reinforcement and mending of old textiles are a second, and less frequent type of soil. Usually these are glues that may be attacked by wet processing with acids, alkalies, or digesters. Occasionally shellacs, gums and resins, that do not respond to wet processing may be found. Many of these are alcohol soluble. Either concentrated ethyl alcohol or methyl alcohol may do the job. Complete rinsing is necessary, because, if diluted with water, the adhesive may deposit back on the fibre. The alcohol solution is not soluble in petroleum solvents and only slightly soluble in the synthetic drycleaners. Some dyes are dissolved in the alcohols so the conservator should test all colours involved with the solvent before using.

Rubber and rubber latex adhesives are commonly used for adhering reinforcements to backs of old rugs. Very often these must be removed for cleaning and repairs. Frequently they will soften or dissolve in one of the aromatic hydrocarbons mentioned above under 'drying' oils. If the rubber has been vulcanised or polymerised with sulphur, it may resist these solvents, and in that case, carbon disulphide (CS_2) a very poisonous, inflammable and foul smelling substance, will often dissolve or soften the rubber. Where softening only is desired, the drycleaning solvents will usually suffice.

Other commonly encountered adhesives, such as cellulose nitrate or cellulose acetate cements, that are insoluble in water, drycleaning solvents and even the aromatic solvents, will dissolve in acetone (CH_3COCH_3), ethyl acetate $(CH_3COOC_2H_5)$ or perhaps amyl acetate $(CH_3COOC_5H_{11})$ or other ketones and esters. Most of these are flammable and toxic to varying degrees. Of these several solvents, only pure amyl acetate is safe for use on cellulose mono- or sesquiacetate fibre. The others will dissolve it.

The lacquers, special paints, and many unknown insoluble polymerised deposits, that do not respond on testing to the conventional wet or drycleaning solvents, will sometimes soften to a point where they may be scraped from the textile by gentle manipulation with spatulas or other tools. If such deposits do not dissolve appreciably, they may swell and disintegrate. Some synthetic rubbers, especially chloroprene, silicones, new kinds of paints and fibre protective treatments, may be of this type. If none of the special solvents mentioned above prove helpful, as a last resort one may try one of the special paint removers often called 'paint strippers'. These are mixtures of many of the solvents already named, perhaps with other additives such as methylene chloride, formic acid, and special detergents and solubilisers to enable them to penetrate a massive deposit, break it up, and emulsify it in a solvent liquid. Some of the ingredients of these mixtures will dissolve or disintegrate cellulose acetate, nylon, and other synthetic fibres, so thorough testing prior to use is advised. The principles of penetration by which these strippers work is explained in the next section.

4.5.4   INSOLUBLE SOILS

Soils that are insoluble in either wet or dry solvents often respond to emulsification by surface active agents. Soaps and other detergents belong to this class of chemicals and the soils they attack best are crusts of earthy materials, partly polymerised sticky airborne deposits like soot, smears deposited under contact pressure, and very finely divided particles from solvent borne slurries and suspensions, e.g. muddy water. Of all of these, the latter seem to be hardest to dislodge because they will be minute enough in size to penetrate into nooks and crannies and deposit on the rough surfaces of the natural fibres. Once these submicroscopic, but insoluble particles have been deposited, the attraction between the fibre surfaces and the particles becomes very great, and it is only by overcoming this surface attraction that removal can be accomplished. At this point, the surface activity agents or 'surfactants' are needed.

Surfactants[12]

When a surfactant works on an absorbed surface-bound particle, a number of things happen. First, the surface tension, or the attraction between molecules, of the cleansing medium is decreased. This permits the liquid to approach the substrate, or fibre, and the soil particle more closely and is called wetting. The second stage of the process then takes place, during which the surfactant molecules are aligned in such a way that one end joins the substrate while the other end extends into the cleansing medium, forming an imaginary furry effect.

To visualise this clearly, one should recall the structural formula of a soap, e.g. sodium laurate $(C_{11}H_{23}COONa)$ the chief ingredient of coconut oil soap. This molecule is composed of a moderately long chain of CH_2

groups connected to a carboxyl and solubilising metal grouping COONa and is pictured thus:

$$CH_3CH_2CH_2CH_2CH_2CH_2CH_2CH_2CH_2CH_2CH_2COONa$$

The long carbon atom chain is attracted to most surface substances, especially the fibres, and is supposed to be especially compatible with oily matter. According to the same theory, the water-attracting group, —COONa, is repelled by the surface, thus causing the molecule to point away. This water-attracting end of the molecule is known as the hydrophilic group, the other end is known as the hydrophobic part.

When the surfactant molecule is quite short, it functions as a wetting agent only because moisture is already very close to the surface to be cleaned. This does not mean that it is a good detergent, although wetting is one of the necessary attributes of a good cleaning agent. A longer chain, however, might be able to penetrate the interface between a soil particle and the fibre surface, thus parting the two. This would help to release the soil from the surface and, indeed, is probably what happens during the second stage of cleaning.

The third step of the detersive process is that of penetrating the soil mass, which we may suppose to be porous (see Figures 4.1, 4.2, 4.3, 4.4). The

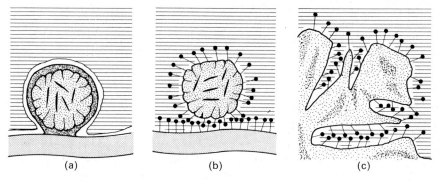

(a)   (b)   (c)

Figure 4.1. (a) A porous soil particle adheres to the surface. (b) Surfactant molecules from the detergent solution penetrate the area of adhesion and orient themselves on surfaces. (c) Section of (b)—surfactant molecules from the detergent solution enter pores and orient themselves on surfaces[12]

attraction forces of the hydrophobic ends of the surfactant molecules, enable the molecules to be absorbed on to the surfaces of any pores or cracks in the soil mass. At the same time, the hydrophilic ends attract water into these spaces producing a swelling force which, if aided by mechanical action, helps in breaking up the soil mass into minute particles, which are theoretically completely surrounded by layers of oriented surfactant molecules. This is referred to as emulsification or peptisation, depending on whether the soil mass is liquid or solid. These individual particles are very large compared to molecules and unless collision is prevented, a gel or collection of particles may occur which would redeposit the soil substance.

At this point in the process, it becomes necessary to maintain separation or suspension of the particles, at least until they can be removed from contact with the substrate. Mechanical disturbance, jet action or heat will do this, but the soil-bearing emulsion must be taken away as soon as possible, lest coagulation and redeposition occur. One of the ways of preventing or delaying this danger is by selecting a detergent of suitable molecular structure and characteristics. This detergent molecule must have a relatively rigid chainlike structure, as illustrated by the chemical formula for the coconut oil soap mentioned earlier, and must bear a strong electrical charge on the

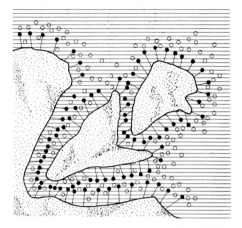

Figure 4.2. Attraction of water (O) to the hydrophilic ends of the surfactant molecules (●) results in swelling of the pores and disintegration and fragmentation of the soil[12]

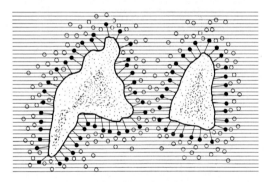

Figure 4.3. Disintegration completed: separated particles form a jelly, or cream-like emulsion. Van der Waal's effect no longer holds[12]

hydrophilic end. It should be soluble to a limited extent, but should be only weakly ionised if at all. When such a molecule orients itself to the soil fragment, the electrically active parts extend out, providing the particle with a charged surface which, when in the vicinity of another similar particle, has a mutually repelling action. This helps to maintain suspension within the cleaning medium.

The length of the hydrophobic chain affects the suspension powers of the detergent molecule. A longer structure appears to produce more buoyancy of soil particles and more protection from accidental collision. The larger and longer molecules, however, unless modified by the presence within the chain of hydrophilic groups or radicals, such as —CH=CH—, —CH$_2$OCH$_2$—, —CH$_2$O, —CH$_2$OH, COOH, —NH—, and other combinations, are less soluble in water than shorter surfactant molecules. From this argument, a general rule as to the effect of the length of the molecule may be set up. Those shorter than 10 carbon atoms may be soluble in cold water, but are not especially good cleaners. At about 20 carbon atoms in length, unless modified as noted above, the compounds are usually so little soluble, even in very hot water, that they fail as cleaners but may be very good lubricants. The short-chain molecules are useful wetting agents and emulsifiers for gels and creams.

Some textiles, because of their very fragile condition, cannot stand mechanical agitation or handling, especially when wet. In these cases, one may try soaking techniques employing a 'solubilising' agent. Solubilisation is a phenomenon, midway between that of dissolving a substance to form a molecular dispersion and that of emulsification or suspension of larger particles. During attack by a substance which is appreciably soluble both in an encrusted soil, for example, and water, a complex of a single molecule of the soil plus one or more molecules of the solubilising agent and numerous molecules of water is formed. This grouping or micelle is relatively small and easily distributed into the surrounding water, because it approaches molecular

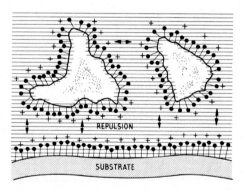

Figure 4.4. Electrostatic repulsion[12]

distribution conditions. A continuing attack of this sort eventually disintegrates the soil deposit into an almost clear mixture with the cleansing medium (Figure 4.5).

Many detergents and soaps possess this valuable property, some more than others for specific soils. For this reason, a knowledge of the probable composition of the soil would enable one to select a compatible surfactant. The effectiveness and speed of penetration and solubilisation also depend on the temperature, the pH and the concentration, which in this case may be lower than when emulsification is desired.

The importance of lather or foam on a cleaning solution is chiefly that it indicates a satisfactory concentration of detergent micelles in the cleansing medium. Although some authorities mention the floating power of stable suds for light soil particles such as fibre fragments and surface deposits of dye crusts, this contributes very little to the overall cleaning job.[13] When the lather is fine and stable, however, the detergent and water mixture is usually in the best condition for emulsification and suspension of the soil. Lack of satisfactory suds or a sudden change indicates poor cleaning conditions. This may be due to acidity or temperature changes, addition of salt or overworking the solution mechanically.

Excessive suds sometimes may be a nuisance and for gentle soaking a

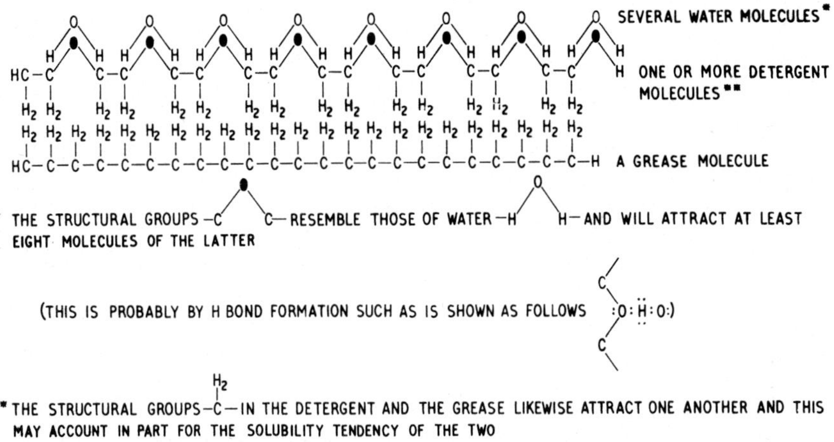

Figure 4.5. *The solubilisation process. Chemical formulae + explanatory text, as given in this figure*

minimum of lather may be best because this indicates a favourable proportion of single detergent molecules rather than collected micelles in the cleansing mixture.

Lubrication is often mentioned as a desirable characteristic of a detergent, and may be described best as that property of a detergent that enables it to spread over surfaces and form a protective film of appreciable depth. If this film sticks tenaciously to the surface and is thick enough to overcome the Van der Waal's effect of attraction of like molecules when brought very close together, then soil is unlikely to redeposit. For this reason, detergents with long molecules make the best lubricants.

4.6 TYPES OF DETERGENT

Colloidal chemistry studies over the past half century have shown that detergents, or substances that help cleaning through surface activity principles, may be divided into three main groups, according to their behaviour in an electric cell. These, in order of their usefulness in cleaning are anionic, non-ionic and cationic detergents.

4.6.1 ANIONIC DETERGENTS

The anionic types are the most widely used in cleaning. Structurally, as discussed earlier, these consist of a moderately long hydrophobic carbon atom chain joined to a hydrophilic group bearing a strong positive electrical charge. For simplicity, these molecules are often represented thus: ————————————O^+; where the hydrophobic end is shown as a line bearing the negative charge and the hydrophilic end is represented by O, the symbol for oxygen, and bears a positive charge indicating a strong basic element.

Many hundreds of individual anionic compounds have been studied and patented, but for our purpose, two main subgroups are recognised. We designate these soaps and synthetic detergents or 'syndets' for short.

Soaps

Soaps may be defined as esters or salts of fatty acids and metallic hydroxides or strong bases. The true soaps are soluble in water and because very few bases, other than the alkali metals sodium and potassium, and the strong organic bases ammonia and ethanol amines, donate sufficient solubility, their number is limited. This is especially true because the length of the fatty acid carbon chain is also limited to between 12 and 18 atoms unless modified.

The metallic soaps, which comprise compounds of other metals with fatty acids, are either nuisances if formed in the cleaning process or are special use products not particularly for soil removal processes.

The cleansing soaps have several defects. They react with calcium, magnesium and iron ions, in hard water, to form soap curds, which are sticky gel-like masses that deposit out on fabrics or washing equipment. This not only reduces the useful soap concentration but adds to the insoluble soil problem. It is one of the reasons why soft water is needed for cleaning. Soaps are decomposed by acids into salts and free fatty acids, thus:

$$C_{11}H_{23}COONa + HCl = NaCl + C_{11}H_{23}COOH$$

soap	mineral	salt	insoluble
	acid		fatty acid

The fatty acid has no cleansing action in water.

Soaps coagulate in salt brine and if the brine is concentrated enough, will precipitate out. This is the way that soap is separated from solution in manufacture. It also reminds us that soaps do not work in sea water.

Neutral or built soaps, which may be necessary to overcome residual acidity in a textile, may be alkaline enough to promote shrinkage or even felting in wool. Superfatted soaps that are incompletely saponified are usually safe in this respect, but may not provide best cleaning. They are excellent lubricants, however, and for that reason are employed in leather cleaning.

Unless made from highly purified fatty acids, ordinary soaps are obtained from natural oils and fats, and thus are seldom composed of precise chemical constituents. These natural fats are usually mixtures of glycerides of many different saturated and unsaturated fatty acids, so that soaps of exact chemical compositions such as used for our illustrations are rare. However, if a soap is decomposed into its fatty acids and these are dried and melted, we may measure a solidifying or melting point of the mixture which has a worthwhile meaning. This temperature when reported in degrees Celsius is called the 'titer'. As a rough practical rule, the best working temperature for a soap solution is about 12–14°C above its titer. Because the titer is indicative of the solubility of the soap, we often hear the terms high titer used for a hot water soap, medium titer for a warm water soap, and low titer for a tepid water soap. Very few soaps are efficient in cold water.

The particular alkali that makes up the soap also affects its solubility. Sodium soaps are least soluble, potassium soaps more so, and ammonium soaps still more readily dissolved. Solubility is also dependent upon whether the principal fatty acids in the soap are saturated or unsaturated chains. The latter form the more soluble soaps. This is the reason why Castile soap which contains a large percentage of oleic acid ($C_{17}H_{33}COOH$), an unsaturated fatty acid from olive oil, dissolves in tepid or even cool water, whereas a soap made from beef or mutton tallow, which is mainly the saturated fatty acid ($C_{17}H_{35}COOH$) does not dissolve satisfactorily until the water temperature is about 70°C. One should note that the two fatty acids are the same carbon atom chain length.

For washing woollens, Castile soap might be an excellent product were it not for the fact that when the oleate oxidises in ageing, peroxides are formed across the weak double bond. These are supposed to continue oxidation to form vile smelling aldehydes similar to perspiration odours.

True soaps may be decomposed by biological processes and are unlikely to poison beneficial bacteria in sewerage disposal systems and streams.

The high titer soaps are rated as very efficient cleaning agents, when used in hot water and rinsed thoroughly at high temperatures. Synthetic detergents compete with moderate and low titer soaps especially for cleaning wools, and in some cases are considered more satisfactory.

Synthetic Detergents

Because the anionic syndets can, by controlled planning and manufacture, be produced so as to avoid many of the defects of soaps, they are displacing the fatty acid compounds for general cleaning usage. For example, the chemical composition can be restricted to uniform products that are more soluble than soap and will work better at lower temperatures. They can also clean satisfactorily at pH levels below the felting or damage points of wool. These anionic detergents may be affected by calcium, magnesium or iron in hard water, but because the resulting precipitates are not sticky curds or slimes, their deposits are much less noticeable than those of soaps. Salt brines also have less drastic coagulation effects on this class. In fact, in some cases, salt may even be required to produce a favourable micelle concentration within the cleaning suspension. Most of the syndets are less sensitive to acids or moderately low pH conditions than soaps. Neither soaps nor anionic syndets are compatible with cationic syndets.

There are a number of different classes of chemical compounds that have been studied and patented for detergent usage. For simplicity, we will try grouping them into three main classes which are:

1. the fatty alcohol and alkyl sulphates and sulphonate esters (F.A.S.);
2. the alkyl-aryl sulphonate esters; and
3. all other anionics.

Groups (1) and (2) comprise most of the syndets marketed in the U.S.A. today for textile cleaning.

Of these three rough groupings, class (1) behave most like the true soaps as far as cleaning effectiveness is concerned. The fatty alcohol sulphates are produced from natural fats, such as coconut oil, in which lauric acid ($C_{11}H_{23}COOH$) is reduced to lauric alcohol ($C_{11}H_{23}CH_2OH$), which in turn is treated with sulphuric acid and neutralised to produce $C_{11}H_{23}CH_2$—OSO_3Na, or sodium lauryl sulphate. The hydrophilic portion in this molecule, —O—SO_3Na, is much stronger and more active than the —C—OONa of the corresponding lauryl soap. Thus, this particular syndet turns out to be soluble in cooler water than the soap and is preferred by professionals for wool cleaning. Other similar sulphates are by-products of petroleum cracking.

The sulphonates which are also by-products of petroleum cracking have a very similar hydrophilic radical, —SO_3Na, but in this case we might expect a little less activity towards water than from the sulphates. This class cleans much like soaps but is more soluble and less affected by acids, salts and hard water. The members of the class also work better at lower pH levels than soaps.[14, 15] We would expect them to be biodegradable.

The alkyl-aryl sulphonates (A—A—S), sometimes known as the alkyl-benzene sulphonates (A—B—S) are perhaps the most widely used chemical class of anionic syndets. Their main chemical characteristic is that the structural formula, in addition to a straight alkyl chain, contains an aryl or benzene ring to which a sulphonic acid radical is attached. Upon neutralisation, with one of the solubilising metallic ions, the aryl sulphonate metal complex becomes strongly hydrophilic. A typical formula for one of these is $CH_3(CH_2)_xC_6H_4SO_3Na$.

These detergents are synthesised mainly from by-products of petroleum cracking and refining. In general, they are more readily soluble than the F.A.S. types. For heavy duty cleaning, they require salts such as sodium sulphate or other thickeners to be added to build up a favourable micelle concentration. They are affected adversely by hard water, forming ions such as calcium, magnesium or iron, but this is not so visibly apparent as in the case of soaps. They are less sensitive to sea water, and to acids, than either soaps or F.A.S. types and can be used at lower temperatures. Some members of this class are rated as non-biodegradable and it is possible that their present widespread use may be restricted unless some way of removing them from spent wash waters is devised.

The third general anionic class comprises all the very many different syndets of other chemical families. Most of these have been developed for special cleaning purposes, so only a few examples will be given here. Alkyl-aryl sodium phosphates are highly regarded as detergents for use in dry-cleaning media. Others, some of which contain nitrogen atoms in the chain, have various special properties such as for cosmetic use or hair care.

4.6.2   THE NON-IONIC DETERGENTS

The non-ionic detergents bear no distinctive electrical charges, and a molecule is represented by a simple diagram thus ——————————O or ——————————O° because in an electrolytic cell there is no deposit on either the cathode or the anode.

This main group of detergents is employed where an excess of stable foam or lather would be a nuisance, e.g. in home-type washing machines and mechanical dishwashers. As a rule, the non-ionics are excellent solubilisers and give good results on soaking jobs where mechanical action is inadvisable. They are not affected by acids, alkalies, or salts in concentrations customarily employed in cleaning, and may be used in hard water. As a rule, they are quite soluble, although some which are primarily lubricants may be sparingly so. In order to form usable micelles for heavy duty cleaning, a thickener such as sodium carboxy-methyl cellulose (C.M.C.) must be added. For soaking jobs, they must be used at the right temperatures. They are useful stain and grease removers, but may bleed dyes.

The non-ionic surfactants can be used in the same bath with anionics. There are three principal chemical classes of the non-ionic detergents:

1. the saponins;
2. the ethylene oxide condensation types;
3. the amine condensates.

The saponins, although not widely used commercially, have found favour with textile conservation workers perhaps for the generally admirable qualities of the non-ionics as listed above. They are natural detersive substances obtained from the barks of certain trees, and nuts and fruits of a few plants. Some of the saponins are poisonous but detoxified extracts are rated as excellent cleaners. They are expensive. The chemical formulae are more complicated than the classic soap chain and just how the molecules do their work is not easily explained.

The ethylene oxide condensation non-ionics are probably equal in detersive properties to the saponins, far cheaper and more easily obtained. There are two chemical types as illustrated by the following diagrams:

1. ———o—o—o—o, an alkyl ethylene oxide where ——— indicates an alkyl chain and —o—o—o—o an ethylene oxide chain;
2. ———— —o—o—o, an alkyl-aryl ethylene oxide, in this case ——— indicates an alkyl-aryl group and the o—o—o—o an ethylene oxide chain.

Type (1) is apt to be grease solubilisers, or perhaps, in longer chains, semi-soluble textile lubricants. Moderately long molecules of type (2) configuration have been suggested as drycleaning detergents. Others may be good dye solubilisers.

The amine condensates differ from types (1) and (2) above, mainly in that a nitrogen atom is introduced into the alkyl chain or into the aryl group along with several ethylene oxide condensation units. Properties are similar to the above class.

4.6.3   CATIONIC DETERGENTS

Cationic detergents are the third major group of surface active substances and the customary schematic way of representing them is $^{+}$———O^{-}.

Note the strong positive charge on the hydrophobic end. They are not compatible with the anionic detergents and often form precipitates with that type. This is not true of the non-ionics which are sometimes used with them as synergists. The cationics are not considered as good general cleaners but do find use in special cases such as removal of bacteriological slimes and in disinfection work. At such times, when used for cleaning, a pH on the acid side increases detergent action.

Cationic detergents will exhaust out on fabrics and other surfaces, whereas the other detergent types may not. This can be noticed by a definite reduction in concentration in a solution to which a fabric has been exposed and extracted. This exhaustion factor is important in considering some of the special uses for cationics. One of these is as an antistatic agent for nylon and woollen carpetings, or sheets of plastic film, or glass plates which tend to stick together when in contact. Surfaces so treated are easily separated afterwards.

Other important uses are as softeners for paper and textiles. They make cheap paper napkins easier to spread and help them to cling to laps or garments. An example of their use in textiles is that they make babies' nappies softer and more sanitary. When cleaning an old fringed shawl or scarf, hours of laborious combing of the tassels after cleaning and drying may be saved by rewetting the fringe with a cationic solution and drying before the job of combing is attempted. Tangled fringes usually fluff out on shaking afterwards.

A great many cationic type chemical compounds have been developed and patented in recent years, many of which are for highly specialised uses as indicated briefly above. They may be roughly grouped into three main classes:

1. long chain or fatty amines;
2. quaternary ammonium salts;
3. basic sulphonium, phosphonium and antimonium compounds.

The first two named are, at present, the most common. The fatty or long chain amines are apt to be principally lubricants, softeners and antistatic producers, and the quaternary ammonium salts are likely to be disinfecting agents and deodorising sprays. Little has been published about uses for the third type.

4.7   PHYSICAL AND MECHANICAL AIDS TO CLEANING

Even with the best of the cleansing media and additives, most problems involving textiles need additional help in the way of mechanical and physical manipulation. Many of these are so well known and familiar to us that we take them for granted and do not relate them to particular problems or hazards. For this reason, a discussion of these physical and mechanical operations may be worth while. Ways in which cleansing media may need help include close temperature control, timing of contact, and a means of forcing contact between the solutions and the soil. Generally, in cleaning, all three factors will vary according to the condition and constitution of the individual specimen. For this reason, a careful study of each is advisable before starting. The result of this study will be a handling plan which may be suggested by the descriptions and discussions that follow.

The first step in the cleaning process is to estimate the physical conditions of the specimen. This may be done by visual inspection, microscopic examination, miniature cleaning behaviour tests on limited areas with the various cleansing media and chemical agents, and even more sophisticated chemical analyses. This study should result in decisions as to how well, or how long, the textile may be exposed to the mechanical or physical steps in the usual cleaning process. These, in sequence, are:

1. preparation for cleaning;
2. selection of cleansing medium and the necessary additives;
3. choice of cleaning techniques, allowable temperatures, kind and timing of mechanical action, replacement or removal of spent cleansing mixture, number and time of rinses, removal of rinse solution, method of drying;
4. finishing.

4.7.1   PREPARATION FOR CLEANING

This step is not undertaken until all information as to the composition and condition of the specimen has been collected and evaluated. If it is very weak and fragile, it may have to be protected and supported so as to immobilise it, without breaking it or causing undue loss of fibres. This may be done by placing it carefully and smoothly on a stretched piece of synthetic fibre gauze such as nylon or saran and fastening it down by sewing, pinning, or adhesion. In some cases it will be necessary to use a very fine silk netting or crepelene next to the sample, both over and under. Depending on the amount of handling expected, the sample may also be covered with another piece of synthetic gauze. If the specimen happens to be a garment, it may be protected with a fine net bag of nylon or cotton. Fabrics made of synthetic fibres are preferred for protective layers because they do not shrink in water except under unusual temperature conditions. When it has been decided to clean the article in a washing machine, the two outer layers may be of aluminium or galvanised iron wire gauze. This preparation is time-consuming and tedious, but should not be neglected. Of course, with strong rugged fabrics of good construction, these precautions may not be necessary.

Occasionally, in a composite specimen where fugitive colours, a special finish or other problems might prevent cleaning in a particular medium, a 'resist' protective treatment may be applied to prevent penetration of the solvent. For example, a starchy type chintz glaze should not be exposed to water. It may be protected by applying molten paraffin to guard during the wet phase. After drying, the paraffin may be removed by drycleaning. A second case is a painted area which would be protected during drycleaning by a coating of gelatin carefully applied. This might be removed by digestion, if necesary, after drycleaning. Other preparation steps include removal of linings, buttons, and trim of various types, where possible.

4.7.2   SELECTION OF CLEANSING MEDIUM

Choice of the cleansing medium will depend on the simple performance tests for dye bleeding and soil removal. The latter is made by rubbing a small test area with a white cloth moistened with water, followed by one moistened with detergent solution. Where dye bleeding is noted or where no soil pick-up can be seen on the white cloths, a test for effect of drycleaning solvents is made in the same way on a new area. It is important that all component colours, yarns, appliqué work, embroidery, painted or printed figures, be tested. Where the specimen is extremely delicate and fragile, the tests may be made by means of cotton tipped wooden medical applicators dipped in the various test mixtures. If necessary, the conservationist may have to improvise other tests in miniature to arrive at a decision.

As a general rule, fugitive dyes behave better in dry solvents. Very old and fragile textiles are less affected chemically by dry solvents and the fabrics are less apt to shrink. On the other hand, wet cleaning, properly managed, does a better cleansing job in most cases and is easier to control. Although solubilisation soaking can be done in both mediums, water soaking is able to remove more soils and stains. Bleaching is not feasible in dry solvents nor can digestion, sequestration, acid or alkaline reactions be employed.

4.7.3   CHOICE OF CLEANING TECHNIQUE

Mechanical handling is beneficial in almost every case of cleaning. After wetting the specimen, it is necessary to help the wetting and spreading action by submerging the specimen, or bringing fresh solution into contact with it. Temperature control and judicious choice of surfactants are helpful. Time of contact or opportunity of contact is also important.

In each individual case, the extent of mechanical action will depend on the physical condition of the fabric. This is judged partly by the age and general appearance of the specimen and partly by the miniature cleaning tests described above. An experienced worker can soon tell by rubbing a small area gently with a dry cloth, and again with cloths moistened with the cleansing media, whether it will withstand mechanical treatments as desired. Tests for more drastic action may be made by brushing, flexing or squeezing as desired.

Soaking

For very fragile pieces and fragments of textiles, soaking techniques with the specimen immobilised as described earlier, so as to prevent further disintegration, are suggested. There are five important aids to this technique. First, one must select a solubilising agent which will act on the stain or soil. For example, if the soil is slightly acidic, a mildly alkaline detergent may be indicated by the preliminary tests. Secondly, the soaking bath should be at the right concentration. This will range from about 1000 to 2000 parts per million, $0 \cdot 1$–$0 \cdot 2 \%$. The detergent chosen should be one of predominantly solubilising characteristics such as a non-ionic or an easily dissolved anionic type. (The patented or trademarked mixture should be about 40% alkali to 60% detergent diluted to the concentration recommended above.)

Thirdly, the temperature of the bath is of very great importance. For wet soaking, this may be maintained at about 37·5°C (100°F) or blood temperature. This temperature is high enough to help the detergent molecules bombard the soil or dye particles vigorously, but not so elevated as to promote rapid chemical degradation of weakened fibres.

Fourthly, provision for circulation of the bath is necessary, to bring fresh solution in contact and remove spent liquor from the fabric. This may be done by stirring or by moving the immobilised sample gently through the bath. Finally, since the exchange is quite slow, enough time must be provided for the penetration and solubilisation to take place. Frequently, this time must be extended by refilling the bath with fresh solution. When this is done depends on observations of samples of the solution for colour, turbidity, and other signs of soil removal activity, taken from time to time.

Soaking out techniques in drycleaning fluids are sometimes worth while. This is true especially where wetcleaning would cause dye bleeding or where it would engender fibre disintegration. In these cases, the drycleaning solvent is mixed with about $\frac{3}{4}$–1% of a drycleaning soap containing a very small amount of water. The temperature is maintained at 20–25°C (68–77°F). Circulation and mixing in the bath is important and the job may take a longer time than wetcleaning. Oxidation or other degradation factors are minimised, however, and the danger of damage is much less than in a wetcleaning bath.

Sponging

Sponging techniques are perhaps second in importance as far as minimising the damage potential to a textile during cleaning is concerned. The fabric is spread out flat on a surface and the cleansing medium is forced into it by sponge pressure to create a flow through and back. This system has a great many of the advantages of simple soaking but is much faster and cleaning is more complete, but obviously, the possibility of damage increases with heavy pressures and transverse rubbing. Slightly higher detergent concentrations are more effective in this case (0·18–0·25%) and temperatures of 27–32°C (80–90°F) are usual since at this point, emulsification is desirable. Drycleaning by sponge action would be more practical and less likely to cause pile crushing on velvets or other pile goods, and, if carefully done, on satins.

Brushing

Occasionally, an encrustation or massive soil deposit resists wetting and penetration by mere soaking or sponge pumping, and must be broken up by scraping or brush action. Where the fabric construction is reasonably rugged and fibre oxidation not advanced, brushing is a rapid way of soil removal. It is an especially good technique where overwetting is to be avoided. There is less danger of damaging the fibres when soft bristles are used, and when transverse motion is necessary, the bristles should be slanted away from the direction of motion. Sometimes an obstinate crust will disintegrate by gentle tamping or stippling with the bristles vertical.

This, of course, would not be a good way to treat a satin or a velvet, but heavy pile goods such as rugs, especially if relatively new, will withstand brushing very well. Brushing with approved drycleaning solvents is considered safer than with wet cleaners.

Occasionally, a deposit of dried paint or adhesive becomes set so thoroughly that it can only be removed by scraping with a blade-like instrument. A bone or wooden scraper may be purchased for this work. Metal instruments such as knives should not be used because of the danger of cutting the fibre and staining from chemical action.

Tumbling and Jet Action

Modern washing machines are based on jet action in some form. In the conventional horizontal tumbler which reverses direction every 12–20 revolutions, the jet principle is subordinate to flexing. These machines are less damaging then they appear and the danger of damage occurring is much less if they are lightly loaded, and operated with a relatively large volume of the cleansing medium at a slow speed. If garments or large specimens are prepared carefully by securing them between two layers of metal cloth, and rolled into a cylindrical coil to fit into the machine, excellent cleaning can be accomplished with a minimum of harm. This is especially true of drycleaning.

Unfortunately, this type of equipment is being replaced by machinery which is smaller, crowded and operates very rapidly. This machinery is unsuited for museum textile cleaning. Likewise, the usual home laundry machine which operate on a reversing jet effect by changing the rotation direction of fins on a spindle rapidly, is not considered suitable and would probably tear up a fragile textile quickly even if it were protected.

Resoiling

Redeposition of soil may be brought about by continuing the washing for too long in either wet or dry processing. It is most likely to occur when the temperature or pH condition within the water changes, especially in cooling. In drycleaning, a build-up of static electricity within the solvent will cause it. Whenever soil is redeposited, the fabric appears dingy and subsequent removal of soil is much more difficult. Resoiling may be avoided by changing the cleaning bath before suspended soil can settle.

Rinsing

Rinsing is an important step. Sometimes as many as five complete changes are necessary to get rid of soaps and some alkalies. Synthetic detergents, because of their greater solubility at lower temperatures, may require fewer changes. It is usually a good plan to reduce the temperature gradually through the several rinsing changes. This is especially necessary when working with woollen goods where sudden changes in temperature may contribute to excessive shrinkage.

In cases of dye bleeding, especially in woollen or silk materials, the final rinse is usually acidified up to about 1 or 2% concentration of a mild acid, such as acetic, or an acid salt, such as zinc or ammonium silicofluoride. The pH should be about pH 3 to pH 4. This is called 'souring' and is also beneficial because it neutralises absorbed alkalies on cellulosic fibres which have been accused of catalysing brown stain development as the fabric ages.

Some dyes used for cottons or linens require salt brine as a setting agent. In this case, the concentration of salt may be as high as 5% in order to prevent bleeding.

Extraction

Removal of excess moisture as soon as possible after rinsing is very important. If the fabric remains saturated, dye bleeding or transfer is still a serious threat. Quick extraction by any means that the fabric will withstand, will minimise this dye staining and will help to speed up the drying process.

Extraction methods vary according to the size of the specimen and individual estimates as to how well it will withstand the physical stresses and strains. Perhaps the simplest method is drip drying with the fabric suspended. In this case, the excess liquid drains to the bottom and the lower edge is usually stained. If the specimen is not very large, this may be overcome by spreading it out horizontally on a screen or net. If the fabric is very weak, it may not withstand hanging.

A second simple method is by blotting and absorption. For this, the article is laid out on a flat surface between layers of absorbent materials such as cotton cloths, paper towels, or felts. Flat weights are placed on top to provide contact pressure. If this is done quickly and the absorbent materials frequently replaced by dry blotters, this technique gives satisfactory extraction with the least dye transfer or structural damage. In those cases where protective gauze or layers of permeable temporary reinforcements are necessary, the excess fluid removal is not hindered appreciably.

Wringing by twisting or torsion, although probably safe for strong fabrics, produces shrinkage and is apt to cause wet dye transfer stains. It is not recommended for fragile or worn specimens.

Squeezing between rubber covered rollers is a rapid way of removing excess fluid from flat goods. If the fabric is not wrinkled when feeding it between the rollers and the pressure is adjusted according to the particular condition of the materials, very little structural damage is likely. It is not a good way of handling garments, however, because of possible crease setting.

Extraction by centrifuge is probably the most widely used method in professional cleaning and in home washing machines. It is suitable for garments and small articles and, if operated intelligently, will remove as much or more moisture than squeeze rollers, but not as rapidly if time is compared by the piece. It is not so good for large flat work because the whirling basket must be loaded so that the weight is distributed equally around the circumference. If the work is not arranged carefully in a smooth neat coil, wrinkling and crushing is likely and occasional contact dye bleeding is possible. Excessive compacting and wrinkling may be avoided by placing garments in net bags before loading in the machine. If the garments are very old and fragile, they may be rolled between two pieces of wire gauze before coiling around the inside of the centrifuge basket. Medium-sized household articles such as bed spreads, table linen and rugs, if not too large, may be treated in the same way. After bringing the machine up to top speed, the power should be cut off and the machine allowed to come to a stop. Whether the load is spun for a longer time depends on the size and rotating speed of the machine, also the apparent physical condition of the load.

Centrifuging or the blotting method of extraction is preferred in drycleaning. For fairly strong unlined rugs and tapestries, squeeze rolling is a preferred way of extracting excess water. The solvent in drycleaning will damage the rollers and in this case, extraction or blotting is safer. Linings must be removed or loosened in any case, because unequal shrinkage is the cause of much creasing and damage in extraction.

Drying

In wetcleaning, speedy drying after extraction is very important. The reason for this is that fibres that are just damp and exposed to the air, oxidise rapidly. In cellulose fibres, a brown coloured intermediate substance resembling an acid dye is formed at the line of drying. If the residual moisture is not evaporated in place, it will travel out by capillary action to a line or border where evaporation and the supply of water are in equilibrium, and at this point the stain concentrates and becomes more easily recognised. If the line happens to be at the end of a pile yarn or a yarn surface, it may result in an overall stained spot. If it is a candlewick tufted construction, a heavy brown line will result. The colour can be removed from cotton or other cellulosic products by wetcleaning or mild bleaching unless it has been mordanted accidentally. If, however, the stain has contacted wool, a fast dyeing occurs and it will not wash out. Drastic bleaching is about the only remedy.

This staining does not happen in drycleaning except where the cleansing medium contains a heavily moisturised soap-solvent, and even then, it would probably be on a sugar stained spot where a colour difference could not be detected before cleaning was started.

The best natural drying of textiles occurs when they are exposed to a warm dry wind on a sunny day. This illustrates the three main requirements for good drying, which are:

1. Heat to evaporate the moisture or solvent;
2. Dry or low humidity air, which will accept the moisture or solvent quickly; and
3. Rapidly moving air to overcome stagnant surface film resistance to heat transfer and moisture acceptance by the air.

Although heat may be applied to a textile by radiation or by conduction from contact with a hot surface, the safest way is by forced convection with air as the carrier of heat. When air is heated, its relative humidity is lowered and its moisture acceptance ability is increased. In addition, it can give up more heat to the wet material. If this air is forced through or past the textile surface rapidly, the evaporation rate is greater than if the fibres are sur-rounded by a stagnant air film. Nevertheless, there are certain limits to the air temperature, velocity and humidity that should not be exceeded in drying many fragile or aged fabrics.

As long as the fibre surfaces are wet, the air temperature may be main-tained at a high safe point of about 60°C (140°F) because if the air before heating is assumed to be at 20°C (68°F) the evaporating water and the fibre surface will be much cooler than the drying air. This final surface temperature will depend on the air speed and how fast the cleansing liquid passes from the interior of the fibre out to the surface. When the fibre surface becomes dry, its temperature will rise to that of the air stream and at that time cellulosic dehydration products tend to form more intensely coloured substances. As the temperature increases above this assumed safety level, the dehydration effect becomes even more noticeable. This can be avoided by lowering the temperature of the drying air as soon as the surfaces appear dry. During the final stages of the drying period, the air temperature and relative humidity should be the same as that of the room where the textile is to be stored.

From empirical tests and calculations made a number of years ago, the author established a reasonable figure for air speed in drying suspended rugs of about 400 ft/min (about 110 m/min). This corresponds to a gentle breeze of about $4\frac{1}{2}$ mi/h and is not likely to cause whipping or snapping damage.[16] If the textile is flat and protected by a supporting gauze, this air velocity may be increased considerably, perhaps to four or five times the speed of a hair dryer.

Textile conservationists may find it necessary to set up special drying facilities for very fragile problems. Drying equipment will vary in each case, but in the main will consist of portable electric fans and electric or steam heated radiators. As long as the textile surface is wet, damage is small even though radiant heat is directed on the fabric, but this must be cut down as soon as surface drying is apparent.

Commercial cleaning establishments have developed several different types of mechanical dryers, such as drying tumblers, drying cabinets and lofts, curtain stretchers and dryers, wind whips and combination drying and pressing machines. Whether any of these would be suitable for a particular job would depend on the strength and ruggedness of the individual specimen.

Drying tumblers are perforated metal cylinders that revolve inside a metal enclosure through which heated air is passed. They are commonly used in both wet and drycleaning plants and home laundry installations. These machines are satisfactory for drying garments and individual small textiles especially if they are relatively new and strong. They may also take delicate goods where the individual pieces are secured in protective net bags or packages. Because there is much flexing and dropping, and the time in the machine is half an hour or more, these dryers may not be suitable for old and much worn specimens.

Drying cabinets or rooms are enclosed spaces where the articles may be hung or draped over poles or on hangers and heated air circulated between. Temperatures range below 60°C (140°F) for wetcleaning or about 32°C (90°F) or 49°C (120°F) for drycleaning (depending on whether Stoddard solvent or 140°F flash solvent is used in the cleaning process). According to the space available, they are suitable for drying garments on hangers, rugs, tapestries, and other moderate sized to large pieces. Rate of drying depends on the temperature of the air, its relative humidity, the effectiveness of the circulation within the space and the air supply. Usually drying is much slower in this kind of equipment than in drying tumblers, but there is much less likelihood of damage or wear.

A 'wind whip' is a machine for drying wetcleaned garments. The garment is buttoned and clamped or pinned over a form and suspended from a hanger. Heated air from inside the form is forced through the garment fabric. Drying is very rapid and when draping and suspension is done with care, there is very little possibility of wear or damage. Staining, either from oxidation or from dye bleeding, is minimised because the evaporation rate is faster when the air passes through the fabric than when it travels parallel to the surface. There is also less opportunity for the moisture to move laterally by capillary action.

A drying system for textile fragments which works similarly may be improvised from a box, the top of which is covered with an air permeable cloth or screen, while the bottom is fitted to an electric vacuum cleaner nozzle. By blanking off those parts of the screen not covered by the fragment, a positive air flow through the fabric can be assured, when the vacuum is operated. A moisture trap between the vacuum cleaner and the box may be necessary if the fragment has not been extracted completely. This improvisation must not be used for drycleaning work because of fire, explosion or toxic gas hazards. Heavy duty professional vacuum cleaners can be purchased, however, and these are considered safe for this work.

Household flat work and linens are usually dried commercially by passing them over heated rolls. This system irons them at the same time. Curtains, especially after starching, are stretched to size and dried by radiant heaters. This type of drying is not recommended for most museum textiles.

Finishing

The last step in fabric manufacturing is finishing. It is also the last thing done in cleaning and is necessary so as to present the completed job in a smooth or otherwise attractive condition. The basic reason for this is that with natural fibres under the usual processing and manufacturing techniques used for producing most historic textiles, precise uniformity of fibres and of the scouring, dyeing, spinning and weaving is not possible. This in turn, results in variations of moisture, dye and other chemical acceptance, causing differences in wrinkling, shrinkage, lustre, flexibility and feel in two similar textiles or even in parts of the same piece. For this reason, it is the usual practice to try to even out the overall appearance with after-treatments or finishing.

In finishing processes, there are three main things to be done. First, the fabric must be plasticised, secondly, it should be dimensionally restored and smoothed out and thirdly, it may be necessary to stabilise it in that condition.

By plasticising, we mean restoration of the textile to its customary smoothness and appearance. This is nearly always necessary, especially if the fabric has been dried by heat and air, because it will have been over-dried. This is true in drycleaning as well as wetcleaning.

If the fabric is over-dried the material will be harsh, wrinkled and, if it is old, it may be brittle. All these are fundamentally due to lack of proper moisture content in the fibres, sometimes known as regain. At any temperature, there is a corresponding moisture content for every relative humidity condition of the air in contact. The moisture content increases as the humidity increases, but not in direct proportion. The shape of the curve of moisture content against humidity differs for each fibre. Unfortunately, after over-drying, the textile does not recover quickly unless moisture is forced into the fabric, the yarns and the individual fibres.

The best quick ways of moisturising the fibres are by dampening the fabric with water and by steaming. Water applied by spraying requires an appreciable time for penetration and is not uniform. Steaming, if properly done, is far more satisfactory if suitable equipment is available. A suggestion is that an electric steam iron, set to produce steam, is held just above the fabric but not in contact. The material should be laid out flat on a padded surface such as an ironing board. When the area under the iron appears to be conditioned, a mitt made of a cloth pad is pressed on the area to smooth out wrinkles. The iron is not permitted to come in contact with the specimen unless the fabric is strong and can withstand ironing. By alternating steaming and pressing with a pad, the whole area of the specimen can be covered. If more sophisticated steam pressing equipment is available, larger areas can be smoothed and time saved. For napped goods, a soft brush or whisk broom may be drawn lightly over the steamed area to produce a pleasing effect and avoid flattening.

In some cases, a good surface appearance may require fixing or starching. When this is necessary, the specimen must be wetted with the fixing agent before it is shaped and ironed. The type of fixing agent or starch is important, as is the temperature of ironing. If the starch has been broken down by cooking or has been treated to make it cold water soluble, it may become yellowed or turn brown after ageing for a while. Potato and corn starch are more inclined to do this. Wheat and rice starch are finer grained, more easily dissolved, and less likely to be degraded towards coloured substances. Ironing temperatures should be as low as possible because the starch is easily toasted and degraded to a point where the colour will show.

Instead of starch, gelatin, gum arabic, gum tragacanth and flaxseed, are used on occasion to provide special degrees of stiffness, lustre, and handle to the finished textile.[17]

NOTES AND REFERENCES

1. FULTON, G. P., 'The Effect of the Chloride Ion on Silk'. *Applied Science for Drycleaners*, National Institute of Drycleaning, Silver Spring, Md, U.S.A., 322 (1951). MATHEWS and MAURERS-BERGER, *Mathews Textile Fibers*, 5th edn, John Wiley and Sons, N.Y. 723 (1947)

2. FULTON, G. P., 'Effect of Alkalies on Shrinkage of Wool', *Applied Science for Drycleaners*, National Institute of Drycleaning, Silver Spring, Md, U.S.A., 305

3. 'Photomicrographs of common textile fibers'. *Appendix to Standard Methods of Identification of fibres in textiles*. ASTM designation D–276, American Society for Testing Materials, 1916 Race St., Philadelphia, Pa., U.S.A. (1959)

4. For other identification tests for the fibres *see* reference 3 above, and also latest annual published by American Association of Textile Chemists and Colorists

5. RICE, J. W., 'Fiber surface roughness and pitting', *Textile Museum J.*, **1,** No. 2 (1963)
   POWE, W. C., 'The Nature of Tenaciously Bound Soil on Cotton', *Text. Res. J.*, **29,** No. 11 (Nov. 1959)

6. RICE, J. W., 'Dyeing of wool, Theory', *Textile Museum J.*, **1,** No. 2 (1963)

7. For practical discussion of alkalies and builders, *see* BERG, N. J., *Wetcleaning,* National Institute of Drycleaning, Silver Spring, Md, U.S.A. (1945)

8. For further information on alkalies and builders, see RICE, J. W., 'The Wonders of Water in Wetcleaning', *Textile Museum J.*, **2,** No. 1, 17 (1966)

9. For approximate pH values and ranges of usefulness in cleaning, *see* reference 8, p. 18 and Fulton reference 1, p. 56 (Table IV)

10. Damage by digestion has been reported in Technical Bulletins published by the National Institute of Drycleaning, *Fellowship Bulletin F.6,* and described by Fulton, p. 360, reference 1.

11. SCHEFLAN, LEOPOLD AND JACOBS, M. J., 'Maximum allowable concentrations for various solvent vapors', *Handbook of Solvents,* Table II, p. 12, Probable safe concentration of exposure for solvent vapors, D. van Nostrand & Co., N.Y. (1953)

12. RICE, J. W., The ways in which surfactants work are illustrated and discussed in detail in 'Characteristics of Detergents for Cleaning Historic Textiles', *Textile Museum J.*, **2,** No. 1, 23 (1966)

13. The value of lather is discussed by BERG, *see* reference 7, p. 40. *See* also MARTIN, A. R., and FULTON, G. P., *Drycleaning, Technology and Theory,* Textile Book Publishers Inc. Interscience Publishers Inc., N.Y., p. 82 (1958)

14. SISLEY, J. P. and WOOD, P. J., *Encyclopedia of Surface Active Agents,* Vols. 1 and 2, Chemical Publishing Co., N.Y. (1963–64)

15. *McCutcheon's Detergents and Emulsifiers, 1967 Annual,* John W. McCutcheon, Inc., 236 Mt. Kemble Ave., Morristown, N.J., 07960, U.S.A. (1967)

16. RICE, J. W., 'Air speed in drying rugs', *How to Dry Rugs,* p. 65. National Institute of Rug Cleaning, 1815 N. Fort Meyer Drive, Arlington, Va, U.S.A. (1957)

17. Starches and gums for finishing. See reference 7 *Wetcleaning,* Chapter VII

18. Reprinted by permission of the National Institute of Dry Cleaners from its book: GEORGE P. FULTON, *Applied Science for Drycleaners*

19. Reprinted by permission of the Textile Museum and of the author from the *Textile Museum J.*, **2,** No. 1 (1966)

FURTHER READING

HOFENK-de GRAAF, JUDITH H., 'The Constitution of Detergents in Connection with the Cleaning of Ancient Textiles', *Stud. Conserv.*, 13, 122–141 (1968)

Plate 5.1. Lace. Before treatment

Plate 5.2. Lace. After mild bleach in saturated solution of sodium perborate at 35°C

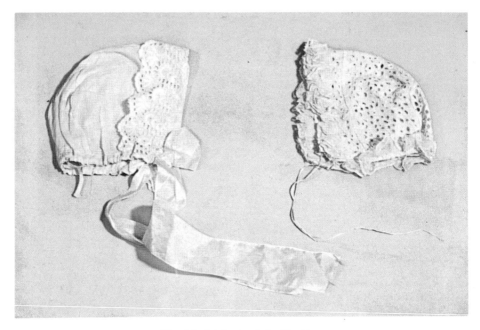

Plate 5.3. Baby's caps. Before bleaching

Plate 5.4. The cap is in the bleaching bath

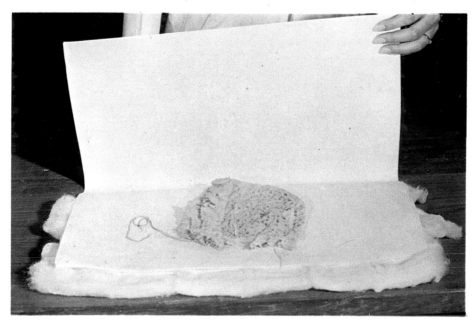

Plate 5.5. The cap has been taken out of the bleaching bath, laid down on filter paper, with an underlying layer of absorbent cotton wool

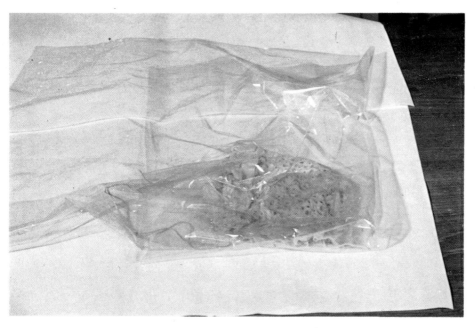

Plate 5.6. The cap wrapped in a piece of polyester foil

Plate 5.7. After being taken out of the foil, the cap is rinsed in cold running water

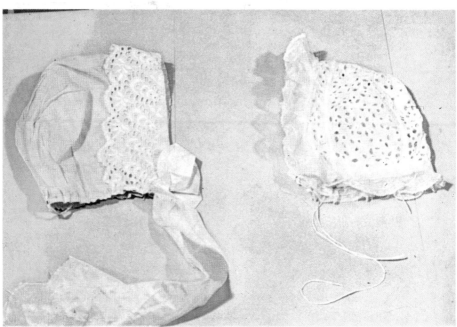

Plate 5.8. The cap on the right has been bleached, the one on the left is untreated

5
Bleaching

JENTINA E. LEENE, D.Sc.
Senior Reader, Laboratory for Textile Technology, Delft University of Technology

In textile collections, laces and linens are very often yellowed, and sometimes even browned by age (*see* Chapter 4). In a few cases an evenly yellowed surface would not matter so much from an aesthetic point of view, but when the yellowing is only local, e.g. at the folds or hems, a bleaching treatment will often have to be considered. This is also the case when dark spots (from mildewing or weathering) are present.

Before deciding on such a treatment it is absolutely necessary to consider the advantages and disadvantages. In general, when dealing with a very fragile textile, it is advisable to be extremely careful with chemical treatments. When all necessary precautions have been taken, it is possible, more often than not, to get a satisfactory result, i.e. an improved appearance and a better handle.

An argument against bleaching is that textiles, especially laces, may become too white to look authentic and art historians may become alarmed at the degree of whiteness which can be attained. It has been shown, by past experience, however, that this whiteness is nearly impossible to get by bleaching alone. Centuries ago, linens got an aftertreatment with a blueing agent, because, even after repeated bleaching, the 'white' still had a yellowish shade.[1] The blueing agent (ultramarine, indigo, or an aniline dye) was added to the rinsing water, and the resulting colour could be 'white' in varying degrees, up to blueish white.

Formerly, when lace was an important part of underwear, it had to be white, because any deviation could be considered evidence of an inefficient housewife. This was also true of lace which served to embellish dresses and other kinds of costume. Only recently has lace been coloured to be more in keeping with the other colours of the garments.

It is difficult to estimate how 'white' these white textiles were in former days, particularly since optical brightening agents are now added to commercial soaps and household detergents to improve the whitening power. They are unlike the blueing agents, in that they are colourless dyestuffs which reflect the invisible ultraviolet light as visible blue light, and in this

73

way give the impression of a 'brighter white'. This effect is greatest in day-light or the light of fluorescent tubes without ultraviolet absorbing filters. In incandescent light there is hardly any effect at all.

When these dyestuffs deteriorate they no longer reflect the ultraviolet as visible light, and the yellowish white of the textile reappears. If these optical brighteners did not deteriorate in a relatively short time, fluorescent dyestuffs would accumulate in the textiles, even though they were washed regularly. A high light fastness would, therefore, be an unwanted property in these agents, especially when applied on those museum objects which are laundered more than once.

Everyone has become accustomed to a bright white, because of the widespread use of these optical brighteners. In consequence, the unwritten housewife's standard of 'white' from former times has been lost. A good guess is that the best that could be achieved is the white which nowadays can be attained by a mild bleach, without application of blueing agents and optical brighteners (Plates 5.1, and 5.2).

A much more important argument against any bleaching treatment is the possibility of a severe degradation of the cellulose fibres. Cellulose fibre can be greatly damaged, and may lose all its strength, when it is bleached under uncontrolled conditions. From experiments at our laboratory, as well as from those mentioned in reference 4, it appears that a mild hydrogen peroxide bleach is very satisfactory.[2, 3] It has a good whitening effect and the degradation, measured as diminution of the degree of polymerisation (DP), is negligibly small. Another advantage of this treatment is that the white produced is very much more stable than when a sodium hypochlorite (NaOCl) bleach has been applied.[4] This means that there is less yellowing with time after the hydrogen peroxide bleach, than after the sodium hypochlorite bleach. Moreover, when the procedure is followed precisely, the degree of whiteness can be easily controlled.

For the bleaching method, developed at our laboratory, the following solution is used:

5 g NaOH (sodium hydroxide, in the form of purified pellets)
5 g Na_2CO_3 (sodium carbonate, anhydrous, purified)
20 g Na_2SiO_3 (sodium metasilicate, anhydrous, purified)
5 volumes % H_2O_2 (hydrogen peroxide solution, strength 30% H_2O_2).
1 litre water.

The fabric to liquor ratio is 1 : 10, i.e. 1 litre of the bleaching solution is needed for bleaching 100 g of fabric. The temperature of the solution has to be about room temperature (20°C, 68°F).

The textile is immersed in a bath of the prepared bleaching solution. (Plastic trays, as used in photographic work, available in different sizes, can be very helpful here.) After 5 min the specimen is taken out and dabbed with filter paper to remove any excess bleaching solution (Plates 5.3–5.8). It is then wrapped in polyester foil to prevent it from drying and the bleaching continues for about 1½–3 hours. The bleaching proceeds slowly and can be stopped when the desired degree of whiteness has been reached. (With very yellow material the whole procedure can be repeated.)

After bleaching, the material is taken out of the foil, rinsed thoroughly in cold running water for at least 2 min and dried in the air. It is preferable sometimes to dry it between sheets of filter paper, or between towels, and then to iron it on the reverse side, using an ironing board with an elastic covering. The iron should be as cool as possible (*see* also Chapter 14).

REFERENCES

1. Greup–Roldanus, S.C. Regtdoorzee, *Geschiedenis der Haarlemmer Bleekerijen*, Martinus Nijhoff, 's Gravenhage 323–329 (1936)
2. POOT, A. H. A., 'Chemical bleaching of ancient textiles', *1964 Delft Conference on the Conservation of Textiles*, Collected reprints, 2nd edn, The International Institute for Conservation, London, 53–64 (1965)
3. LEENE, J. E., *Restaurierung und Konservierung von Kostümen, Waffen und Kostümkunde, Jahrgang*, **9**, 57–60 (1967)
4. LEWIN, M. and ETTINGER, A., 'Oxidation of Cellulose by Hydrogen Peroxide', *Cellulose Chem. Tech.*, **3**, 9–20 (1969)

6

Textile Pests and Their Control

Dr H. J. HUECK
Head of Department of Biology, Central Laboratory TNO, Delft

Specimens in museums and art collections may be attacked by a number of organisms, but the present review is restricted to those pests which bear a special relation to textiles. Damage may also be caused by a number of general nuisances, such as rodents and termites. It would, however, be a mistake to deal with such severe pests from the narrow point of view of textile protection only. Any building that contains a textile collection should be protected in its entirety against polyphagous rodents and termites. In very serious cases this should either be left to a local specialist, or the advice of health authorities should be sought. Readers interested in these pests, and their control, may consult Mallis.[1]

6.1 ORGANISMS AND DAMAGE CAUSED

Damage of biogenic origin to textiles is caused mainly by two types of agents:

1. Insects.
2. Micro-organisms.

Damage by other organisms, such as snails, is of too rare an occurrence to be discussed here.

In general, insects are considered to be the more serious pest in museums, especially in moderate climates.[2] Damage by insects may only appear to be the most important, however, since it can be detected with the naked eye, whereas damage by fungi and bacteria, in its initial stages, can only be detected through microscopic inspection and chemical or mechanical tests. The attack by micro-organisms is only readily observable without artificial means in cases where the damage has progressed to a large extent or, quantitatively, is very considerable indeed.

Of the various types of textiles, wool is most vulnerable to insects. Cotton (together with other cellulosic fibres, such as jute, ramie, sisal, hemp, linen, etc.) is more vulnerable to micro-organisms. Keratinous materials, e.g. fur and felt, in this respect behave like wool, and so does silk, although it is not a keratinous protein. This does not mean, however, that there are no insects that attack cotton nor micro-organisms that attack wool.

Wool and silk will, under conditions of severe microbiological stress, e.g. in contact with moist soil, deteriorate nearly as rapidly as cotton and linen. Silverfish, fire brats and termites, on the other hand, may damage cellulosic fibres. As a general rule, however, the relationships 'insects to wool' and 'micro-organisms to cotton' hold good.[3]

Synthetic fibres, e.g. nylon and polyester fibres, are not susceptible to biodeterioration, although occasional insect damage is reported.[4, 5] It has been noted that superficial growth of mildew may occur on nylon, etc., without impairing the strength of the fibre. Such rare growths are apparently a result of either impurities in the fibre or soiling. Rayon, being cellulosic in type, behaves like natural cellulose fibres. Nowadays many mixtures of synthetic and natural fibres are made and with respect to biogenic deterioration they behave just as the natural fibres, which they contain.[6] As synthetic fibres are comparatively rare in textile museums, this chapter will only deal with damage to natural fibres.

Major textile pests are the organisms that feed directly on the material itself, e.g. clothes moths living on wool, and fungi breaking down cellulose for their nutrition. A number of pests, however, may cause damage because they thrive on secondary substances present in textiles, such as sizing, or because they live in the neighbourhood of the textile fabric and then inflict accidental damage without really feeding on it. Wood boring beetles are an example of the latter group. Their larvae actually live in wood, but they may penetrate textiles that are in close contact with it. Such damage may occur if textiles are stored on wooden shelves, in wooden containers or mounted on wooden panels.[4] Only the very hard varieties of wood which are plastic-like or plastic-covered provide some protection in this respect.

6.1.1 INSECT PESTS

Some of the better known insect pests are summarised in Table 6.1. Many others may occur occasionally. Laibach analysed 700 cases of textile damage occurring in West Germany in 1956–1958 and 1961–1963.[7, 8] He recorded over 50 species, most of which, however, occurred only once. The following list shows the number of cases (in percentages) of the more important pests:

Tineola bisselliella (common clothes moth)	25%
Hofmannophila pseudospretella (brown house moth)	9%
All clothes moths and house moths together	38%
Anthrenus verbasci (varied carpet beetle)	18%
Attagenus pellio	14%
All carpet beetles together	38%
Lepisma saccharina (silverfish)	2%
Niptus hololeucus (golden spider beetle)	9%
Cockroaches	1%
Wood-boring beetles	2%

This shows that, in moderate climates, moth and carpet beetle larvae are about equally important as textile pests, and together they account for the

Table 6.1 INSECT PESTS OF TEXTILES*

Name	Substrate	Type of damage
MOTHS		
Tineola bisselliella Humm (common clothes moth)	Preferably wool, fur, felt, but they accept other proteinaceous food. Occur naturally in birds' nests.	Superficial grazing. Holes. Silk and excrements produced.
Tinea pellionella L. (case-bearing clothes moth)		Same as above, larvae build cases from silk and bitten thread.
Trichophaga tapetzella (tapestry moth)		Same as above; larvae form tunnels in the material, made of silk and bitten threads.
Hofmannophila pseudospretella Staint (brown house moth) *Endrosis sarcitrella* (white shouldered house moth)	Occurs on wool. Feeds on wool, etc. and stored food. Prefers stored food, but occurs on wool.	Same as above; produce a mess of frass stuck together with silk threads.
CARPET BEETLES		
Anthrenus museorum L. (museum beetle) *Anthrenus verbasci L.* (varied carpet beetle) *Anthrenus scrophulariae L.* (common carpet beetle) *Anthrenus vorax Waterh.* (furniture carpet beetle) *Anthrenoceros australis Hope* *Attagenus piceus Oliv* (black carpet beetle) *Attagenus pellio L.*	Wool, fur, felt and proteinaceous stored materials, without preference.	Mainly holes of irregular shape. No silk. On microscopical examination, typical bristles from the larvae are found. Excrements very fine, hardly visible.
OTHER PESTS		
Lepisma saccharina L. (silverfish)	Rayon and many types of stored food, paper and related materials.[13]	Irregular holes in rayon and, occasionally, other textiles.
Niptus hololeucus Fald. (golden spider beetle)	Stored food and debris of vegetable or animal origin.	Holes bitten by adult beetles generally more knurled than of carpet beetle larvae.
Cockroaches (many species)	Polyphagous, including sizing of textiles, glue, etc. Not specific for textiles, although rayon is eaten.	Superficial grazing and irregular holes if amenable food is present.
Termites (many species)	Wood and many other cellulose-containing materials. Textiles are readily eaten.	Complete devastation, often progressing from the dark back or inside of attacked materials. Many termites build tunnels.
Wood-boring beetles (many species)	Wood. No preference for textiles, acceptance as food doubtful.	Neat round holes in wooden boards may be continued in stored textiles.

*Illustrations and descriptions of the pests mentioned may be found in references 82 and 84, or the handbooks listed in Section 6.5.

majority of insect damage to textiles. The only other species of some quantitative importance appears to be the adult golden spider beetle. This species, however, should not be a pest in well-kept museums; its life history shows that it is a pest of neglected store houses, and may occur during the restoration of old buildings.[9]

It is important to identify the causative insect when damage has actually occurred, and this should be left to a specialist. If no local entomologist can be contacted, the *International Directory of Biological Deterioration Research*, which lists a great number of laboratories in this field of research, should be consulted.[10] The following notes on the biology of the insects under consideration may be helpful.

Most moths mentioned above are not only able to use wool as their food, but they may even complete their life cycle in the infested wool itself. The damage is done by their larvae; the adult moths are only instrumental in the propagation of the pest. Instead of pursuing flying moths which have probably dropped their eggs already, it is better to search for larvae, and their remains, and then eliminate this source of infection.

Carpet beetles, too, cause damage only through their larvae. Although some species may complete their life cycle on wool, etc. as the sole source of food, it is more usual that the adults spend their life elsewhere. They feed on pollen of flowers outdoors, and lay their eggs indoors. Because of this habit, and the more polyphagous nature of their eating habits, the infestation of dwellings may be rather widespread and not confined to textiles.

The golden spider beetle causes damage only in its adult form. The larvae feed on animal or vegetable debris, found in many places. It is, therefore, an invader rather than a resident, and care for textiles alone will not prevent its occurrence. The same is true of the remaining species mentioned in Table 6.1. Prevention of damage to textiles caused by these general pests *must* be based on general methods of control; it cannot rely on specific methods for textiles only. The best prevention of termite damage, for example, is a termite-proof building.

The life history of the silverfish, in relation to damage done to paper and textiles in archives, etc., has been described by Herfs and Laibach.[11−13] Silverfish usually live on carbohydrates, such as starch and dextrin, provided by sizing. They are also able to digest certain types of cellulose which have suffered from chemical breakdown processes. Such types of cellulose with a short chainlength of glucose units $(DP < 200)$ occur in rayon and paper. They can serve as a source of food, whereas native cellulose, as present in cotton, cannot be used.

The direct damage by insects as a result of eating is of a purely mechanical nature. It is, however, not the only nuisance they may cause. The presence of excrements is also objectionable. With cockroaches this may lead to severe soiling of fabrics.[14] Furthermore, insects may introduce fungi. Whitehouse noted that cockroaches, feeding on the sizing of bookbindings, acted as vectors for fungi that caused further damage.[15]

6.1.2 MICRO-ORGANISMS

Among the micro-organisms attacking textiles, only some broad groups are mentioned here as it is quite impossible to review the hundreds of species involved.[16] For practical purposes anyway, these species do not differ very much from each other, especially with regard to their control. For control purposes, large groups of species only need be considered.

The most noxious group of micro-organisms, in relation to textiles, are the cellulolytic fungi. Most 'mildewing' arises from them. They feed on the cellulose present in cotton and linen. Once they are really established, the cellulose is broken down rapidly, and in less than a week the strength of the fabric may be lost completely. Staining by fungi may also be a nuisance. 'Weather-stains' are often, although not always, produced by fungi. Moreover, they may be caused not only by cellulolytic fungi, but also by micro-fungi thriving on sizing, or on mere dust and soil attached to the fibre.

Bacteria attacking cellulose do exist, although their occurrence in museums should be rare, as they only develop under very moist conditions. In the event of a mishap, such as a leaking roof or burst waterpipe, they may do damage. Their presence is first detected from a very bad smell, and the fabric feeling sticky when handled. With wool the problem of micro-organisms is less severe; keratinolytic fungi and bacteria exist, but their occurrence is rare. Under humid conditions, however, wool may suffer damage from this cause quite unexpectedly.

Kowalik, Nuiksha and Gallo provide detailed information on species of micro-organisms occurring in libraries and archives; the microflora found in these will not deviate appreciably from that of textile museums.[17-20]

6.2 CONDITIONS UNDER WHICH DAMAGE OF BIOTIC ORIGIN MAY OCCUR

In order that biodeterioration may develop, a number of conditions must be fulfilled. In general the most significant conditions are:

1. A source of infestation.
2. Presence of food.
3. Suitable environmental conditions, e.g. temperature and humidity.

6.2.1 SOURCE OF INFESTATION

Cellulolytic micro-organisms are practically omnipresent; they only await suitable conditions to develop and to manifest themselves. This is not true of insects. In this case, it is worth removing known sources of infestation in the neighbourhood, and preventing the entry of insects. It is known that the infestation caused by carpet beetles spreads rather slowly from room to room and from house to house. The first infestation occurs usually in dark, dusty places; there females, flying in from the garden, deposit their eggs.[21] Clothes moths, on the other hand, frequently develop in discarded pieces of wool deposited in a quiet corner. Wool kept in storage, once it is infected, may be a source of infestation for its environment. Frequent inspections, and general hygiene, are, therefore, desirable to keep out insects.

6.2.2 PRESENCE OF FOOD

It is self-evident that, to sustain themselves, all organisms need a source of food. Clothes moths and some carpet beetles, as was discussed in Section 6.1, carry out their full life cycle in the presence of wool and similar keratin-containing materials. Since we wish to preserve the textile itself, the withdrawal of this food which would kill the pest, is impossible. Starvation is possible, to some extent, with other insects, i.e. the ones which have to rely on additional sources of food. The larvae of the golden spider beetle, for example, are unable to live on textiles. With many other species (cockroaches, silverfish and even carpet beetles) the presence of sources of food other than textiles may contribute materially to the infestation. It is essential, therefore, to remove all secondary sources of food from any place near the textiles to be preserved. Stores of food in kitchens should be inspected and edible waste, left by visitors or personnel, should be removed regularly. Such regulations for cleanliness may seem obvious, but their wisdom may not be clear to everyone concerned. Lack of personnel may easily cause trouble in this respect.

The attractiveness of human food to these small organisms is readily appreciated. We should remember, however, that nearly all naturally occurring materials, or their derivatives, may well be sources of food to them. Glue, dust and debris in seams of floors, birds' nests, wood under certain conditions, refuse from gardens, etc., are a few of the items to be watched carefully.

Although the above advice mainly applies to insects, it is relevant also to fungi and their secondary sources of food. Evans has shown that the presence of sizing enhances the mildewing of their main source of food, e.g. cellulose.[22]

6.2.3 ENVIRONMENTAL CONDITIONS

The great importance of suitable environmental conditions (mainly temperature and humidity) for the occurrence of biodeterioration is well known. Among these factors, humidity appears to be the most important and, fortunately, the one that can best be controlled. Some interrelations exist; we will therefore first discuss these factors individually and then consider their simultaneous influence.

Temperature

The general influence of temperature on living things can be described by an optimum curve. At a certain temperature, the activity of organisms will be optimal: both an increase and decrease of temperature will bring about a decrease in activity. If the temperature becomes extreme, the organisms will be killed either by heat or by cold.

For practical purposes the range of temperatures in which biodeterioration organisms may occur is rather wide. The mould *Pullularia pullulans*, for example, has been observed to thrive at temperatures as high as $83°C$.[23] On the other hand it is well known that fungi and bacteria may develop in refrigerators at around 0°C. To kill some micro-organisms requires extreme temperatures. Insects have somewhat narrower temperature limits. In both instances, however, we must distinguish between active living organisms and the preservation of life in special resting stages, such as spores of fungi and bacteria or insect eggs.

These resting stages can generally withstand much more extreme temperatures and, under suitable conditions, may give rise to new infections. It may even be suspected that low temperatures are beneficial to the preservation of the resting stages. In this respect, Sykes[24] may be quoted:

Refrigeration at low temperatures, and the lower the better, is popularly considered to be fatal to all forms of life. Whilst this may be true for the larger forms of organised life, it is certainly not true for the smaller plant life, including that of micro-organisms. When cultures of bacteria are frozen, it is true that a proportion of the cells is always rendered non-viable. Sometimes the death rate might be as high as 99%, but once frozen at a sufficiently low temperature the surviving cells can be preserved for long periods.

In any study of temperature limits, it must be taken into account that the length of time during which a certain temperature is maintained is important. The general rule holds that the more extreme the temperature, the shorter the period for which it need be maintained. Keeping these restrictions in mind, some temperature effects may be discussed.

Clothes moths, especially *Tineola*, have been investigated rather thoroughly and it appears that their larvae can withstand temperatures as low as −15°C. On the other hand, development is practically arrested at temperatures below 15°C. Optimum activity is found at 20–30°C for all stages of the insect and 33°C appears to be the highest temperature at which complete development is possible. Finally, 41°C appears to be lethal to all stages within 4 h. For house moths these temperatures are somewhat lower, for carpet beetles slightly higher.

From these considerations, it would appear that insect damage can be prevented by storing textiles at relatively low temperatures. In fact, 10°C may suffice, but as most refrigeration facilities provide temperatures of about 4–5°C, the advice of Busvine[25] to store at such a temperature may be practical. This method is reliable, but the necessity to maintain the low temperature makes it expensive. Moreover, it cannot be applied to textiles on show. To prevent damage by fungi and bacteria requires lower temperatures.[24, 26–28]

To summarise, we may say that no practical limiting temperature can be given for killing spores. Active life is found from around 0°C to 70°C, with some exceptional organisms even exceeding these limits. Optimal activity of organisms, related to textiles, is found between 20°C and 40°C, but appreciable breakdown of cotton still occurs at 5°C which is the normal temperature of refrigerators.[29] To kill these organisms requires temperatures well over 100°C, though much depends on secondary factors. For practical purposes, therefore, no temperatures acceptable for general use can be given which may prevent the occurrence of micro-organisms. Storage in commercial deep-freezing utensils (−20°C), however, will provide a degree of protection which might be considered fair for the preservation of unique specimens, should control of humidity not provide an easier solution.

Humidity

It is common knowledge that a dry atmosphere will prevent nearly all damage that arises from organisms, especially micro-organisms. However, answers to the question how dry the atmosphere should be generally lack definition.

Block *et al.* have investigated a number of materials, including wool and cotton, for their behaviour as a substrate for development of fungi under the influence of a range of well-defined relative humidities.[30, 31] They found that an under-limit of relative humidity exists below which no growth occurs. This limit, however, varies with temperature and with type of material. The water content of each material is in equilibrium with the humidity of the surrounding atmosphere. The position of this equilibrium is specific for each material (some materials are more hygroscopic than others).

Block suggested that the water content of the material is the thing that really matters and that it is more important than the relative humidity of the surrounding air. He proposed a critical water content of $12 \pm 2\%$. It became clear, furthermore, that a sharp limit does not exist. The chance of material becoming mildewed generally decreases when the (relative) humidity of ambient air is decreased. As a general idea, Block posed that below 70% relative humidity growth of fungi on textiles will be negligible or impossible. Bacteria require even higher humidities. Klens and Stewart arrived at a somewhat lower level of safety, namely, 60% relative humidity and Werner quoted a figure of 65%.[23, 32] Nuiksha is of the opinion that, in libraries, a relative humidity of 45–60% is optimal.[20] In practice, perhaps, humidities lower than 70% will be required owing to complicating factors that are discussed in the next paragraph. A very thorough study has been reported by Ayerst.[33] Although rather definite conclusions may be reached as to the desirable humidity to prevent mildewing, the case is less clear for insects. Insects can generally stand lower relative humidities than micro-organisms. Even as low a relative humidity as 20–30% will not stop moths and carpet beetles fully, though they will be retarded in growth. The optimum for development is not very pronounced: with *Tineola* it is about 65–75% relative humidity; in *Hofmannophila* it appears to be higher (about 90%). The same is true for carpet beetles; all species can stand relative humidities of 90–100%. The conclusion, therefore, is that no practical levels of relative humidity can be found that will prevent textile damage by insects.

The Total Environment

Temperature and humidity in museums are not separate factors, they must always be considered together. A very helpful discussion, for the point of view of museums, is given by Padfield.[34]

The relation between temperature and relative humidity is rather precise and can be expressed graphically, as in Figure 6.1. It can be seen, from this graph, that with a given amount of moisture in the air, changes in temperatures will generate changes in relative humidity. In general, we may say that a decrease in temperature causes an increase in relative humidity.

A complication, under practical conditions, is that temperature and humidity are not the same in all parts of fairly large buildings. Moreover, we must even reckon with 'micro-environments', whenever overcrowded rooms prevent proper replacement of air. Werner gives an interesting practical example, when he describes a case of books mildewing in a library which was maintained at an overall relative humidity of 50%.[35] In a pocket

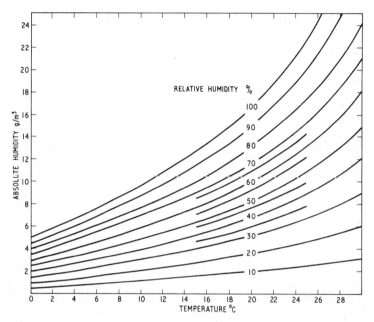

Figure 6.1. The relation between absolute humidity, relative humidity and temperature. Based on hygrometric tables H.M.S.O.

of stagnant air, where mildew occurred, a relative humidity of 83% was measured. Such conditions first of all would involve a constant level of both temperature and humidity.

A quite unexpected result of the interrelation of temperature and humidity is that differences of temperature—which may easily occur due to radiant heat from stoves, or sunlight through windows, or contact with cold walls— may lead, in more or less closed containers, to a partial rise in relative humidity that may cause trouble. Padfield shows theoretically (compare Figure 6.1) that if the inside of a showcase has a temperature of 20°C and a relative humidity of 55%, and if the glass has a temperature of 15°C, the relative humidity at the glass will be 75%, which is well beyond the critical limit.[34] Hazeu and Hueck have shown experimentally that Padfield's theoretical supposition holds true.[36] This means that not only relative humidity but, at the same time, temperature should be controlled, if one wishes to implement ideal conditions.

In practice, less perfect conditions have to be dealt with, but, by manipulating heating and ventilation, the ideal may be approached.[32] Special attention must be paid to fully or nearly closed packaging units, such as showcases, or containers used for dispatch of museum objects. In this respect, several solutions have been offered. Padfield has stressed the importance of ventilation holes in showcases and calculated their dimensions.[34]

For dispatch, cases with holes drilled in them cannot be used, because hermetically sealed containers may be desirable in order to keep out vermin. In this situation it has been suggested that the safety limits should be lowered to about 50% relative humidity and that packaging should be carried out under that condition.[36] Various experts have pointed out that the presence of wood, or large amounts of cotton (cellulose), has a remarkably stabilising effect on relative humidity, if occurring in closed environments with a given and acceptable amount of moisture.[34, 37, 38] The same effect can be reached by adding silica gel or saturated salt solutions. Of these materials, silica gel is easiest to handle. It should be checked before use, however, because its capacity to adsorb moisture is limited.

It has been suggested, as a general rule, that taking all these possible secondary influences into account, a relative humidity of 50% would provide an ample margin of safety.[39] One must be careful in being too rigorous, however, as dry atmospheres may be harmful to the objects under custody. According to Werner, the lowest permissible limit where organic materials, including textiles, are involved, should be taken as 50% RH.[32] This, combined with the advice above that it should be the upper limit, leaves no margin of safety. Leene has suggested a figure of 40% RH as possible.[40] In ideal conditions, perhaps air-conditioning could be used, aiming at a constant RH somewhere between 40 and 50%; in less ideal conditions, the advice of Werner could be followed to maintain the atmosphere at humidities between 50 and 65% RH.[32] Rapid fluctuations of temperature or uneven distribution of temperatures must be avoided for the reasons given above. The actual value of the temperature is relatively unimportant (20°C is a good choice), but constancy is important.

6.3   CONTROL OF BIODETERIORATION OF TEXTILES

The preceding paragraphs already contain some information on the control of insects and micro-organisms, based on general considerations of the biology and ecology of the organisms in question.

In this section, we shall discuss a number of special methods that allow a more active control of these organisms. It will be appreciated that preventive measures are preferable to curative measures; the latter aim at destroying the organisms when they have become apparent. The damage to the textile has already been done then, and is difficult to repair. Moreover, curative measures tend to be rigorous and may make use of poisons, which in itself is an objectionable approach. Curative methods, therefore, should be used only when they cannot be avoided.

Since control of organisms is a complicated affair,[41] experts should be consulted if possible, and care must then be taken that all measures proposed are carefully scrutinised as to their compatibility with the objects to be protected. Some outlines of useful methods are given below, but it must be realised that many details for individual specimens cannot be mentioned, also that all measures possess advantages and disadvantages which must be weighed carefully on the basis of local circumstances.

6.3.1   PHYSICAL METHODS OF CONTROL

As a preventive measure, an inert and invulnerable barrier between the attacking organism and the fabric may be erected. Clothes bags are a well-known example, and antique chests, containers, suitcases and the like are also used. These will provide protection only to stored goods and one must be certain that no infection (especially eggs of clothes moths or carpet beetles) is introduced, either during, or before parcelling, otherwise ideal circumstances are created for the quiet and destructive development of these keratin eating insects.

A number of instances are on record where plastic foils have been penetrated by insects, such as carpet beetle larvae, so that the protection afforded by physical barriers must not be over estimated.[5, 42, 43] It is rather difficult to make containers absolutely insectproof. Polythene foils, for example, should have a thickness of at least 0·1 mm.[44] Moisture in hermetically sealed packages may be a problem, as discussed earlier. The introduction of p-dichlorobenzene in the bag, as advocated by Plenderleith, 'to ensure against the risk of moth eggs being present', is of rather relative value;[2] this will be discussed below. Moreover, this chemical is a solvent for certain plastics; its use in plastic bags, therefore, is not advisable.

To protect book-bindings against cockroaches, Block developed a coating of ethylcellulose.[45] Other coatings are discussed by Gallo.[46, 47] Baynes-Cope, however, warns that varnishes 'are a poor sort of preservation that destroys the utility of the object'.[48] His opinion is based on the stiffening and the deleterious effects of some chemicals that may be sealed in the varnish.

Physical methods of a curative nature involve the application of heat (dry or wet) for the deinsectisation and disinfection of materials.

The use of moist heat for disinfection of books is a technique of long standing and is still one of the widest used general purpose methods.[28, 49] The equipment required is generally not available in museums, though any hospital can help out. With antique textiles it should be used carefully, if possible after pre-treatment of small samples. Helwig has given a critical review of such disinfection methods for books and papers.[50] It appears that moist heat is indeed effective, and relatively harmless. For this purpose, she recommends 95°C and 40% RH for 4 h. Dry heat should not be used, because of the high temperatures involved.

For the same purpose, different types of radiation are used. As many dyes, and cellulose, are sensitive to ultraviolet radiation, treatment in this way is not recommended. Though these methods are highly effective, they have the disadvantage that, in general, specialised and expensive equipment is needed, equipment which must be handled by specialists. The compatibility with delicate textiles is doubtful. For further details the following references should be consulted, 24, 26, 27 or 28.

6.3.2   CHEMICAL METHODS OF CONTROL

Chemical methods, like physical methods, can be used preventatively or curatively. Most of the methods used depend on the killing of the organisms in question. This is a rather specific property of such chemicals; only a few can be used for control of both insects and micro-organisms. We shall consider insecticides and fungicides separately.

Insecticidal Treatments

Nowadays an astonishing number of insecticides is available. A practical review of them is given by Johnson *et al.*, and many other reviews, handbooks, etc., exist.[51] An index of technical preparations, commercially available for this purpose, is given by Hueck-van der Plas.[52]

From Johnson's list, the insecticides in Table 6.2 are chosen as examples

Table 6.2 INSECTICIDES USEFUL FOR THE CONTROL OF TEXTILE PESTS

Name	LD_{50} *(Oral)* *	*Remarks*
A. Insecticides with pronounced residual activity		
D.D.T.	100	
Methoxychlor	6 000	
Lindane	125	chlorinated
Chlordane	460	hydrocarbons
Dieldrin	60	
Endosulfan	110	organophosphorus ester
Diazinon	100–150	
B. General purpose and 'knock-down' insecticides		
Pyrethrins	820	knock-down
Rotenone (derris)	132	
Lethane 384	90	knock-down
Malathion	1 400	organophosphorus ester
Sevin	500–700	carbamate
Thanite	1 600	knock-down
C. Insecticides active as a gas		
D.D.V.P.	56–80	organophosphorus ester
p-dichlorobenzene	2 950	
ethylene oxide	330	explosive, if used pure

*In this table, LD_{50} means the dose as mg/kg body weight lethal for 50% of experimental animals (rats).

of the different types. The higher the LD_{50} figure, the lower the toxicity. LD_{50} is only a rough approximation of the real danger to humans to be expected. Over 1000 suggests rather harmless compounds, under 100, compounds to be handled with great care and respect. It is, however, a good rule never to be careless with any insecticide. Gallo has, in some detail, discussed the risks involved in the application of pesticides in museums.[53] Most insecticides of Group A are used in solutions, or emulsions, containing a few per cent of active compound. Powders are available that contain about 1–5% of active compound. Many commercial preparations contain mixtures of insecticides from Groups A and B, apart from many additives. In general, one should not rely on insecticides that are only indicated by brand; their packing, etc. should also bear a specification of active agents.

The proper use of insecticides with residual activity is in spraying floors, wall and ceilings. In general, amounts of 1 g of the active compound per m^2 of walls, etc. should be used. Much depends, however, on local circumstances. Such high amounts can best be applied from sprays. Aerosols are almost useless for this purpose, as the amount of active ingredient seldom exceeds 2%. Protection periods up to one year may be expected, depending on the insecticide used. D.D.T. is especially known for long-lasting activity. For toxicological reasons, its general use, however, is not recommended in some countries.

During the protection period a high level of general safety against insects may be expected; this may render a treatment of the textiles themselves superfluous in environments where the incidence of general insect damage is low. In this way the problem of finding an insecticide compatible with the textile under custody is avoided. Many manufacturers of sprays containing D.D.T., Lindane or Dieldrin recommend their products for direct spraying of textiles. In the author's experience, no untoward effects from direct spraying are seen on modern textiles, apart from a slight 'blooming' in some instances, owing to crystals of the insecticide. Antique textiles, however, may be more vulnerable, especially to the action of solvents of the insecticide on the dyestuffs of antique fabrics. No experience exists on long-term effects of the action of insecticides on textiles. Jedrzejewska carried out some short-term experiments with D.D.T., covering this problem and suggested that HCl might develop from this compound, especially if used as a technical preparation containing impurities.[54] Observed effects were, however, only slight or negligible. Further research in this direction is highly desirable.

Apart from spraying with residual contact insecticides, long-term protection can be acquired with mothproofing agents known under the brand names of Eulan (Bayer, A.G.) and Mitin (Geigy, A.G.). Under the name of 'Eulan', a variety of rather different preparations is offered.[55–57] The use of Eulan BLS for museum textiles has been advocated. This is a sulphanilid-derivative, applied in organic solvents and used as an addition to solvents in drycleaning processes. Though the compatibility of such substances with modern textiles is excellent, the type of process (drycleaning, aqueous dyeing) that is implied in their application makes one feel reluctant to use them on antique textiles.[58] If it is established that the textiles involved can stand the treatment, then this type of protection has merits, in that it is invisible and lasts many years. Hase[59] with Eulan and Wälchli[60] with Mitin established experimentally that the protection lasted over 20 years. A drawback of any treatment of this kind may be that it is specific, i.e. it kills moths and carpet beetles, but cockroaches, etc. are not harmed. To apply these mothproofers requires some technical skill. The guidance of the manufacturer's representatives should be sought.

P-dichlorobenzene (moth balls) and the more modern D.D.V.P. (dichlorvos) are applied in gaseous form. They certainly have a killing action but p-dichlorobenzene especially is not as effective as it is popular, particularly since it is hardly ever used in the correct way. It should be used in hermetically closed containers, preferably at temperatures over 20°C (68°F) and be renewed every 6 months. Opinions differ as to the amounts to be used; this may be due to the fact that in large containers this insecticide is much less efficient than in smaller ones.[61] A reasonable recommendation appears to be about 100 g for each m^3 of closet space.[62] If all these requirements are fulfilled, one should still not expect the vapour to penetrate through piles of fabric, neither does repellent action occur to any appreciable extent.[63] Its use, therefore, is not recommended as it may too easily lead to false ideas about security.

D.D.V.P. may well prove to be useful. Its high activity[64] makes hermetically closed containers unnecessary. Incorporated in resins, it is useful against house flies, giving protection for some months' duration. Unpublished results from our research institute show that it is effective in this form, also against clothes moths and carpet beetles; somewhat higher amounts, though, are required than are used for killing flies.[88] The high toxicity of D.D.V.P. restricts its use to areas not generally exposed to the public.

Paper impregnated with Lindane, D.D.V.P., etc. is commercially available, and may be useful if piles of textiles are to be protected. It should be inserted between individual pieces of fabric, and constant renewal will be necessary, as its useful life is only a few months.

The measures discussed above aim at prevention of insect pests. If insects are already present insecticides from Group B may be used advantageously, although the slower acting insecticides from Group A are just as effective. Many commercial aerosols for household use contain mixtures of insecticides which gives them a broad applicability. Treatments should be thorough, and care should be taken to track down, if possible, the source of infestation. After eradication preventative measures should be taken.

At one time, treatment of materials with fumigants (in gas chambers) was deemed necessary if severe outbreaks of insects occurred. With the present high efficiency of contact insecticides, this is hardly ever necessary now. Treatments by fumigation may still be useful on admittance of new and complicated articles, e.g. furniture from suspected sources. Fulton *et al.* state that ethylene-oxide is very effective for the purpose.[65] It has the added advantage that micro-organisms may be killed by the same treatment. This gas can be advantageously used according to the simple procedure which Rice devised for the control of micro-organisms.[66] The ethylene oxide is applied to the material, which is packed in polyethylene bags or tubing, and as the ethylene oxide diffuses through the wall of the bag, it leaves the material inside uncontaminated and, as long as the polythene bag is kept sealed, properly preserved. As already mentioned insects may penetrate the polythene foil if it is too thin.

Fungicidal Treatments

The problem of choosing the correct fungicide is still more difficult than that of selecting insecticides. The number of available anti-mildew agents is large. Johnson *et al.* give a review, mainly about agricultural applications, Hueck-van der Plas provides a compilation of preparations available for

Table 6.3 FUNGICIDES FOR TEXTILES

Compound	Toxicity LD_{50} oral	Remarks
Phenylmercuric acetate	2 080	
Zn dimethyldithiocarbamate	1 400	
Cu-8-quinolinolate	c. 10 000	slightly brown
Cu-naphthenate	460	blue-green
2·2'methylene bis(4-chlorophenol)		
= DDM = dichlorophene	2 000	
Salicylanilide	>2 000	
Br-salicylanilide (Diaphene)	1 500	
Benzalkoniumchloride	210–260	
Pentachlorophenol	210	
Na-pentachlorophenate	80–200	
Triphenyltinacetate	125	
Triphenyltinhydroxide	500–600	
Formaldehyde	800	
P-dichlorobenzene	2 960	active as a gas
Ethylene oxide	330	

technical applications, including the impregnation of textiles, and Darby and Kempton evaluate the relative effectiveness of a number of fungicides for textile application.[51, 52, 67] Table 6.3 has been compiled from these sources, and contains the more usual technical fungicides for textiles.

The concentrations of fungicides currently used are about 0·5–1% of the weight of fabric, except for phenylmercuric-acetate and triphenyltin compounds which are used in lower concentrations.

Although insecticides can be advantageously used as a spray, this is not the case with fungicides. Only impregnation of fabrics provides full protection, because the microscopic size of fungi renders any superficial protective layer rather unreliable. It must be admitted, however, that Kowalik and Sadurska report good results from alcoholic sprays containing about 3–5% p-chloro-m-cresol, applied as 1 g of active substance per m³ air, in mildewed book storerooms.[68] According to the said authors, the spray settles 'on surfaces where dust settles and renders them microbicidal for prolonged periods under ordinary conditions'. It is still doubtful whether, in such complicated structures as furniture and dressed mannequin dummies, a superficial treatment would be sufficient. In any case, since p-chloro-m-cresol evaporates slowly, permanent protection should not be expected. Sprays containing quaternary ammonium compounds or laurylpentachlorophenol have been tried in specific cases.[69, 70]

Not all the fungicides listed above are recommended for use with delicate textiles. A number of them, especially the widely used and convenient copper-containing compounds, are coloured. The phenolic derivatives and the tin compounds are slowly broken down when exposed to daylight. The breakdown products may be undesirable and activity is eventually lost.

It has been found that pentachlorophenol is weakly acidic (the pH of a saturated aqueous solution is about 4·6) and can cause deterioration of paper due to this property alone.[48] The same may be true for cellulosic textiles, eventually. Experiments have been carried out by Jedrzejewska on the development of HCl from chlorine-containing fungicides and insecticides like pentachlorophenol, p-chlorometacresol, D.D.T., chloronaphthalene and dichlorobenzene.[54] In closed containers traces of acid can be demonstrated on reagent paper with the first three substances mentioned above.

The purity of the preparation is of importance, as impurities may catalyse the breakdown of the compounds. Heat (for ironing or drying) and exposure to strong light, especially if ultraviolet light is present, can be dangerous. In conclusion, sensitive materials in contact with the preservatives mentioned should not be kept in closed containers and should be stored in subdued light. Further research in this field is necessary.

Formaldehyde hardens the proteins found in wool. According to Baynes Cope it may cause fading of (unspecified) blue dyes.[48] Naphthalene, according to Jedrzejewska promotes an alkaline reaction on wool and according to Lehmann both naphthalene and p-dichlorobenzene have a damaging influence.[54, 71] For the special purpose of preserving museum pieces salicylanilide may be a good choice. Czerwinska et al. have shown its effectiveness for archives.[74] It is very active against fungi, being colourless, odourless, non-volatile and quite stable to heat, etc. As a technical fungicide, however, it fails because it is easily leached from fabric and does not stand a soil burial test, presumably due to its low activity against bacteria.[62] The technical shortcomings are hardly of consequence in museums as leaching does not occur and bacteria are rare. To remedy this, combinations with quaternary ammonium compounds and with halogenated derivatives have been suggested.[73] The use of quaternary ammonium compounds alone is standard procedure for archives and libraries in France.[69]

Though such compounds may be promising, more data are wanted on compatibility with delicate antique textiles and on permanency. In general, impregnation with fungicides should be considered only when everything else fails. Apart from the fungicides, either organic solvents or emulgators, for making an aqueous emulsion, are necessary for impregnation. Such compounds in themselves may be objectionable. The process should therefore, if possible, be tried out on small pieces, before treating the whole fabric. If superficially mildewed spots occur anywhere near textiles, these spots may be sprayed with 1% pentachlorophenol in kerosene, 5% laurylpentachlorophenol in turpentine or an alcoholic spray with 3–5% p-chloro-m-cresol.[68, 70] Generally, however, this mildewing is an indication of too humid conditions, wet walls, etc., and it is better to remedy this, although in practice it is not always feasible.

The gaseous fungicides formaldehyde and ethylene oxide are considered too poisonous (maximum allowable concentrations in air, respectively, 5 and 100 p.p.m.) for continuous use. Although formaldehyde was previously used for disinfection purposes, nowadays ethylene oxide is in general use.[2, 20, 66] Ethylene oxide is a rather dangerous compound, being both poisonous and explosive. Mixtures of it with CO_2, or other inert compounds, are less dangerous and still effective.[74] Such mixtures are commercially available in convenient aerosol containers. Nevertheless, special apparatus (sterilisers) is generally required for treatments. Rice has given a description of an ingenious and simple method for use of a mixture of Freon and 11% ethylene oxide (Cryoxide, American Sterilizer Co., Eric, Pa., U.S.A.), which is sealed, together with the material to be sterilised, in polyethylene tubing.[66] After sterilisation, the material remains in the tubing, while the ethylene oxide diffuses through the bag. As long as the bag is sealed, the material is safe from mildewing, even under temporarily adverse environmental conditions. As ethylene oxide is a rather reactive compound, it is advisable to first apply the treatment to a small piece of fabric.

Although best known for its anti-insect properties, p-dichlorobenzene can be used for the prevention of mildew in storage.[40] Block recommends an amount of 40 g/m^3 of air.[75] If the unpleasant smell is no drawback, it can be used continuously in store rooms to prevent mildew. Though its toxicity is low, exposure to vapours for months or years may cause some unpleasant reactions in man. General use, therefore, cannot be advocated. Its use in closed storerooms may be considered, taking into account what has been said about it when used as an insecticide. In the author's opinion it is not the first choice in mildew prevention, but it may prove helpful in special circumstances.

The most efficient way to use gaseous fungicides like ethylene oxide, then, is curatively when mildew or bacteria are apparent. They can also be used as a general hygienic measure, when textiles are admitted into collections. In this way, one can be sure that no organisms (insects included) will be introduced inadvertently. Municipal sanitary authorities of larger towns generally have the equipment necessary to carry out these treatments. Failing that, large hospitals and some commerical firms may be consulted.

Such a policy will not prevent outbreak of mildew when proper storage conditions are not maintained. Gallo has shown that the air in libraries contains enough spores for reinfestation of stored books.[18] There is no reason to expect otherwise in textile museums.

6.3.3   ADDITIONAL METHODS OF CONTROL

When a calamity such as water leakage or a flood occurs, soaked textiles may be completely destroyed in periods ranging from a few days to a few weeks, depending on temperature. Mildew growth should be checked as soon as possible, either by drying or autoclaving (and subsequent drying), or by application of powerful water-soluble disinfectants (quaternary ammonium compounds, phenolics, etc.) whenever climatic or environmental conditions do not allow drying or autoclaving.

The use of ultrasonics is a modern development that appears to have interesting possibilities for modern textiles, but for fragile ancient textiles it cannot be recommended.[76] The pertinent literature, however, should be consulted for its practical application.[77]

Boucher *et al.* mention that ethylene-oxide and ultrasonic waves are synergistic, possibly due to accelerated gas diffusion.[78] Such a treatment could perhaps, in specific situations, be valuable.

6.4   RECOMMENDATIONS FOR CONTROLLING TEXTILE PESTS

1. Good housekeeping, regular inspection and vigilance provide a sound basis for the control of undesirable insect pests and micro-organisms in collections of textiles.

2. If possible, the atmosphere in textile museums should be conditioned at 50% relative humidity in order to prevent development of mildew.
3. If air-conditioning is impracticable, a relative humidity of between 50% and 65% should be achieved, if possible, by manipulating ventilation and heating. Rapid fluctuations or uneven distribution of temperature should be avoided.
4. Constant storage of textiles below temperatures of 10°C (preferably 5°C) will prevent damage by insects.
5. Insecticides and fungicides should be used preventatively only, if other methods of prevention fail. If organisms are already present, these compounds should be used after checking their compatibility with the textiles concerned.
6. For preventative purposes with respect to insects contact insecticides (D.D.T., Lindane, etc.) may be used, preferably applied as a spray on walls, floors, ceilings, etc.
7. For protection against mildew, salicylanilide or quaternary ammonium compounds are suggested tentatively. In each case, proper care should be taken to investigate compatibility with the textile to be treated.
8. For the curative control of both insects and micro-organisms, commercially available mixtures of ethylene oxide and inert gases may be used. Rice's method[66] appears to be both simple and effective.

6.5   SOURCES OF INFORMATION

The problem of textile pest control in museums and art collections has received very little attention, so that literature on the subject is scarce. A review, based on information about similar damage to stored textiles for household and technical use, was made by Hueck.[39] Another source of information is the literature on biodeterioration in archives and libraries, institutions which have to cope with comparable problems; the basic material—cellulose—is common to books, and a number of types of textiles.

Recent reviews of this related problem are by Wälchli and Gallo and Gallo.[41, 60] Furthermore, the books by Langwell and Plumbe should be consulted.[79, 80] See also reference 81. Information on relevant insect pests can be found in Busvine, Herfs and Stotter, Hickin, Kemper, Lepigre, Malis and Munro.[1, 9, 25, 55, 82–84] Damage by micro-organisms (mildew) is described by Turner and also in the famous book by Siu.[16, 62]

A compilation of literature on damage by all kinds of organisms to a wide array of materials (textiles inclusive) was made by Greathouse and Wessels.[3] The book by Plenderleith on the general problems of conservation of antiques and works of art, contains a short chapter on biogenic damage to textiles.[2] An article by Leene, dealing with the conservation of costumes, in general, also touches on this problem and so does Lehmann in his articles on the conservation of historical textiles.[40, 85, 86]

Most of the books and articles mentioned provide information on methods of control, too. From the many handbooks that deal with the chemical substances involved in the control of insects and micro-organisms, and related subjects, the one by Chalmers deserves mention as a practical guide for anyone not acquainted with the rather specialist field of household pesticides.[87]

REFERENCES

1. MALLIS, A., *Handbook of Pest Control*, 3rd edn, Mac Nair Dorland Comp., New York (1960)
2. PLENDERLEITH, H. J., *The conservation of antiquities and works of art*, 2nd edn, London, University Press, Oxford (1962)
3. GREATHOUSE, G. A. and WESSELS, C. J., *Deterioration of Materials*, Reinhold Publishing Corporation, New York (1954)
4. LAIBACH, E., 'Zoologische Probleme in der Textilforschung', *Melliand TextBer.*, **37**, 1220–1225 (1956)
5. LAIBACH, E., 'Do moths feed of Perlon, Nylon and Man-made Fibres?', *Spinn. Web., TextVeredl.*, **84**, 975–984 (1966)
6. LAIBACH, E., 'Das Verhalten der Raupen der Kleidermotte *Tineola bisselliella Humm.* gegenüber einem Mischgarn aus Wolle und Chemiefasern', *Melliand TextBer.*, **38**, 677–678 (1957)
7. LAIBACH, E., 'Insekten als Schädlinge an Textilien', *Z. angew. Ent.*, **47**, 142–48 (1960)
8. LAIBACH, E., 'Lästlinge und Schädlinge en Textilien', *Anz. f. Schädlingskunde*, **38**, No. 3, 33–36 (1965)
9. KEMPER, H., '*Die Haus- und Gesundheitsschädlinge und ihre Bekämpfung*', Duncker & Humblot, Berlin (1950)
10. Organization for Economic Cooperation and Development, *International Directory of Biological Deterioration Research, Paris*, 2nd edn (1968)
11. HERFS, A., 'Termiten und Silberfischchen als Papier—bzw. Bücherschädlinge', *Anz. f. Schädlingskunde*, **32**, No. 12, 178–181 (1959)
12. LAIBACH, E., 'Warum wird Kunstseide von Silberfischchen *(Lepisma saccharina L.)* gefressen', *Melliand TextBer.*, **29**, 397–401 (1948)
13. LAIBACH, E., '*Lepisma saccharina*, das Silberfischchen', *Z. hyg. Zool. und Schädlingsbekämpfung*, **40**, 321–370 (1952)
14. HERFS, A., 'Insektenschäden an Kunstseide', *Melliand TextBer.*, **17**, 689–704 (1936)
15. WHITEHOUSE, J. A., 'Apparent mildewing of new bookbindings', *Aust. J. Sci.*, **18**, No. 2, 60–61 (1955)
16. SIU, R. G. H., '*Microbial decomposition of cellulose*', Reinhold Publ. Comp., New York (1951)
17. GALLO, F., 'Biological agents which damage paper materials in libraries and archives', *Recent Advances in Conservation*, Edited by G. Thomson, Butterworths, London, 55–61 (1963)
18. GALLO, F., 'Continuto microbico dell' aria e infezioni secondarie dei libre', *Boll. Ist. Patol. Libro.*, **23**, 2–18 (1964)
19. KOWALIK, R., Micro organisms destroying paper in Polish archives, *Med. dosn. mikrobiol.*, **4**, 359 (1952), Ref.: *Rev. Appl. Mycol.*, **32**, 583 (1953)
20. NIUKSHA, I. U. P., 'Mycoflora of books and paper' (in Russian), *Bot. Zh.*, **41**, 797–809 (1957), *Prev. Det. Abstr.*, **15**, PDL 30325 (1957)
21. WOODROFFE, G. E. and SOUTHGATE, B. J., 'An investigation of the distribution and fieldhabits of the varied carpet beetle, *Anthrenus verbasci L.* in Britain', *Bull. ent. Res.*, **45**, No. 3, 575–584 (1954)
22. EVANS, D. M., 'The deterioration of bookbinding materials', *Microbiological Deterioration in the Tropics*, SCI (Society of Chemical Industry) Monograph, No. 23, London, 179–184 (1966)
23. KLENS, P. F. and STEWART, W. J., 'New developments in textile preservation', *Am. Dyestuff Rep.*, **46**, 346–350 (1957)
24. SYKES, G., '*Disinfection and sterilization*', 1st edn, Spon, London, 183 (1958)
25. BUSVINE, J., *Insects and Hygiene*, 2nd edn, Methuen & Co., Ltd, London (1966)
26. LAWRENCE, C. A. and BLOCK, S. S., *Disinfection, sterilization and preservation*, Lea & Febiger, Philadelphia (1968)
27. REDDISH, G. F., *Antiseptics, Disinfectants, Fungicides and Chemical and Physical Sterilisation*, Lea & Febiger, Philadelphia (1957)
28. WALLHÄUSSER, K. H. and SCHMIDT, H., *Sterilisation, Desinfektion, Konservierung, Chemotherapie*, Georg Thieme Verlag, Stuttgart (1967)
29. HUECK, H. J., 'An analysis of the soil burial test', *Proc. IVth Int. Congress of Crop Protection*, **2**, 1773–1776, Braunschweig (1960)
30. BLOCK, S. S., 'Humidity requirements for mould growth' *Appl. Microbiol.*, **1**, 287–293 (1953)
31. BLOCK, S. S., RODRIGUEZ-TORRENT, R., COLE, J. B. and PRINCE, A. E., 'Humidity and temperature requirements of selected fungi', *Devs. Ind. Microbio.*, **3**, 204–216 (1962)
32. WERNER, A. E. A., 'Heating and ventilation', *Museums J.*, **57**, 159–166 (1957)
33. AYERST, G., *Microbiological Deterioration in the Tropics*, SCI (Society of Chemical Industry) Monograph No. 23, 14–20, London (1966)

34. PADFIELD, T., 'The control of relative humidity and air pollution in show-cases and picture frames', *Stud. Conserv.*, **11**, 8–30 (1966)

35. WERNER, A. E. A., 'Scientific methods in the examination and conservation of antiquities', *Sci. Prog.*, **50**, 527–539 (1962)

36. HAZEU, W. and HUECK, H. J., 'Changes of humidity inside packages due to environmental conditions', *Microbiological Deterioration in the Tropics*, SCI (Society of Chemical Industry), Monograph No. 23, 224–231, London (1966)

37. HAZEU, W., 'Vocht, materialen en schimmel', *TNO-Nieuws*, **21**, 323–327 (1966)

38. THOMSON, G., 'Relative humidity variation with temperature in a case containing wood', *Stud. Conserv.*, **9**, 153–168 (1964)

39. HUECK, H. J., 'The biodeterioration of textiles and its prevention in antiquities and works of art', *TNO-Nieuws*, **20**, 301–307 (1965)

40. LEENE, J. E., 'Restaurierung und Konservierung von Kostumen', *Waffen- und Kostümkunde*, 55–69 (1967)

41. GALLO, F. and GALLO, P., 'Bücherfeindliche Insekten und Mikroorganismen', *Papier Geschichte*, **16**, No. 3/4, 7–28 (1966)

42. HUECK, H. J., 'The biological deterioration of plastics', *Plastics Lond.*, **25**, 419–422 (1960)

43. REUMUTH, H. and LOSKE, TH., 'Fälle von Mottenhissen in Zellulosefolien und "mottensicheren" Kunststoff–Folien–Beuteln', *Melliand TextBer.*, **41**, 871–873 (1960)

44. GERHARDT, P. D. and LINDGREN, D. L., 'Insect penetration of films', *Mod. Packag.*, **28**, No. 4, 216–219 (1955)

45. BLOCK, S. S., 'Protection of paper and textile products from insect damage', *Ind. Engng Chem.*, **43**, 1558–1563 (1951)

46. GALLO, F., 'Richerche sperimentali sulla resistenza agli agenti biologici dei materiali impiegati nel restauro dei libri. IV. Saggi su polivinilpirrolidone, calaton, marange e aquapel, *Boll. Ist. Patol. Libro*, **23**, 39–47 (1964)

47. GALLO, F., Idem. 'V. Saggi sui films plastici e considerazioni sulle loro carratteristiche'. *Boll. Ist. Patol. Libro*, **24**, 96–105 (1966)

48. BAYNES-COPE, A. D., 'The conservator's point of view', *Microbiological Deterioration in the Tropics*, SCI (Society of Chemical Industry) Monograph No. 23, 121–124, London (1966)

49. BALLNER, F., *Über die Desinfektion von Büchern, Drucksachen u. dgl. mittels feuchter heisser Luft*, Franz Deuticke, Leipzig und Wien (1907)

50. HELWIG, H., 'Bücher mit Schimmelpilzbefall. Disinfektions und Konservierungs-möglichkeiten', *Das Papier*, **7**, 235–239 (1953)

51. JOHNSON, O., KROG, N. and POLAND, J. LLOYD., 'Pesticides, a CW Report', *Chemical Week*, May 25, 118–148; June 1, 56–90 (1963)

52. HUECK-VAN DER PLAS, E. H., 'Survey of commercial products used to protect materials against biological deterioration', *Intern. Biodet. Bull.*, **2**, 69–120 (1966)

53. GALLO, P., 'Problems in the use of insecticides on occupied premises', *Recent Advances in Conservation*, Edited by G. Thomson, Butterworths, London, 48–54 (1963)

54. JEDRZEJEWSKA, H., '*The damaging influence of disinfecting agents on sensitive ancient materials*', IIC (International Institute for Conservation of Historic and Artistic Works), London Conference on Museum Climatology. Preprints, 95–101 (1967)

55. HERFS, A. and STÖTTER, A., *Wollschädlinge und ihre moderne Bekämpfung*, Edited by Farbenfabriken Bayer A.G., Leverkusen (without year)

56. LAIBACH, E., 'Wollschutz, ein Sondergebiet in der Schädlingsbekämpfung, *Melliand TextBer.*, **39**, 1389–1391 (1958)

57. MONCRIEFF, R. W., *Mothproofing*, Leonard Hill Ltd, London (1950)

58. RICE, J. W., 'A dry cleaning technique for textile conservation', *Stud. Conserv.*, **9**, 83–90 (1964)

59. HASE, A., 'Wollschäden und Dauerschutz der Wolle durch 'Eulan'—Behandlung', *Mitt. Biol. Zentralanstalt Ld- u. Forstw.*, Berlin, No. 72, 1–56 (1951)

60. WÄLCHLI, O., 'Papierschädlinge in Bibliotheken und Archiven', *Text. Rdsch.*, **17**, 63–76 (1962)

61. BURGESS, R., 'Experiments on the preservation of wool against harmful insects', *J. Soc. Dyers Colour.*, **51**, No. 3, 85–89 (1935)

62. TURNER, J. N., *The Microbiology of Fabricated Materials*, J. A. Churchill Ltd, London (1967)

63. MEEUSE, A. D. J., 'Mothproofing from the entomological point of view', Med. Vezelinstituut TNO No. 169, Delft (1951)

64. EICHLER, W., *Handbuch der Insektizidkunde*, VEB Verlag Volk und Gesundheit, Berlin, 205 (1965)

65. FULTON, R. A., YEOMANS, A. H. and SULLIVAN, W. N., 'Ethylene oxide as a fumigant against insects', *J. Econ. Ent.*, **56**, 906 (1963)

66. RICE, J. W., 'Principles of textile conservation science No. 2. Practical control of fungi and bacteria in fabric specimens', *Textile Museum J.*, **1**, 52–55 (1962)

67. DARBY, R. T. and KEMPTON, A. G., 'Soil burial of fabrics treated with minimal concentrations of fungicides', *Text. Res. J.*, **32**, 548–552 (1962)

68. KOWALIK, R. and SADURSKA, I., 'The disinfection of infected storerooms in archives, libraries and museums', *Acta microbiol. pol.*, **15**, 193–197 (1966)

69. FLIEDER, F., 'Lutte contre les moisissures des matériaux constitutifs des documents graphiques', *Recent Advances in Conservation*, Edited by G. Thomson, Butterworths, London, 70–72 (1963)

70. WHITMORE, T. C., 'Laurylpentachlorophenate protecting herbarium specimens', *Taxon*, **14**, No. 5, 164–165 (1965)

71. LEHMANN, D., 'Conservation of textiles at the West Berlin State Museum', *Stud. Conserv.*, **9**, 15 (1964)

72. CZERWINSKA, E. and SADURSKA, J., 'Actinomycetes damaging old manuscripts and documents' (in Polish with English summary), *Acta Microbiol. pol.*, **2**, 160–164 (1953)

73. PARTRIDGE, H. W. and KEY, G. E., 'Textile Materials: rot-proofing', *J. Text. Inst.*, **40**, 1077 (1949)

74. CZERWINSKA, E. and KOWALIK, R., 'Penicillia destroying archival papers', *Acta Microbiol. pol.*, **5**, 299–302 (1956)

75. BLOCK, S. S., 'Experiments in mildew prevention', *Mod. Sanit.*, **3**, 61–67 (1951)

76. LEENE, J. E., Private communication

77. PISANO, M. A., BOUCHER, R. M. G. and ALCAMO, I. E., 'Sterilizing effects of high-intensity airborne sonic and ultrasonic waves', *Appl. Microbiol.*, **14**, 732–736 (1966)

78. BOUCHER, R. M. G., PISANO, M. A., TORTORA, G. and SAWACKI, E., 'Synergistic effects in sonochemical sterilization', *Appl. Microbiol.*, **15**, 1257–1261 (1967)

79. LANGWELL, W. H., *The Conservation of Books and Documents*, Ed. J. Pitman, London (1957)

80. PLUMBE, W. J., *The Preservation of Books, in Tropical and Sub-tropical Countries*, Oxford University Press (1964)

81. Anonymous, 'Bescherming van archiefruimten en dokumenten'. Nederlands Instituut voor Documentatie en Registratuur, Den Haag, Publ. 2e serie No. 27 (1959)

82. HICKIN, N. E., *Household Insect Pests*, The Rentokil Library, Hutchinson & Co., London, 172 (1964)

83. LEPIGRE, A., *Insectes du Logis et du Magasin*, Ed. Insectarium, Jardin d'Essai, Alger (1951)

84. MUNRO, J. W., *Pests of Stored Products*, The Rentokil Library, Hutchinson & Co. Ltd, London, 234 (1966)

85. LEHMANN, D., 'Restaurierung und Konservierung von historischen Textilien', *Textilindustrie*, **68**, 293–299 (1966)

86. LEHMANN, D., 'Die Erhaltung von historischen Textilien', *Melliand TextBer.*, **48**, 1298–1302 (1967)

87. CHALMERS, L., *Domestic and Industrial Chemical Specialities*, Leonard Hill, London (1966)

88. HUECK, H. J. and BRIJN, J. LA., 'The control of textile pests by dichlorvos-vapours', *J. Stored Products Res.*, (in press) (1971)

FURTHER READING

BOUSTEAD, W., 'The conservation of works of art in tropical and sub-tropical zones', *Recent Advances in Conservation*, Edited by G. Thomson, Butterworths, London, 77–78 (1963)

DITTMER, D. S., *Handbook of toxicology, Vol. V: Fungicides*, W. B. Saunders Comp. Philadelphia and London (1959)

EVANS, D. M., 'Cockroaches and Bookbinding', *Penrose's A.*, **54**, 118–120 (1960)

FLIEDER, F., 'Etudes des blanchiments des taches des papiers anciens', *Bull. Ass. Tech. Ind. Pap.*, ATIP Bull. No. 4, 173–184 (1960)

FLIEDER, F., 'Etude de la resistance biologique des procédés de renforcement des documents graphiques', *Recent Advances in Conservation*, Edited by G. Thomson, Butterworths, London, 65–69 (1963)

HINTON, H. E., *A monograph of the beetles associated with stored products*, British Museum (Natural History), London (1945)

LEHMANN, D., 'Die Eulan Behandlung von Textilien und Zoologischen Präparaten', *Ergänzungsbände des Berliner Jahrbuchs für Vor- und Frühgeschichte*, **1**, 67–72 (1964)

LEHMANN, D., 'Mottenschutzbehandlung textiler und zoologischer Museumsobjekte', *Der Präparator. Ztschr. f. Museumtechnik*, **11**, 187–194, 221–230 (1965)

MOUTZ, K., 'Beseitigung von Schimmelstellen und feuchten Flächen in Papierfabriken', *Allg. Pap. Rdsch.*, **12,** 596–600 (1959)

SAREL WHITFIELD, F. G., COLE, J. H. and WHITNEY, G. F. H., 'The bionomics of *Tineola bisselliella Humm* under laboratory culture and its behaviour in biological assay', *Lab. Pract.,* **7,** 210–217, 275–284, 339–343, 408–411 (1958)

SCHMIDT, H., Insekten als Papierschädlinge und ihre Bekämpfung, *Das Papier,* **11,** 309–311 (1957)

United States Department of Agriculture, 'Clothes Moths and Carpet Beetles. How to combat them'. *Home Gdn. Bull.,* **24** (1953)

WALCHLI, O., 'Die Dauerhaftigkeit der Motten- und Käferechtheit durch Mitin', *Textilveredlung,* **3,** 345–349 (1968)

7

Textiles in the Museum Environment

GARRY THOMSON, M.A. (Cantab.)
Scientific Adviser, National Gallery, London

Since prevention is better than cure, control of the museum environment is becoming of prime importance for good conservation of all museum materials. Textiles stand to benefit more perhaps than any other class of material from these improvements.

This chapter is divided into two parts. The first is a basic summary of environmental control for the general museum, and follows the I.I.C. booklet on the subject.[1] The second part deals specifically with textiles and their interaction with the environment.

7.1 BASIC CONTROL OF THE MUSEUM ENVIRONMENT

7.1.1 RELATIVE HUMIDITY

Under ordinary circumstances air at 20°C may contain from about 3 to about 17 g water vapour per m³ (5–35 l of water in an exhibition room of 2000 m³). Water, ever present in the air, is also to be found in a great variety of museum materials. Where the condition of the air remains steady, an equilibrium is reached, so that the amount of water present in solid objects also remains constant. If the air is heated, or if it is replaced by drier air, objects start to dry out, and vice versa. These changes matter very little for materials which contain no water, e.g. metals, very little water, e.g. oil paint, or can release it without strain, e.g. porous ceramics. Wood, ivory, leather and the natural textiles, however, are very water-absorbent (hygroscopic) and undergo appreciable changes in volume as they imbibe or release water. This may lead to warping of wood, and where materials of different water-absorption characteristics are joined (e.g. paint on wood or canvas, textile coverings on wood) to adhesion failure at the joint.

To control humidity we must be able to measure it. Since warm air can hold more water than cold air, it is no good quoting the actual amount of water vapour in a volume of air. If, however, we take this amount, divide it by the maximum amount which the air could hold at that temperature and multiply it by 100, we obtain the percentage *relative humidity* (RH) of the air. Thus, air with as much water as it can hold has an RH of 100% whatever the temperature, and perfectly dry air an RH of 0%.

Objects kept at a constant RH will not give out or take in water vapour even if the temperature varies (within reasonable limits). Although this is a simplification, since an object which is heated, even if the RH is kept constant, gives off some water, within the limits encountered in museums a constant RH will ensure that no damage occurs through moisture-content variation. Lack of humidity control is liable to cause serious change to wooden objects in winter, in the temperate zones, where powerful interior heating is considered necessary for human comfort. This lowers the RH from 50–60% to perhaps 20% and thereby causes serious drying of wood. Dry wood is less plastic than wet, and it may respond by cracking to the stress set up. Paper and other water-absorbent materials also become brittle at low RH. Humidities above 70% are dangerous because of the ease with which moulds and fungi can grow in these conditions. With high humidities there is also the danger of condensation on surfaces cooler than the air. Indeed, pictures and tapestries hung on outside walls may enclose behind them a microclimate quite different from that in the room. The RH in museums, therefore, should not be allowed to rise above 60% or fall below 40%, and should ideally be stabilised at some set value between these two figures. 55% RH is a commonly accepted figure for paintings and furniture. Whatever value is chosen should be maintained as accurately as possible (this normally means to within ±3 or 4%). The temperature, however, is dictated by human comfort (normally near 20°C) and need not therefore be specified here.

7.1.2   DIRT

Substantially all the dirt which reaches museum objects is airborne. In towns much of this is tarry and adheres tenaciously. Precipitated dirt may also form nuclei for undesirable reactions such as corrosion of metals. However safely the cleaning of tapestries and textiles is carried out it is better not to have to clean them at all, especially since some dirt is almost impossible to remove.

If the museum is situated in a town or near an industrial area, high priority must be given to air-filtering. Maritime museums (salt in the air) and museums in arid zones (wind-borne sand and dust) also have special problems which can be cured by filtering the air.

Two ways of removing suspended solids (known as aerosol) from the incoming air may be considered—either forcing the air through tiny passages as in a fabric or foamed plastic filter, or electrostatic precipitation. Electrostatic precipitators are efficient filtering devices, but they are not to be recommended for museums exhibiting textiles and other organic material because of the small amounts of ozone and nitrogen oxides which they produce.

It is possible to install fabric filters which remove more than 99·995% of the incoming suspended dirt, but this involves powerful fans, since there is a considerable pressure drop across the filter. Such high efficiencies are only warranted where other clean air precautions are in force, and this is certainly not the case in public museums. It is reasonable, however, to ask that filters remove 95% or more of the incoming dirt, and this should be not 95% of a coarse 'test dust', but 95% under the actual conditions of use. The pressure drop across such a filter might be 1–2 cm measured by water gauge.

The amount of any air pollutant, whether solid or gaseous, can be expressed in micrograms per cubic metre ($\mu g/m^3$ where $1\mu g = 10^{-6}$ g). The suspended dirt in large towns in winter amounts to several hundred micrograms per cubic metre, but may fall to 100 or so in summer. By removing 95% of this the indoor air contains about as much suspended matter as normal country air.

7.1.3   SULPHUR DIOXIDE

Sulphur dioxide is responsible for much damage to antiquities. It is readily converted to sulphuric acid, in which form it attacks paper, cotton, linen, frescoes, limestone, marble, and metals other than gold.

Whereas clean air legislation is now decreasing the amount of dirt in the air of many cities, it has not been found practicable to remove sulphur dioxide at source, i.e. where fuel is burnt. Consequently, the level of sulphur dioxide is rising with the growth of industry. In London today there is commonly twice as much sulphur dioxide as dirt in the air.

Sulphur dioxide can be removed from museum air by passing the air through an activated carbon filter, or by a water spray. Improved materials may soon be on the market. Activated carbon filters cannot be expected to remove all the sulphur dioxide at one pass (a typical figure is 60%), but where the bulk of the air is recirculated, they can be very satisfactory, if constantly supervised. Some air-conditioning systems use a continuous water spray, and if thorough may reduce sulphur dioxide concentration to low levels. Other water sprays may be more effective if made alkaline with a non-corrosive, non-volatile additive. As with smoke and dirt, a 'country air' level of concentration well below 50 $\mu g/m^3$ can be regarded as satisfactory.

7.1.4   OTHER POLLUTANTS IN THE AIR

Ozone has become a serious menace in certain towns in the U.S.A., notably Los Angeles. The ozone is formed by a series of reactions in the air involving sunlight and the exhaust gases from automobile engines. No comparable quantities of ozone are produced in large European towns. Ozone is detrimental to many organic materials, including cellulose, has a pronounced effect on rubber, and should be regarded as a dangerous museum contaminant. The construction of a cheap and effective ozone remover should not be difficult, however, and in the absence of a special filter, activated carbon should be reasonably effective.

No special precautions need be taken to remove hydrogen sulphide unless present in unusually high concentration, although it is common practice to lacquer silver objects against tarnishing.

7.1.5   LIGHT

Chemical change requires energy, and most of the colour changes on surfaces get this energy from light. For our purposes light in a museum, whether from sun and sky, fluorescent lamps or tungsten incandescent lamps, can be divided into three bands, in order of increasing wavelength:

1. Invisible ultraviolet radiation, wavelength 3000–4000 Å.
2. Visible light, wavelength 4000–7600 Å.
3. Invisible infra-red radiation, beyond 7600 Å.

This is also the order of decreasing potency. Ultraviolet radiation is, in general, the most damaging. Visible light, especially the shorter, blue, end of the spectrum, causes a wide variety of harm, but the effect of infra-red radiation (unless by heating) can be regarded as negligible.

Ultraviolet Radiation

This, being damaging but invisible, should be eliminated by using ultra-violet-absorbing filters in sheet or varnish form. This is particularly important when specimens are exposed to daylight. Some fluorescent lamps emit a noticeable amount of ultraviolet radiation, so they also should be filtered, unless known to emit no more ultraviolet radiation than a tungsten lamp. It is not at present considered worthwile to use ultraviolet filters over tungsten lamps.

Visible Light

Since visible light is also harmful, although to a lesser degree than ultra-violet, it must also be controlled. The illumination value (measured in lux or lumens/ft^2, where 10 lux $\backsimeq$ 1 lumen/ft^2) should never be excessive. An illumination value which is currently being recommended to museums in England allows a maximum of 150 lux for moderately sensitive objects, such as oil and tempera paintings, and no more than 50 lux for very sensitive objects such as textiles, tapestries and watercolours.

Controlling artificial light to a predetermined level causes no great technical difficulty, but daylight is so extremely variable that some automatic control involving photocells and electrically operated shutters is, in most cases, the only way to prevent excessively strong light and to ensure sufficient light at all viewing times. Exposure to light can be greatly reduced by any form of curtain or shutter which masks sensitive material from the light, except when it is being viewed.

7.1.6   LIMITED ENVIRONMENTAL CONTROL

Controlling the environment in the way that has been recommended above is expensive and involves the installation of air-conditioning and lighting control. A more limited approach may seem all that is possible for some museums, though this may in the end prove a false economy. A great deal of good can be done, however, by guarding against extremes.

Relative Humidity

In dry climates, humidity should be maintained as near 55% as possible, and should never be allowed to fall below 40%, by using humidifiers. These are devices which add water to the air, either by atomising it in a fine spray, or by evaporating it from a large surface, or by heating it. They are controlled by a 'humidistat'—a humidity senser which operates an electrical relay. The atomising type of humidifier blows the salts contained in hard water into the air along with the water, so that distilled water should be used in these devices.

In wet climates dehumidifiers should be operated to keep the RH below 70% to avoid danger from moulds and condensation. In these, the room air is drawn through a water-absorbent substance, which is periodically dried by heating and the moist air is ducted to waste.

Relative humidity can often be controlled by heating or refrigeration, according to conditions. Where whole rooms cannot be humidity-controlled it is usually possible to control individual exhibition cases.

Dirt and Air Pollution

In the absence of a central air-conditioning plant, the limited answer here, too, is to keep dust and sulphur dioxide out of the exhibition cases. For instance, a case can be fitted with a breathing hole plugged with a small air filter and sulphur dioxide absorber.

Ultraviolet Radiation

Glass removes the shorter ultraviolet wavelengths (about 3000–3250 Å) but is ineffective against the remainder, even if thick. The common commercial white paints, however, absorb a good deal of ultraviolet radiation. In tropical museums the ultraviolet menace will be mainly overcome if all daylight reaches exhibits only by reflection from a white wall. This will also prevent undiffused sunlight from striking the exhibits. Proper ultraviolet filters, however, are not expensive, even though they have to be periodically renewed.

Visible Light

In many of the older museums of the world, particularly in hot countries, the illumination level may not rise above 100 or 200 lux, even when the sun is high. The pressure to modernise to high illumination levels should be resisted by conservators in these museums.

Using a light meter the pattern of light can be visualised. Screens, blinds, net curtains, and other shading devices will usefully control high spots, and very sensitive material can sometimes be rearranged so as not to receive high light exposures. Where serious control is attempted, the economy of artificial lighting will be apparent.

7.1.7   MONITORING

It is bad practice to install devices to control the environment without, at the same time, ensuring that they remain effective. Particularly with humidity, more damage may be done by malfunctioning apparatus than by none at all.

All controls must, therefore, be either continuously or regularly monitored, and the more 'fail-safe' mechanisms that can be built in the better. For instance, in a season of median humidity, where a humidity control device starts a slow cycle of high and low RH (through faulty feed-back) it may be better to have the RH control cut out automatically and a warning device operated.

RH should be recorded continuously and the records filed. Regular checks, perhaps monthly, will suffice for dust filter efficiency, sulphur dioxide concentration, ultraviolet radiation, and daylight control.

7.1.8   SUMMARY

The mnemonic ALIGHT may help the conservator to remember the factors that should be controlled in the museum environment:

Aerosol   all suspended dirt and dust to be removed with at least 95% efficiency.

Light   illumination value not to exceed an agreed figure. 150 lux is suggested for moderately sensitive, and 50 lux for very sensitive material.

Invisible   ultraviolet radiation to be eliminated with filters from daylight and fluorescent lamps.

Gases   pollutant gases in urban museums to be reduced to below 50 $\mu g/m^3$ by activated carbon filters or water spray.

Humidity   to be controlled to a set level: 55% RH is widely recommended.

Temperature   the least important control, since it is determined in any case by human comfort, usually at about 20°C. Excessive heating by illuminants to be avoided.

7.2   DETERIORATION OF MUSEUM TEXTILES

The controls just described apply equally to textiles as to other museum objects, such as paintings. However, textiles are more sensitive than oil paintings to light, airborne dust and sulphur dioxide, and respond in a different way to humidity. We now, therefore, consider some special points relating to the effect of environment on textiles.

We have to examine here two classes of change which are usually inter-dependent: change in colour and decrease in strength (tendering). Since the deterioration of a dye varies according to the nature of its textile substrate, and vice versa, when considering deterioration it is best to use the term 'dyeing', meaning a dye-textile combination.

It was once supposed that if the lighting is made dim enough no fading will take place. This is not true; light, however dim, causes fading of suscep-tible materials. As far as is known within the range of museum lighting, the amount of fading is dependent on the total exposure received, so that one year under light at a certain illumination value is equivalent in destructive power to two years under light at half this illumination. This is known as the 'reciprocity' principle.

7.2.1   MEASUREMENT OF LIGHT

For museum work two units of measurement are required, illumination value and exposure. The *illumination value*, which can loosely be described as the strength of the visible light as it appears to the human eye, is measured in *lux*. Illumination value is also referred to as illumination level. The word 'intensity' should not be used except where light energy is being measured. Lux is the international unit (Système International) and is a measure of lumens per square metre. In England and the U.S.A. a measure called 'lumens per square foot' (or foot candles) is still in use. Since $1 m^2$ = approx. $10 ft^2$, $1 lm/ft^2$ = approx. 10 lux. The *exposure* to light which an object has received is proportional both to illumination value and to time of exposure, therefore, to lux multiplied by time, or lux-hours. A more convenient unit is 1 million lux-hours, 1 Mlxh, which is an exposure of 1000 h at 1000 lux, 10 000 h at 100 lux, or any other combination of lux multiplied by hours making a product of 1 million.[2] In museums where the light is not too fierce one year amounts to an exposure of 1 or 2 Mlxh,[3] but it can easily rise to 10 or more times this figure if the lighting is very powerful.

7.2.2   HOW FUGITIVE ARE THE TEXTILE COLOURS IN MUSEUMS?

Any textile may find itself in a museum. Some colours may be so fugitive as to have faded out before the object even arrives or may disappear in the first few months of exhibition. Leaving aside these very unstable colours, the conservator is mainly concerned with the natural dyes used on the very valuable exhibits, such as tapestries and historic costumes.

In a recent comprehensive study of the fading of natural dyes, the authors concluded that after about half a century of average conditions (70 Mlxh), many of the natural dyes 'would show only the faintest tint of their original colour, or a faint tint of some other colour. Many of the yellows would have become pale brown and even the fastest dyes, madder, cochineal and indigo, would have changed appreciably in colour.'[4] The lifetimes of many water-colour and manuscript pigments are comparable. Kuehn exposed six rather fugitive colours (magenta, orchil, brazilwood, saffron, yellow and green Persian berries lake), all of which except magenta have been used on old manuscripts.[5] Even with the exclusion of ultraviolet radiation, all of these would have faded significantly in less than a year of exhibition in an average museum.

The rate of fading of colours is matched by the weakening or tendering of the fibres themselves. Among the common natural fibres, silk is the least resistant to photodegradation, wool the toughest, with cotton in an intermediate position.[6] Padfield concludes that 50 Mlxh is likely to cause serious damage to cellulose (cotton and paper).[7] As already stated, this amounts to about half a century of average museum life.

We are a long way from having acquired all the information we need on the rates of fading of the natural colours. Even when all these rates are known for the fresh colours we are not at the end of the road. Many very precious exhibits have no bright colours left and little mechanical strength. How much are they changing now? Have they reached the end of their course? It is never right to assume this, although there are factors which cause rates of change to slow with time. In one series of tests, three Egyptian wool fabrics, probably about 2000 years old, were included. Their dullness (2 dull red, 1 khaki) suggested that some deterioration had already occurred, yet under about 20 Mlxh of daylight, with and without UV, changes were detected in all three.[8]

Statements about rates of fading must be carefully qualified because so many factors influence these rates. For simplicity these factors can be separated into three groups:

1. Preparation of dye and textile.
2. Deterioration which has already occurred.
3. Environment.

Though we do not always have full details of old recipes, there is no refuge in the popular assertion that 'ancient secrets have been lost'.[9] It is possible to prepare natural dyes in the laboratory, thus ensuring that factors (1) and (2) are constant, in order to disentangle the damaging factors in the environment. However, there is reason to suppose that, from the nature of accelerated tests these effects may be exaggerated relative to the primary cause of damage—photo-oxidation. The fading of a dye or the weakening of a fabric rarely takes place in one chemical step, but rather in a series of stages. The first and most important stage gets its energy from light. This is usually the slowest, and therefore the rate-determining step. Imagine the stages in the fading reaction to be represented by a car driven out of town through crowded traffic. There are on the route a number of bottle-necks which could cause traffic jams. But the first one at the town centre is by far the worst. In fact it is so bad that it almost completely determines the time for the journey home. Once out of this jam, traffic flows smoothly. The mid-town traffic jam is equivalent to the first stage of the fading reaction which is slow because of insufficient light. Now accelerated fading tests take place under very strong light, and this is equivalent to removing the mid-town traffic jam. But the driving reader will recall from bitter experience that, as soon as one traffic jam is eliminated another appears at some other part of the route, though the traffic in fact moves faster. The new traffic jam, that is to say, one of the later stages in the reaction, is now rate-determining. But this stage may be strongly influenced by such factors as humidity, heat, or sulphur dioxide, which scarcely affected the primary reaction. Hence in an accelerated test any of these factors may come to have an exaggerated effect.

Before reviewing the small amount of work on natural dyes, we may briefly glance at research on modern dyes. Giles notes that a rise in either RH or temperature causes more rapid fading of dyeings on wool and cotton, though dyeings on wool are usually less susceptible than those on cotton.[10, 11] Most of his figures, however, are for very high humidities. The effect of temperature is small, since the reaction is started by light, not heat. Indeed, local heating of a textile, as by tungsten spotlights, may actually slightly reduce fading rate by reducing the moisture content of the textile.

Much importance has been attached to the effect of moisture on the photodegradation of the fibres themselves. Cotton, wool and silk all photodegrade faster when wet than dry, but there is little detailed information about the extent of the effect at intermediate humidities.[7, 12, 13]

The effect of gaseous sulphur dioxide on modern dyes is limited to a small class, where the original colour can be restored by alkali.[11] However, sulphur dioxide becomes sulphuric acid on absorption by the fibres, and this is discussed with reference to the natural fibres on p. 109.

The beneficial effect of excluding oxygen from the environment of certain natural dyes is mentioned on p. 109, and it is pointed out that no dyed object should be placed in an oxygen-free environment until its effect, on all the constituents of the object, is known. This applies strongly where synthetic dyes are concerned. Many synthetic dyes are sensitive to reducing agents and removal of oxygen will actually increase their fading rates.[14]

With these points in mind, the summary at the end of this chapter can be taken to apply both to natural and synthetic dyes.

7.2.3   NATURAL DYEINGS AND THE ENVIRONMENT

Ultraviolet Radiation versus Visible Light

Cellulose is degraded predominantly but not exclusively by ultraviolet (UV) radiation, whether or not it is dyed.[7, 15] Padfield estimates that about four-fifths of the loss of strength of cotton cloth, irradiated by daylight through glass, is caused by wavelengths between 3000 and 4000 Å.[7] Similarly it has been shown that the short wavelengths, particularly UV, are the most destructive for wool.[16] Silk is the most rapidly degraded of all the natural fibres, and since, like wool, it is a protein one can assume that, for silk also, the rate of photodegradation is strongly dependent on the presence of UV.[6]

Dyes are much more likely to be affected by visible light than fibres, although light may be absorbed by a dye and its energy passed to the fibre, thus degrading it, or vice versa.

One might reasonably suppose that a wavelength that is strongly absorbed by a dyeing (e.g. blue light by an orange dyeing) is more likely to cause damage than one that is almost completely reflected, though this is not always the case. A more reliable generalisation is due to MacLaren.[17]

Dyeings appear to have a threshold wavelength. Any light of shorter wavelength (i.e. more energetic) can cause deterioration, but light of longer wavelength will have no effect. Thus fast dyeings can be faded only by UV. Those in a less stable category may be sensitive to blue light, while very fugitive dyes may be affected by the whole of the visible spectrum.

That removal of ultraviolet radiation reduces photochemical damage of natural colours and textiles is evident from a number of experiments.[4, 8] It would be surprising if the natural dyes behaved differently in this respect from the huge variety of synthetics on which a much greater number of experiments have been performed. However, when we try to obtain quantitative information ('By how much will the lifetime of a dyeing increase if we install UV-absorbing filters?') the picture is very confused, and experiments on modern dyes are of little direct use.

The most recent and complete report dealing with the effect of UV on natural dyeings in quantitative terms is that of Padfield and Landi.[4] These authors give figures for the fading of a wide range of natural dyes under a fluorescent lamp with and without UV. From them it is possible to deduce that removing UV about doubles lifetime under a fluorescent lamp with average UV emission (though fluorescent lamps vary widely in UV emission). With a knowledge of spectral energy distributions, it should be possible to go further and to derive the average benefit to be gained from UV-filtering daylight. Here results are not in accordance with each other, and daylight seems to fade much faster than its extra UV should allow. We can say no more, therefore, than that the UV-filtering of daylight should more than double the average lifetime of natural dyeings. More results are badly needed on fading rates.

Tungsten incandescent lamps and certain fluorescent lamps (e.g. the Philips 37 and 27) emit very little UV, so that it is not regarded as necessary to use UV-absorbing filters over them, at any rate while other far more important conservation measures remain to be taken. However, the newer tungsten-iodine (quartz halogen) lamps *do* require both glass and UV-absorbing filters for really safe use. Information on suppliers of UV-absorbing filters and other equipment relating to lighting and conservation is being collected by a group, including the author, in the Conservation Committee of the International Council of Museums. The information so far collected can be obtained from the above Council or from I.I.C.

Relative Humidity

The previously mentioned finding for modern dyes, that high heat and high relative humidity accelerate fading, is borne out for some natural dyes by Kuehn's work, but the effect in both cases seems too small to stimulate worthwhile conservation measures, except by radically changing the exhibit's environment.[5]

Averaging Kuehn's results shows that a drop in RH from 65% to 45% had very little effect on his dyes (ratio of fading rates at 65%/45% = 1·1), but that a further increase in dryness to 25% RH reduced fading considerably more (ratio of rates at 65%/25% = 3·2).

A drop in reaction rate to one-third of the rate at median RH seems worth while, but there are a number of difficulties. First, does this drop apply as much to normal as to accelerated conditions? Secondly, would the loss of elasticity of the textile at low RH offset the gain in light-fastness? Thirdly, what are the difficulties in exposing certain exhibits to a lower RH than the rest of the collection? Many old textiles are brittle even at normal RH. If they require to be handled from time to time by scholars and students, brittleness becomes an even more important factor.

With so many gaps in our knowledge, the best course would seem not to impose special RH conditions on textile departments of museums (i.e. to keep to the usually advocated 50–55% RH), bearing in mind that avoidance of excessive RH is important in reducing fading as well as in eliminating moulds. However, the possibility of sealed show-cases is briefly mentioned below, and the advantages of low RH should be carefully considered.

Temperature

A reaction which is caused by light should be almost uninfluenced by temperature over the usual climatic range, and indeed this is true for most dyes.[10] We have noted, however, that fading usually takes place in a number of stages, and that, though the first stage needs light, the following ones are likely to be slightly temperature-dependent (since their activation energy is low: Giles[10] quotes 2 kcal/mole, which corresponds to a rate ratio of 1 : 15 at temperatures 10°C apart near room temperature). Kuehn's colours were more responsive than the average to a change in temperature and this is not unexpected for such fugitive colours as he used. If primary activation energies are near to thermally available energies, e.g. around 30–40 kcal/mole, temperature may even influence the primary reaction. A change in temperature from 20° to 30°C resulted in a fading rate of about 1½ times the original rate. This would also be approximately true for a rise from 10° to 20°, but it may well amount to less in a museum than in Kuehn's accelerated conditions. A 50% increase in life might seem worth gaining, but, considering for instance that the illumination value over a picture may vary by 3 to 1 without being noticeable, the benefit to be gained by low temperature does not warrant the trouble, when so much can be done by control of the illumination and possibly the atmosphere.

Airborne Dirt

A textile presents a huge surface area to the air passing round and through it; it is, therefore, an efficient collector of airborne dirt. This dirt becomes partly embedded in the fibres and difficult to remove and, furthermore, may carry agents of destruction, such as traces of iron and adsorbed sulphur dioxide or sulphuric acid. Since even careful cleaning of a fabric weakens it, air-filtering is more important for textiles than for any other class of exhibit.

As with other museum materials, electrostatic precipitators for air-filtering should not be used because of the ozone they produce. A fabric or plastic filter capable of removing more than 95% by weight of the airborne dirt is recommended. Whether filters are installed or not, the pattern of air circulation may greatly affect the soiling of hanging textiles. Whenever air is made to change direction sharply the dust which it carries may be deposited. This explains the pattern of dirt to be seen above room-heating radiators (which by heating the air cause it to rise sharply upwards), around air entry ducts, beside narrow slots and holes, etc. If the sun is allowed to shine directly on a surface it can also cause an air circulation which leads to deposition of dirt.[18]

The safest precautions against soiling are, of course, air filtration or enclosing the textile in a glazed case.[19] Where neither of these is considered possible, care should be taken to observe air circulation, to avoid hanging over heated surfaces, and to diffuse any direct sunlight (which is also important because of fading).

Air Pollution

What has been said in the section on basic control about the damaging effect of sulphur dioxide applies strongly to cellulosic textiles.

In the presence of traces of iron and many other metals, sulphur dioxide is oxidised to sulphuric acid. Light is not necessary for this reaction, and since iron is such a common constituent of airborne dirt there will always be a supply of catalyst on textiles in urban museums. Therefore, we can assume that the sulphur dioxide adsorbed on textiles becomes converted to sulphuric acid.

The damaging effect of sulphuric acid from sulphur dioxide on paper and on other cellulosic materials, e.g. cotton, linen, has been known for years.[20] Less frequently studied is the effect of acid on the protein fibres wool and silk, although it has been shown that photochemical deterioration takes place very much more rapidly if the fibres are acid to pH 3·5 in the case of silk and to pH 1·2 in the case of wool.[21, 22] Since these were relatively fast laboratory experiments it would be safest to assume that the common pH of sulphur-dioxide-acidified material—pH 4—is also damaging in the long run. More data are needed.

Dangerous concentrations of ozone are uncommon outside certain localities such as Los Angeles in the U.S.A., but it should be noted that ozone is generally destructive of organic material, and has been demonstrated to affect cellulose and even dyes in low concentrations.[23, 24] Electrostatic precipitators, which are very effective air filters, should be avoided in museums since they produce traces of ozone.[20]

Oxygen

The Victoria and Albert Museum, London, has a picture by Turner which was enclosed in a 'vacuum' in the 1890s. However sceptical one may be of the extent of this vacuum, the fact that the fading of colours and the deterioration of other materials usually involves atmospheric oxygen was well known at that time. The difficulties and dangers of maintaining a vacuum are sidestepped if an inert gas, such as helium, argon or nitrogen, is used to fill the case instead.

There is no doubt that the rate of photodegradation of cellulose, whether or not it is dyed, is decreased, but not entirely stopped by the absence of oxygen.[25, 26] Nearly all this photo-oxidation is by ultra violet and blue light.[7, 15] The U.S. National Bureau of Standards made good use of these facts when they enclosed the American Declaration of Independence in a helium atmosphere and placed a yellow filter over it.[27]

Demény found that the weakening of cotton yarns by exposure to fluorescent light was retarded by a factor of more than three when nitrogen was substituted for air.[15] This sort of factor may also be operative in the case of wool.[28] The photodegradation of silk is also decreased by the absence of oxygen.[13]

Kuehn's paper provides good evidence for the protective effect of an inert atmosphere (nitrogen) on some natural colours.[5] His figures show that the effect of surrounding his samples with a nitrogen atmosphere instead of air, was to produce a marked improvement in light fastness, averaging out at about 10-fold.

Kuehn warns that the fading of some dyes may be unaffected by the absence of oxygen and in certain cases may actually be accelerated, and we have already noted that this may apply even more strongly to synthetic dyes. Therefore, before a composite object is placed in this special environment, the response of all its components to the special atmosphere should be known. The use of inert gases in sealed show-cases merits close attention for special objects.

Summary

1. The removal of *UV radiation* from daylight can be expected to increase the average lifetime of dyeings, on presently available data, by a factor of at least two, and probably considerably more for the fastest dyes and for the fibres.
2. Low *relative humidity* decreases rate of degradation of both dyes and fibres, but the decrease is not great enough to warrant dropping the RH to the lower tolerance limit for museums, say 40% RH. Unknown factors, such as the extra brittleness of fibres at the lower RH may offset the advantages. However, if objects are one day to be immobilised in sealed show-cases (see 5 below) the arguments for a low RH should be re-examined.
3. Lowering the *temperature* decreases rate of degradation, as with RH, but again the effect is too small to worry about in the applicable range, except possibly for storerooms.
4. It is extremely important to keep soiling by *airborne dirt* to a minimum, either by putting exhibits in cases or by efficient air-filtration.
5. There is every advantage in removing *sulphur dioxide* down to country-air concentrations (see Section 7.1), and no disadvantage except cost.
6. *Oxygen* plays a part in the majority of deterioration processes. The beneficial effect of nitrogen and other inert atmospheres in sealed show-cases should be further studied.

The above precautions having been taken, *visible light* remains in a special category on its own. The painful fact is that in the museum we can only admire as we destroy, whether the damage is large or minute. We can, however, ensure that, as far as possible, when there are no viewers there is no light: blinds should be closed during closing hours, curtains may cover show-cases, automatic illumination devices be used, etc. Beyond this the honest curator may be surprised to learn that a certain element of subterfuge comes into play. Where illumination values are to be brought down from an uncontrolled few hundred lux to the recommended 50 lux, one of the architect's main purposes is to make the museum visitor unaware of the large differences between exterior and interior daytime illumination—by more careful planning than has been customary in the past he must create 'apparently bright situations'.[29]

NOTES AND REFERENCES

1. *Control of the Museum Environment—a basic summary*, International Institute for Conservation, c/o National Gallery, Trafalgar Square, London W.C.2. (1967)
2. To quote exposure as the product of (illumination × time) is to assume the 'reciprocity law'. This is normally accepted within the range of our calculations
3. THOMSON, GARRY, 'Annual exposure to light within museums', *Stud. Conserv.*, **12,** 26–36 (1967)
4. PADFIELD, TIM and LANDI, SHEILA, 'The light fastness of the natural dyes', *Stud Conserv.*, **11,** 181–196 (1966)
5. KUEHN, HERMANN, 'The effect of oxygen, relative humidity and temperature on the fading rate of watercolours. Reduced light-damage in a nitrogen atmosphere', *1967 London Conference on Museum Climatology*, 1st edn, The International Institute for Conservation, London, 79–88 (1967)
6. LITTLE, A. H., 'Deterioration of textile materials', *1964 Delft Conference on the Conservation of Textiles*, 2nd edn, The International Institute for Conservation, London, 67–78 (1965)
7. PADFIELD, TIM, 'The deterioration of cellulose', *Problems of Conservation in Museums*, Allen and Unwin, London, 119–164 (1969)
8. THOMSON, GARRY, 'A new look at colour rendering, level of illumination, and protection from ultraviolet, *Stud. Conserv.*, **6,** 49–70, Figs 11–13 (1961)
9. KIEL, E. G. and HEERTJES, P. M., 'Metal complexes of Alizarin, V–investigations of Alizarin-dyed cotton fabrics', *J. Soc. Dyers Colour.*, **81,** 98–102 (1965)
10. GILES, CHARLES H. and MCKAY, ROBERT B., 'The lightfastness of dyes: a review', *Text. Res. J.*, **33,** 527–577 (1963)
11. GILES, C. H., 'The fading of colouring matters', *1964 Delft Conference on the Conservation of Textiles*, 2nd edn, The International Institute for Conservation, London, 8–26 (1965). Also printed in *J. appl. Chem.*, **15,** 541–550 (1965)
12. *See* reference 6 above, p. 76
13. HARRIS, MILTON, 'The photochemical decomposition of silk', *Am. Dyestuffs Reptr.*, **23,** 403–405 (1934)
14. BEEK, H. C. A. VAN and HEERTJES, P. M., 'Fading by light of organic dyes on textiles and other materials', *Stud. Conserv.*, **11,** 123–132 (1966). Azo-dyes are particularly mentioned as being sensitive to reducing agents
15. DEMÉNY, L., 'Degradation of cotton yarns by light from fluorescent lamps', *1967 London Conference on Museum Climatology*, 1st edn, The International Institute for Conservation, London, 53–64 (1967)
16. *Annual Report 1963–4*, Commonwealth Scientific and Industrial Research Organisation, Australia, 14 (1964)
17. MCLAREN, K., 'The spectral regions of daylight which cause fading', *J. Soc. Dyers Colour.*, **72,** 86 (1956)
18. REUMUTH, HORST, 'Der Schmutz in seiner ganzen Vielfalt', *Repr. Reiniger Revue Chem. Reinigung/Färberei*, Nos. 5-9, 26 (1965)
19. FELLER, R. L., 'Control of deteriorating effects of light upon museum objects' (in English and French), *Museum Unesco*, **17,** No. 2 (1964)
20. THOMSON, GARRY, 'Air pollution—a review for conservation chemists', *Stud. Conserv.*, **10,** 147–167 (1965)

BRYSSON, R. J., TRASK, B. J. and COOPER, A. S., 'The durability of cotton textiles: the effects of exposure in contaminated atmospheres', *Am. Dyestuff Reptr.*, **57,** 512–517 (1968)

21. HENDERSON, S. T. and HODGKISS, D., 'The spectral energy distribution of daylight', *Br. J. appl. Phys.*, **14,** 125–131 (1963) and **15,** 947–952 (1964)
    COLLINS, J. F., 'The colour temperature of daylight', *Br. J. appl. Phys.*, **16,** 527–532 (1965)

22. SMITH, A. L. and HARRIS, M., 'Oxidation of wool in photochemical oxidation', *J. Res. natn. Bur. Stand.*, **17,** 97–100 (1963)

23. BOGATY, H., *et al.*, 'The oxidation of cellulose by ozone in small concentrations', *Text. Res. J.*, **22,** 81–83 (1952)

24. SALVIN, V. S., 'The effect of atmospheric contaminants on light fastness', *J. Soc. Dyers Colour.*, **79,** 687–696 (1963)

25. EGERTON, G. S., 'Some aspects of the photochemical degradation of nylon, silk and viscose rayon', *Text. Res. J.*, **18,** 659–669 (1948)

26. PADFIELD, TIM, *see* reference 8 above, p. 22

27. 'Preservation of the Declaration of Independence and the Constitution of the U.S.A.', *N.B.S. Circular No. 503* (1951)

28. HARRIS, M. and SMITH, A. L., 'Photochemical reactions of wool', *J. Res. natn. Bur. Stand.*, **20,** 563–569 (1938)

29. BRAWNE, MICHAEL, 'Museum design for conservation', *1967 London Conference on Museum Climatology*, 1st edn, The International Institute for Conservation, London, 77 (1967)

8
Storage and Display

ANNE BUCK, B.A., F.M.A.
Keeper of The Gallery of English Costume, Manchester City Art Galleries
JENTINA E. LEENE, D.Sc.
Senior Reader, Laboratory for Textile Technology, Delft University of Technology

In Chapters 6 and 7, the importance of the control of pests and of the museum environment is stressed. In this chapter some practical conclusions and suggestions will be discussed. These suggestions come from a curator of a costume collection and so apply particularly to textiles in this form, but they are generally applicable to all kinds of textile collection.

The curator's problem is to work within the limits of comparative safety, and at the same time to organise the collections efficiently and present them effectively. The museum climate affects all specimens in different ways, at every stage of their museum existence; those in good condition of recent date, as well as earlier examples, which are already faded, tendered and repaired, must be considered.

8.1 LIGHT

Protection from light can easily be given to stored textiles. The exclusion of light from cupboard or storerooms, except for short-period lighting for occasional examination, presents no practical difficulty, however limited the curator's means may be. In the display of costume, however, lighting is a major problem. The curator, knowing all light to be harmful, must still make the collection visible.

In a newly designed museum an exhibition room should be designed to exclude daylight. In existing museums, it is usually possible to block out daylight from the exhibition room, but in some cases, where the museum itself is an architectural exhibit, there has to be compromise. Showcases should be arranged within the room so that no daylight falls on them, or if this is impossible, windows can be curtained and treated with UV absorbent varnish.

For the lighting of displays, the lamps (incandescent as well as fluorescent) should be separated from the cases by a glass screen which should be treated with a UV absorbent. Another problem is the reduction of the level of lighting, whatever the source, so that it is as weak as possible, but still acceptable to the viewer, who must not have a sense of strain or discomfort. Even in this weak light, objects should be exposed for as short a time as possible (*see* Chapter 7). The time of exposure can be lessened most easily by limiting the actual hours of viewing, but this solution is not in accordance with present museum policies. It must be limited, therefore, by ensuring that the exhibits are illuminated only when there are eyes viewing them. Attendants must be trained to switch off lighting whenever the room is empty and switch it on again as needed. This can, of course, be done by visitors themselves, but checking is still necessary. Time switches can be irritating especially to a serious viewer, and as they give minimum protection at the same time as they give maximum irritation, are no real solution. Time of exposure can also be limited by short-period exhibitions, although this means that the curator has to balance a slight deterioration over a large part of the collection against a greater deterioration of a smaller part. Objects already in a fragile state should, however, only be exposed to light for very short periods between long periods of protection in store. In a room which has been completely darkened, it will be necessary to have room lighting for cleaning purposes, but this will normally be used only when the display lighting is switched off.

If daylight is excluded as a protective measure, and artificial lighting used to light the displays, the eye will accept a fairly low level of illumination as adequate. The maximum level for safety is now given as 50–150 lux (*see* Chapter 7). The eye will adapt itself to this level but suffers some loss of discrimination. Brommelle states that this loss can be minimised by employing backgrounds less bright than the object, in similar rather than contrasting colours.[1] However, as the compensating effect of such backgrounds becomes negligible if the field subtends an angle of more than 12° at the eye, this does not help when a full-length costume is on display. Since a number of light and dark colours are nearly always involved, the choice of background must be experimental and will be governed by the purpose of a particular display. If the emphasis is on the history of the changing styles of dress, the dresses should be seen clearly defined against their background. A light background gives efficient viewing, except in cases where all the dresses within the group are white or have little colour, when a slightly darker and toning colour is more effective. Any sacrifice of detail in a main display of full-length costume can be countered by secondary, possibly more didactic displays in which detail is emphasised. Where the object to be viewed is smaller and can be closer to the eye, a more subdued background is advisable. If there is detail in relief, as for instance in many types of embroidery, quilting, ruching and applied trimmings, lighting from the side at a lower level of brightness than the lighting from above gives effective results. Seeing in a museum involves more than the level of illumination. Eyes unpractised in visual apprehension often need direction rather than greater intensity of light. The lower the level of light in a case, the more important it is that the display itself has form and clarity. If there is overcrowding in a case, when the level of illumination is low, the visitor will have to make a physical effort to see anything clearly and will at once become aware of strain and, consequently, of the lack of illumination. More spacious display, emphasising carefully defined shapes, textures or colour uncluttered by too much detail, make a lower level of illumination acceptable. A dress shown in the setting of its own period with contemporary furniture and domestic impedimenta, where a general impression rather than detail is the aim of the display, loses little by being shown in a dim light, although here also economy in display usually produces the effect of a brighter light.

8.2   POLLUTION

A polluted atmosphere is one of the greatest dangers to textiles whether they are exposed to light or not. Textiles and costume are particularly susceptible to the dirt in the atmosphere. The disfiguring effect of this, apart from its share in hastening deterioration, makes a high degree of protection from dirt essential. Dirt falling on a piece of pottery makes a film which is comparatively easily removed, but it penetrates deeply into a fabric, so that the washing or cleaning of a garment is not a simple operation, but one which brings new hazards. Therefore, preventive rather than remedial conservation is particularly desirable against the action of dirt.

If only cleaned air enters the storeroom, a costume can be stored in darkness, without additional protective enclosure; otherwise it will need some protective covering. The most general method is to hang garments full length, or to store them lying full length on trays in wardrobes, and to store the smaller garments and accessories in purpose-designed or adapted units, in boxes or in polythene bags. To prevent dust from entering, all wardrobes and cabinets should be designed with extra rebating at the doors. Foam strip can be used in addition, but is not a substitute for protective construction. For added protection from soiling, and for other reasons (see below), garments may have to be placed in bags within the wardrobes. In theory, show-cases protect the exhibits from dust. To achieve this, they have to be made as dustproof as possible, even more so than the storage units, as displayed objects can have no other protection. In practice, ideal conditions are rarely achieved, although this becomes obvious only in the more polluted industrial areas or museums where displays are not changed. Cases give some protection against the sulphur dioxide in the air, which is exhausted rapidly unless the case is frequently opened. Cases must be ventilated because of other hazards, however, and although dirt can be excluded by filters in the ventilators, these will not exclude gaseous pollution. If the museum atmosphere is controlled so that only washed, chemically clean air enters the room, it may be possible to do without cases altogether, an advantage since they themselves can make other problems.

8.3   HUMIDITY

As moisture in the atmosphere accelerates fading, the internal atmosphere of the cases must be controlled so that specimens displayed therein are not subjected to this danger. Costumes need large cases for their full-length display, in some instances, small rooms within the exhibition galleries. Dr. Plenderleith has shown that the daily variation in RH within a show-case at the British Museum was negligible compared with the variation within the museum itself, but not all cases are safe. A large case built some years ago at Platt Hall, Manchester, against an existing wall, gave so dangerous a variation that it has since been dismantled. The economy of building a large case straight on to a wall can be dangerous, especially if the wall is an outside one. The case will hold the seasonal and day and night variation of external temperature out of step with the controlled temperature of the room itself, with consequent danger of a critical level of relative humidity. Ventilation is needed to regulate the contact with the room atmosphere, but cases should also be insulated from outside walls.

Excess of humidity is likely to be a greater danger in the storeroom than in the exhibition rooms. For this reason costumes and textiles should not be stored in sealed polythene bags. In this respect, cellophane which allows for a rapid permeation of water-vapour is preferred to other plastic foils.

In museums where insect damage is more to be feared than fungus attack, light packaging in thick plastic foils may be considered, according to the material of the specimen.[2] The need to protect a woollen garment from moth attack may justify enclosing it in a sealed package, especially as wool is less susceptible to fungus attack. On the other hand, cotton and linen, less susceptible to moth attack than wool, but more susceptible to fungus attack, should not be sealed. Material used for any storage container should allow ventilation and permeation so that sharp variations in temperature and relative humidity are avoided. Wood is, therefore, to be preferred to steel for wardrobes, and ventilators should be fitted to them. It is also desirable to have as free a circulation of air as possible around the wardrobes, cabinets and other storage units. They should not be placed close to the wall of a room, particularly not an outside wall, but allowed sufficient space for free movement of air.

8.4   EXTERNAL HAZARDS

Even when precautions have been taken against dangers from light, variation in temperature and excessive humidity, and air pollution, costume is still subject to a number of hazards. Many of these have not yet received scientific attention. Neither are they a matter for those who specialise in conservation in its secondary aspect of individual treatment and repair, although the need for remedial treatment may well arise from neglect of them. It cannot be emphasised too often that such treatment, always costly in skilled time, is wasted if the object is afterwards stored, displayed or handled in conditions, favourable perhaps as far as light and climate are concerned, but containing elements of hazard for that particular type of object. Aftercare of all objects which have been treated is particularly necessary to enable us to assess possible effects of treatment.

Ease of access to stored material is a basic museum requirement. If this is lost, the museum's value as a place of study is lessened. It may be possible to give objects excellent conditions for conservation provided that one makes them almost inaccessible. If, in the interests of conservation, storage methods involve excessive handling and disturbance when reserve collections are used, this protection becomes a hazard.

Contact of the textile with other materials can be dangerous. In all storage trays, drawers or boxes, specimens should be protected from the surface of the container by layers of acid-free tissue paper. Polyurethane foam has many possible uses in storage. As a lining to drawers in which small accessories, for example, bags and purses are stored, it makes a soft padding and its slight suction holds the objects just sufficiently to prevent movement. It is also useful as a padding for the wire frames of storage hangers where the same quality of suction keeps the dress from slipping. However, exposure to air causes discoloration of the foam, and further testing of this material is needed before it can be thoroughly recommended as a contact material for textiles. In the meantime, direct contact should be avoided.

For full-length dresses, a variety of different frameworks are in use. Whatever type is used, all wood and metal sections should be padded and covered so that the textile is not in contact with any sharp edges or stretched over hard surfaces. If garments are mounted on boards these should be fabric covered.

In any museum treatment, pins should be used with care and their removal carefully checked. They have to be used in conservation and preparation of garments for display, but their permanent use in display should generally be avoided. They often conceal themselves in the garment and may cause damage as the exhibit is dismantled, or remain unnoticed and a potential cause of damage later. Any pins used should always be fine entomological pins and they should be placed between threads of the fabric, not piercing a thread.

8.5   INTERNAL HAZARDS

Costume conservation involves not only the basic problems of textile conservation, but also conservation of fur, feather, leather, metal and ivory and other substances which are used for dress accessories and are closely combined with textiles in the construction or ornament of garments. Often these other elements in dress represent a hazard to the main fabric.

Pins sometimes appear in a garment, surviving *in situ* as originally used. The early pins which fix the small bustle of an early nineteenth century dress, and those which pin in place the bonnet ribbons of the same date, are evidence which should be spared, although the state of the pins should be checked at intervals.

Dress shields attached to the armholes of dresses have often deteriorated badly, the inner layer of rubber having dried and disintegrated with discoloration of the covering fabric, and sometimes of the dress itself. If the shields themselves are suitable for preserving they should be removed and preserved separately.

Most of the textile fibres which come into museums are weakened by age through past exposure to light and air. When textiles are made up into garments, the fabric may also be bearing a strain caused by shaping and construction. To avoid strain on fibres in storage and display is an essential part of costume conservation.[3] Garments are subjected to the least strain if they are stored lying flat. This should always be the method for certain groups of material:

1. Very fragile garments of all kinds, particularly if the weaker fibres appear to run vertically from shoulder to hem.
2. Dresses of delicate fabric which have heavy trimming, particularly if this is at the hem, e.g. dresses of bead-embroidered chiffon of the 1920s and dresses of the 1820s of silk gauze with padded ornament at the hem.
3. Dresses of the 1930s, cut on the cross, which stretch out of shape if hung up.

With a small collection, the method of laying each dress flat and full-length in a wardrobe designed for this purpose, or in racks if the storeroom is air-conditioned, provides the best form of storage. However, if three or four

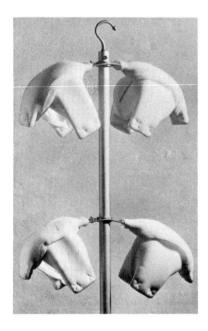

Figure 8.1. Storage hangers (originally designed by the Costume Institute of the Metropolitan Museum of Art, New York). The wire shoulder and hip frames are covered with polyurethane foam. At present a layer of tissue paper is placed over this foam until it has been proved completely safe as a contact material (Courtesy City Art Gallery, Manchester)

dresses have to lie in each tray, this method is less safe and less efficient. When frequent reference has to be made to a number of dresses, ease of access, with less handling, by hanging them may be the safest way. Dresses will then need a special hanger of the type designed at the Costume Institute of the Metropolitan Museum of Art, New York (Figure 8.1), with an upper framework giving support at shoulder, and a lower one taking the weight of the skirt—the wire just flexible enough to adjust slightly for width at shoulder and hip. The wire framework should always be covered with pads. This hanger not only gives support but enables the dress to be taken out by the pole which can be set in a holder, to make the dress available for study and sketching, and the dress itself need receive no handling at all. The frames give sufficient three-dimensional form to the dress to suggest its line to anyone who has already studied comparable examples on display. Dresses which are light-weight and not bulky, like the muslin dresses of the early nineteenth century, can, if in a good condition, be stored on the usual type of hanger, but this must be well padded.

Strain on fibres must be taken into account in costume display, and whenever garments are being carried or handled they should be kept flat. The showing of heavy robes and vestments, scarecrow-wise, on horizontal rods, or in any way which makes the weight of the garment hang continually from a single point in each thread, or from a limited number of threads, is harmful to the fabric. Such garments should be displayed over a cone-like support, so that the fabric does not hang vertically but is on a slight incline. The shaped forms of dresses are most safely shown on models moulded to their individual forms. Appropriate frames and petticoats beneath not only give the dresses their original form, but act as a support for the fabric. Smaller garments or accessories shown two-dimensionally, mounted on a board, should never hang so that the weight falls from one or two points only. The boards should never be placed vertically, but should always be given a slight incline to help support the mounted textile. Ideally, the angle with the vertical should be that at which the object remains in position without any other support.

Garments have other internal hazards, apart from their own weight. Silk garments, in particular, can be damaged by sharp creasing, which will, in time, cause the fibres to break completely. Creasing and folding in storage should be avoided as far as possible, and acid-free tissue paper layered within all folds. Shaped specimens should be padded out with tissue-paper so that the lines of their shape are preserved. In storage, as in display, we should work with the construction of the garment, never against it. Large flat garments like shawls are best stored on rolls and the smaller accessories, like lengths of lace and ribbon, should also be rolled.

In display, if garments are shown two-dimensionally so that they have to be folded, all the folds should be rounded by a roll of tissue-paper or lightly padded with cotton wool. Many dresses have some form of permanent creasing, such as pleating, in their construction, and present a particular problem. A very light padding of cotton wool or tissue-paper in trimmings like bows and puffs, will not only ease creasing, but will also restore the softer shaping that the trimmings would have had originally.

The silk covers of parasols and umbrellas also have this hazard inherent in their construction, and avoiding one hazard only produces another. Suffering from creasing when closed and from strain when open, the parasol is a difficult accessory to store and display. The method described by Mrs. Karen Finch, of attaching a tape to the ribs, slightly less than the circumference of the opened parasol, to take the strain when the parasol is displayed open, lessens the danger in this position.[4] To store parasols in this way, however, is not likely to be practical for a collection of any size. They should never, of course, be tightly rolled, which from time to time has been the fashionable appearance for the umbrella. In display, however, conservation has to give way to accuracy of presentation for at least one example, for it would be incorrect to show, with the dress of a fashionable man of the 1880s or 1890s, an umbrella which was not rolled as slender as a walking stick.

Possible methods are to store them vertically, secured at the ferrule end by the handle, in an adaptation of the umbrella stand, or to store them horizontally, slightly open to release the folds (Figures 8.2, 8.3). Neither method is entirely satisfactory and the complication of the different forms of ferrule and handle, and the great variation in size, adds to the difficulties of providing storage, which is both safe and easy, and efficient for reference.

Sharp creasing is a cause of deterioration in another important costume accessory—fans, with silk, vellum or paper leaves. Most fans were originally

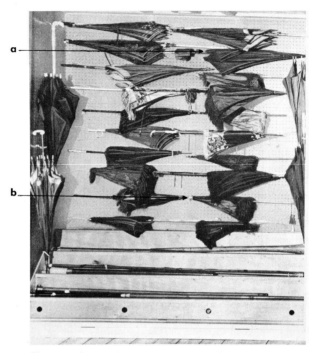

Figure 8.2. Storage of parasols.
1. The parasols are held horizontally (a) by clips which hook into the pegboard back and hold the stick and ferrule; (b) by square metal frames which also hook into the pegboard back; the handle and ferrule are supported on these; the frames extend beyond the clips so that two parasols can rest on a pair of them and the cover of a parasol above, supported by clips, can fall free behind them. Clips and holders are adjusted according to the lengths of the parasols.
2. Very long parasols are stored, held by clip or clips, vertically on the sides of the cupboard.
3. At the base of the cupboard, grooved steps hold walking sticks (Courtesy City Art Gallery, Manchester)

kept closed in boxes when not in use, and even when they were in use, they were closed for most of the time. The leaves of many fans show the effect of this. When they come into the museum they should be stored open and supported. The Gallery of English Costume, Manchester, has three different sizes of small tray; according to size, two, three or four of these fit into the large sliding drawers of a cabinet. The trays are made of a sheet of hardboard, covered with felt, with a small wooden block along each side, to form handles to lift the tray and also to support the tray above. The drawers are deep enough to take three trays, one above the other, so that according to the size of fan, six, nine or twelve are stored in each drawer. The fan lies open

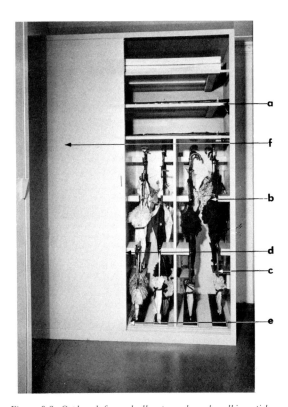

Figure 8.3. Cupboard for umbrellas parasols and walking sticks. (a) Shelf for walking-sticks; (b) clamps for tall umbrellas; (c) supporting shelf for the tall umbrellas; (d) clamps for short umbrellas; (e) supporting shelf for the short umbrellas; (f) sliding door (Courtesy Historisches Museum der Stadt Wien, Modesammlungen, Schloss Hetzendorf)

on the felt-covered board and can be removed for study without any handling of the fan itself.

Garments can cause damage to each other as they are moved. A hook and eye left unfastened on one dress can catch on the flimsy fabric of a dress hanging beside it. In some periods, particularly 1900 to 1914, the fastenings of dresses were extremely complicated and hooks and eyes could appear almost anywhere. A dress should be fully fastened when stored, but as it can hardly be stored exactly as worn, the fastenings often tend to come undone. The sharp-edged beads of some trimmings and the metal tags of laces need care. Dresses which for these or similar reasons may be a danger to themselves and others, should have a protective covering separating them from adjoining garments in store.

8.6   STORAGE

The problems of storage and display from the point of view of a curator of costume collections have been discussed and there now follows a description of how collections of other textile objects are housed and stored in a few newly built museums in the U.S.A.[5-9] The storage buildings of The Henry Francis du Pont Winterthur Museum are of cement-block construction with an open air space between the block- and plastered-wall to

Figure 8.4. Curtain storage (Courtesy Colonial Williamsburg)

prevent condensation. All museum rooms and storage areas are air-conditioned at $21°C$ and a controlled relative humidity, the level of which ranges from a low of 45% to a high of 55%. The adjusted level is dependent on the kind of materials present in a room.

The storage rooms are windowless, and lighted by fluorescent tube lamps protected with UV absorbing plastic shields. They are protected from fire by an automatic CO_2 fire-extinguishing system.[5]

At Colonial Williamsburg, the textiles are kept at a temperature between 20° and 22°C and at a relative humidity of 50–55%. Provisions have also been made to avoid damage by fluorescent light.[8]

8.6.1   CURTAIN STORAGE[5,7,8]

In storage, curtains should hang free from folds. In the Winterthur Museum they are hung on racks of copper pipe and furnished with rope, pulleys, and hooks. The racks run on sliding tracks suspended from the ceiling. When removed from storage the curtains are lowered on to a clean pad spread out on the floor before being folded and laid on a truck or cart the dimensions of which being determined largely by the width of corridors and doorways in the museum, and of the elevator.[5]

At Colonial Williamsburg, another device has been developed on the same principle, but before storing them, 'the curtains are lined and inner-lined, with the antique textiles tacked to the inner-lining, at intervals of eight inches throughout the curtain. This transfers the stress to the inner-lining and prevents the total weight of the curtain from being supported by the antique fabric'.

In this museum, there are racks, which consist of a sliding sleeve on a rectangular frame. This sleeve can be moved up and down for placement or removal of curtains, which are attached to them by drapery pins (Figures 8.4 and 8.5). The walls of the curtain storage rooms are lined with pegboard for easy hanging of valances and tassels. The valances are attached with nylon-pile tape to wooden boards of the same length, which are hung on the pegboard (Figure 8.6).

In the Winterthur Museum, the bed and window valances are hung flat on the furred-out walls by means of snap fasteners attached to tapes. Nylon-pile tape is also used.

8.6.2   STORAGE OF BEDSPREADS, AND OTHER LONG PIECES

In the Winterthur Museum the bedspreads are hung over wooden rods supported in a metal frame that hangs from the ceiling and runs on an aluminium track. The round poles, which are made of varnished, seasoned wood, prevent centre creases in the spreads.[5] A similar arrangement (Figure 8.7) exists at Colonial Williamsburg.

8.6.3   STORAGE OF SMALLER FLAT FABRICS

In the Costume and Textile Study Collections of the University of Washington, Seattle, flat fabrics are rolled on cardboard tubes of about 160 mm diameter, which are covered with polyethylene foil, held in place with tapes. Special cases have been designed to take the rolls, installed in such a way that the space available is used at the optimum.[9]

Figure 8.5. Curtain storage room with two floor levels (Courtesy Colonial Williamsburg)

Figure 8.6. Storage of valances (Courtesy Colonial Williamsburg)

At Colonial Williamsburg, textiles are also stored on shelves. When folded, provisions have to be made for limiting any damage at the folds (Figure 8.8).

8.6.4 STORAGE OF RUGS

In the Winterthur Museum, rugs up to about 5 m (16 ft) are rolled on heavy-gauge aluminium tubes protected with muslin sleeves. Several tubes

Figure 8.7. Storage of bedspreads and other long pieces (Courtesy Colonial Williamsburg)

Figure 8.8. Storage of smaller flat fabrics (Courtesy Colonial Williamsburg)

are suspended vertically by means of S-hooks linked through eyebolts and connected to metal chains which also move on sliding tracks. Very large, heavy rugs, however, are rolled and stored on metal shelves.[5]

At Colonial Williamsburg there are specially designed racks, which support chains on which as many as five lengths of wooden rollers can be hung. These chains, despite the full weight of the rugs, can be moved with trolleys from side to side with minimal effort (Figure 8.9). The rugs are rolled on heavy cardboard sleeves which fit over the rollers, allowing the rugs to be removed from the rollers and transported to an exhibition building while still supported by the cardboard sleeve.[7] There is accommodation for rugs

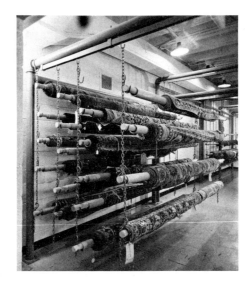

Figure 8.9. Storage of rugs, rolled on cardboard sleeves (Courtesy Colonial Williamsburg)

of about 3 m (10 ft) width, and up to about 5 m (16 ft) long (*see* also Chapter 12).

8.7   DISPLAY

It is outside the scope of this book to discuss in detail principles of display. In general, it is not the task of the restorer, although often he lends a hand. The rules laid down in Chapter 7, and in the paragraphs referring to display, in the first part of this chapter, should be followed. In Chapter 16 the different points of view concerning manikins with or without head (schematic or realistic) are mentioned. The structure of show-cases will always be dependent on the objects to be exposed, and the curator shall have to decide on the structural and aesthetic demands in close co-operation with architects.

REFERENCES
1. BROMMELLE, N. S. and HARRIS, J. B., 'Museum Lighting' (4), *Mus. J.*, **3,** 180 (1962)
2. HUECK, H. J., 'Biodeterioration of Textiles and its Prevention', *Delft Conference on Conservation of Textiles*, 2nd edn, The International Institute for Conservation, London, 98 (1965)
3. GREENE, F. S., 'The Conservation of an Historic Robe', *Mus. News*, 23–32 (Sept. 1964)
4. FINCH, K., *Costume Society Bulletin*, **1,** No. 2, 17 (1966/67)

5. Private communications of Mrs. Charles F. Montgomery on the facilities for textile collections in the Henry Francis du Pont Winterthur Museum, Winterthur, Delaware 19735, U.S.A.
6. Private communications of Mr. John M. Graham of the Colonial Williamsburg, Williamsburg, Virginia 23185, U.S.A.
7. GRAHAM, J. M., 'Solving Storage Problems', *Mus. News*, 24–29 (Dec. 1962)
8. LANIER, M. B., 'Storage facilities at Colonial Williamsburg', *Mus. News*, 31–33 (Feb. 1967)
9. Curator of the Costume and Textile Study Collections, University of Washington, Seattle, Space and Textiles, *Mus. News*, 28–33 (Nov. 1963)

9

The Equipment of a Textile Conservation Workroom

Mrs SHEILA B. LANDI

Conservation of Textiles Department, Victoria and Albert Museum, London

9.1 GENERAL CONDITIONS

The first and most important requirement, and probably in many cases the most difficult to obtain, is space. It must be remembered that there will always be an object which fits into no known category and for which individual treatment will have to be devised. No specially designed equipment ever seems to be the right size or shape. In general, working conditions that are pleasant and comfortable are conducive to greater working efficiency.

The room itself should be as large as can be acquired, reckoning that each worker will need as a minimum 25 m² (270 ft²) of space, inclusive of storage cupboards and general equipment. There is much to be said for dividing the available space into two separate areas, one for 'wet' work (i.e. washing, dyeing, drycleaning and preparation of chemicals) and one for 'dry' work (i.e. sewing, application of adhesives, etc.).

The use of the term area rather than room is to emphasise that the two sides of the work are closely related so that it would be unsuitable to have, for instance, two rooms divided by a corridor. If two separate rooms are provided they should be linked by a wide archway, not an ordinary door, as objects will have to be carried from one section to another. All workrooms should have a good north light, some of which comes from directly above so that all parts are equally well lit. If the daylight source cannot be from the north, care should be taken to provide means of exclusion of direct sunlight. Artificial light will obviously be necessary at times and there are a number of fluorescent tubes on the market which are considered to give good colour rendering.[1] These should all be investigated to establish individual preferences, but in any case should provide general lighting of at least 500 lux. Care should always be taken to avoid unnecessary exposure of objects not under treatment. In addition, adjustable spotlights may occasionally be needed.

The next thing to be considered is ventilation, the importance of which cannot be too strongly stressed. Normal ventilation facilities must be supplemented with a hood and a powerful extractor fan for use when toxic or strongly smelling chemicals have to be employed.

Decor should be pleasing in colour, but not too obtrusive, and chosen with the light requirements in mind. There is at present a wide choice of floor coverings available, all of which are easily cleaned and resist penetration by water.

9.2   BASIC FURNITURE

It is essential to provide as many working surfaces as space permits, the design of which takes into consideration the different operations that will have to be undertaken. All workers need personal tables and chairs where they will be 'at home'. These tables should be approximately 0·75 m (2½ ft) high and at least 1·5 × 1 m (4½ × 2 ft) in area, and provided with drawer space, situated to one side so that there is still room for the legs. There should be other tables available, of the same height and on castors, that can be pushed together when large objects have to be dealt with. There should also be one or two that are rather higher than average, perhaps 0·85 m (2·8 ft), for there are some jobs which can only be done while standing, and stooping over a table of normal height can be very tiring.

If space and funds permit, a glass-topped table, lighted from underneath, would provide an admirable means of viewing the other side of work in progress without the necessity of turning it over. (Both the Bavarian National Museum at Munich, Germany, and the Abegg-Stiftung at Riggisberg, Switzerland, have similar tables in their conservation workshops.) Yet another idea is to have a sloping surface provided with tee-square and set-square to aid the correct setting of warps and wefts. This could, of course, be made to fold away when not in use.

There should always be available, at any working surface, a chair that is adjustable in height and in the angle of the back. A great deal of study has been given, in recent years, to correct height and shape of furniture intended for use at work, and consultation with a specialist in the subject could prove well worth while. The nature of conservation work is such that a high degree of concentration must be maintained and this cannot be achieved in conditions of physical discomfort.

As far as possible all working surfaces should be positioned at right angles to the main source of daylight and have at least two electric power points close at hand. Over the workroom these power points should be provided in abundance, together with a number of extension leads long enough to reach any part of the room. The local regulations concerning the protection of electrical installations from penetration by water, water vapour and the fumes of inflammable solvents must be strictly observed.

The material from which the table tops are made can be varied according to the function for which they are intended but all must be easy to clean. Some must also be resistant to water, others to heat and adhesives. The former requirement can be met by a phenol-formaldehyde surface, the latter by a film such as tetrafluorethylene which, when stretched on boards previously covered with a strong cotton material, can provide a sympathetic and convenient surface on which to perform many operations.[2, 3] It can easily be replaced when necessary. As the intensity of light required is very high, attention should be given to the colour of these surfaces. A neutral colour of mid-tone is the most restful for the eyes.

As it is always necessary to keep good records of the practical work done, an allocation of filing cabinets should be made in which paper, note-books, photographs, etc., can be stored. There should also be a bookcase in which to keep reference books.

A valuable piece of extra equipment is a small trolley, with at least two shelves on which to keep personal tools. This can be wheeled to any part of the room in which the conservator may have to work.

9.3   PERSONAL TOOLS

Some personal tools will be collected in the course of time as a particular job creates a particular need, but there are also a number of items which will always be required by each worker. It should be understood that everything in the following list that is made of metal must be of stainless steel if possible. It should also be noted that the best tools for textile conservation work are often made for quite other purposes than for the use of the needlewoman.

Needles—There are a number of standard shapes: sharp, crewel, straw, darning, tapestry, bead, and curved surgical needles that are round in section. (Some surgical needles have a cutting edge and these are of no use in the present context.) In general, sizes between 5 and 12 are the most common, although they are available down to No. 1. For tapestry needles the sizes run from 17 to 24. *N.B.* Sizes range from thick to fine, the higher the number the finer the needle.[4] All these kinds of needles should be provided in as wide a range of sizes as can be acquired.

Thimble—One of the right size.

Scissors—In at least three sizes: a large pair of cutting-out scissors, a pair with fine blades about 150 mm in length over all, and a pair of short, but pointed, surgical or embroidery scissors. There should also be a pair of pinking shears for departmental use.

Surgeons' scalpels—A separate handle can be bought and used with a number of differently shaped blades, the most useful of which are the long pointed ones.[5]

Measures—A good metal tape at least 3 m (10 ft) long, a dressmaker's tape and a short ruler.

Tweezers—The best ones are to be found amongst surgical and laboratory equipment. For general use the surgeon's blunt-nosed forceps which are serrated on the inner surface are ideal, although there are times when those intended for handling microscope slides are more appropriate. If at any time a pair of very finely pointed tweezers are required the answer may be found among watchmaker's equipment.

Pins—Entomological pins are very fine and excellent for pinning out delicate fabrics. The long, strong, plastic-headed pins, sometimes known as toilet pins, are also very useful for heavier work, but are not stainless. Plated brass pins should be avoided as they are clumsy and can damage fabric.

Brushes—Large, medium and small, in all kinds of shapes and in all kinds of bristle (hog, sable, squirrel, camel, nylon, etc.) will be needed for all kinds of purposes.

Magnifier—A pocket lens with magnification of at least × 10.

9.4 GENERAL TOOLS AND EQUIPMENT

In this section the items are very numerous indeed.

Embroidery frames—A number of different sizes must be available. Figure 9.1 shows the basic principles of these frames. Naturally the larger the object

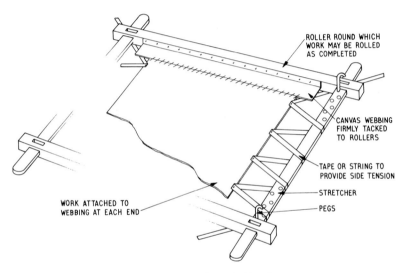

ROLLER ROUND WHICH
WORK MAY BE ROLLED
AS COMPLETED

CANVAS WEBBING
FIRMLY TACKED
TO ROLLERS

TAPE OR STRING TO
PROVIDE SIDE TENSION

STRETCHER

PEGS

WORK ATTACHED TO
WEBBING AT EACH END

Figure 9.1. Diagram of an embroidery frame

to be restored the bigger and heavier the frame. For tapestries, the principle may be the same (see also Chapter 11).

Binocular Microscope—This has to be mounted on a frame which will support it over the work when needed, leaving both hands free. Magnification × 10 will be needed if a wide field of vision is required, × 20 if more detail is wanted.

Magnifying glass with a magnification of × 4 over a wider area, and which is on an adjustable arm, can also be of great help at times.

Microscope—A students' microscope for identification of fibres, etc. Magnification should be at least × 100.

Irons—Large and small, with a temperature control and properly earthed. For the small irons this may mean they will have to be especially adapted or even made. As a guide, a drawing is given of one that has already been found of great use (Figure 9.2). There have recently come on the market one or two spatula irons made principally for painting restorers and work with prints and drawings, but which are also very suitable for textiles.[6]

Steam table—A very expensive item, both in money and space, that can only really be justified in a large department. However, if there happens to be an extensive collection of costumes, or ecclesiastical vestments, which are

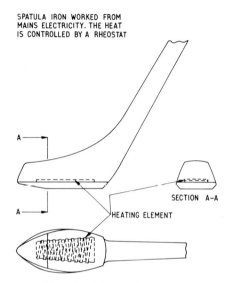

SPATULA IRON WORKED FROM
MAINS ELECTRICITY. THE HEAT
IS CONTROLLED BY A RHEOSTAT

SECTION A-A

HEATING ELEMENT

Figure 9.2. Diagram of a spatula iron

so often made of velvet, the cost is well worth while. A domestic steam iron is no substitute.

Ironing Boards—There should be several of these, in different shapes, together with a sleeve board.

Hair dryer—The kind that is held in the hand. This is an excellent aid to quick drying.

Electrical fan heater—This is also to assist drying large objects which would otherwise take a very long time.

Carpenters' tools—A small hammer, one pair of pliers, a screwdriver and a small tenon saw. These items may seem surprising until a little experience shows how useful they can be.

Apparatus for treating material with adhesives—If only one side of the material needs to take the adhesive, a table or board into which pins can be pushed will suffice, together with plenty of expendable plastic sheeting. When large quantities have to be treated or when both sides of the material must retain adhesive a more elaborate apparatus is necessary. The important factor is to keep the material from contact with any surface during treatment. A diagram is given of a simple machine on which this can be achieved (Figures 9.3 and 9.4).

Miscellaneous—A dressmaker's dummy, a sewing machine, some soft boards into which pins can be stuck, plenty of plastic film such as polyethylene teraphthalate and polyethylene in wide widths, and a roll of silicone parchment[7] Other items will be a stock of drying paper (a kind of paper that is

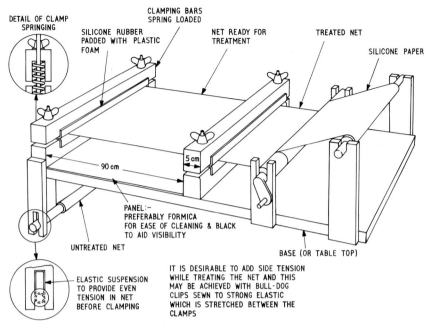

DETAIL OF CLAMP
SPRINGING

CLAMPING BARS
SPRING LOADED

SILICONE RUBBER
PADDED WITH PLASTIC
FOAM

NET READY FOR
TREATMENT

TREATED NET

SILICONE PAPER

90 cm

5 cm

PANEL:−
PREFERABLY FORMICA
FOR EASE OF CLEANING & BLACK
TO AID VISIBILITY

UNTREATED NET

BASE (OR TABLE TOP)

ELASTIC SUSPENSION
TO PROVIDE EVEN
TENSION IN NET
BEFORE CLAMPING

IT IS DESIRABLE TO ADD SIDE TENSION
WHILE TREATING THE NET AND THIS
MAY BE ACHIEVED WITH BULL-DOG
CLIPS SEWN TO STRONG ELASTIC
WHICH IS STRETCHED BETWEEN THE
CLAMPS

Figure 9.3. Diagram of an apparatus for treating materials with adhesives

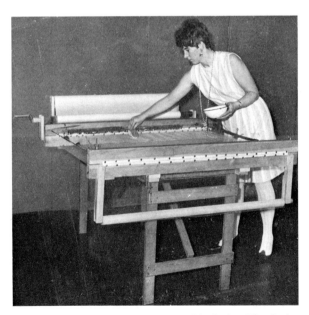

*Figure 9.4. Apparatus for treating materials with adhesives. The adhesive
is applied on the fabric by means of a sponge*

fluffless and has great wet strength and is used by photographers for drying prints) or thick blotting paper, cotton wool, absorbent tissues and tissue-paper.

Textile materials—A stock of textile materials in a variety of weaves, weight, yarns and fibres in white or cream can be very useful. The choice has to be made according to the kind of textiles belonging to the museum collection.

9.5   LABORATORY EQUIPMENT

Proper laboratory equipment is absolutely essential. A catalogue should be consulted to choose beakers and flasks in a range of shapes and sizes, storage jars for both dry and liquid goods (ensuring that some are in dark glass for those chemicals affected by light) and measuring cylinders in varying capacities, up to one litre. Further items are stirring rods, watch-glasses for beaker covers, corks, pH papers, filter paper, a scoop, thermometers, and a retort stand or two.

For weighing, either a student balance or a balance of the type with a weighted arm, is sufficiently accurate for most purposes. In addition to glassware a few larger plastic bowls, made of a plastic that will resist boiling water and most acids and alkalies, and one or two stainless steel bowls for dyeing, will be needed. For heating, electric hot plates are very useful and much better than gas bunsen burners.

Cupboards should be reserved for the storage of chemicals and chemical glassware.

9.6   STORAGE

For the temporary storage of the objects which have to be restored, the same principles apply as for the storage of textile collections. One has to be careful that light, excessive changes in temperature and relative humidity are avoided. The work must be organised in such a way that objects are usually in the restoration rooms for only a short time. As a general rule the textile objects will be kept in cupboards, but if this is not possible there should be shelves behind curtains which shut out the light.

There are, in general, three kinds of objects to be stored:

1. Costumes. These must be hung at full length, unless they are at all weak on the shoulders in which case there should be several shelves available where they can be laid out without folding.
2. Small and medium-sized flat textiles. These should be kept flat and wherever possible it is also desirable to keep them separate from each other. It follows that the requirement is for many shelves close to-gether, on slides so that they can be drawn out.
3. Large flat textiles. Once an object is too large to be kept flat it is better to roll rather than fold it. A supply of cardboard rollers in varying sizes (diameter and length) will, therefore, be needed. These should be kept on horizontal racks instead of shelves.

If it is planned to provide some very deep shelves they should be accessible from two sides as there is a limit to the stretch of the human arm. Although it would be very convenient to have all doors made of glass, so that the contents of the cupboards could be observed from the outside, this must not be done because of the harmfulness of light.

Shelves should also be available for the stock of new materials. Sewing threads and other small items should be stored in shallow drawers, each partitioned into a number of compartments in which the different colours and kinds of thread can be kept separately. Another piece of furniture which can house many items, such as tissues and drying paper, is a press or chest of large, flat drawers, which is generally used for keeping maps or working drawings.

9.7   EQUIPMENT FOR WASHING AND GENERAL CLEANING (See also Chapter 4)

Objects to be cleaned vary in size from the very large down to the smallest pieces of lace, and in condition from perfectly sound, though dirty, to those whose fibres barely retain any cohesion.

For small objects which require long soaking, the trays that are used for photographic work, are of the right size and shape, as are those used for dissecting. Trays that are heavy should be avoided for with the addition of water they become unmanageable.

Specially designed equipment will be required for large objects. The first consideration for any such equipment is that drainage is over a wide flat area which can be tilted as desired and can be reached freely from all sides. The equipment must be stainless steel for nothing else gives the same freedom in the use of chemicals and from the fear of rust. The input of water (hot and cold) should be in the form of a spray across the whole width of the surface. The simplest way of draining away the water is, of course, by gravity, but if this is not possible a pump will have to be included.

If a completely separate washing area has been provided, some part of the floor could be built with a slight slope towards a water discharge. By using plastic sheeting, or frames covered with netting, which could be put together to create the necessary size, the floor itself could be used for washing the larger textiles. If a trough is required this could be improvised by adding raised borders to the frames already mentioned and covering the whole with plastic sheeting to contain the water. It is very difficult to give exact specifications for such equipment, for local conditions and requirements will obviously differ greatly. In addition to such special equipment there must be a stainless steel or porcelain sink as large as space permits.

The only really safe water for washing is distilled or de-ionised water. Distilled water is cheap to produce but the still needed to provide any quantity would be very large, besides taking a very long time. This means a big storage tank is needed in which to build up a supply. In preference, therefore, it is well worth the initial expense of providing for the de-ionisation of water. Units are available which, by a system of ion-exchange taking place in a cylinder filled with active resins, give pure water on tap. From the larger units the flow is almost that of the ordinary water supply.[8]

9.8 EQUIPMENT FOR DRYCLEANING

For most conservation departments to provide proper drycleaning installations, such as those used commercially, would not be an economic proposition, unless there happened to be a very large collection of costumes in good enough condition to stand the rather violent action of such a plant. There will inevitably be times when drycleaning solvents have to be used, however, and, since they are comparatively toxic and need careful handling the following items should be taken into consideration:

1. A fume chamber to protect against vapour.
2. A trough in which objects can be submerged.
3. A flat space on which spotting can be done.
4. A means of 'mixing' solvent and textile.
5. Some means of recovering the solvent.

It is difficult to give exact specifications for the last two items for, as with the washing apparatus, local conditions will tend to dictate methods. Recovery of the solvent is necessary, from the economic point of view, if the apparatus is to be used with any frequency and freedom; also because it is not easy to dispose of large quantities of dirty liquid which cannot be poured into the local sewerage system. Some effort should, therefore, be made, by filtration or distillation, to re-use the solvent at least once.

REFERENCES AND NOTES

1. THOMSON, GARRY, 'A new look at colour rendering, level of illumination, and protection from ultraviolet', *Stud. Conserv.*, **6**, 49–70 (1961)
2. Phenolformaldehyde surface known in the U.K. as Formica, is also manufactured by other firms
3. Tetrafluoroethylene film known as Teflon and made by Du Pont, U.S.A.
4. Manufacturers of needles in the U.K. include Millwards of Redditch, and Newey and Bros., Ltd., of London
5. Surgeons' scalpels are manufactured in the U.K. by W. R. Swann and Co., Ltd., Sheffield, and Gillet and Sibert, Ltd., of London
6. Spatula irons are made by Willards Electrical Services Ltd., Chichester, Sussex, England and by Todd Electrics, Chelmsford, Essex, England
7. Polyethylene teraphthalate film known in the U.K. as Melinex (I.C.I.), in the U.S.A. as Mylar (Du Pont). In Germany comparable films are manufactured by Hoechst and B.A.S.F.
8. Units for deionisation of water are made in the U.K. by Elga Products Ltd., High Wycombe, Buckinghamshire, and Permutit Co., Ltd., London

Acknowledgements To Mrs. Karen Finch for her helpful suggestions and to Mr. N. S. Brommelle, Keeper of Conservation, Victoria and Albert Museum for guidance and permission to publish

10
Restoration and Conservation

JOHAN LODEWIJKS
Director of Central Research Laboratory for Objects of Art and Science, Amsterdam

JENTINA E. LEENE, D.Sc.
Senior Reader, Laboratory for Textile Technology, Delft University of Technology

10.1 INTRODUCTION

It is probably true that textile mending has been carried out for nearly as long as textiles have been used by man. Mending of holes and tears in garments and other textiles is more or less comparable with what is generally understood by restoration of textiles. It is only when the textiles, in the course of time, have acquired artistic or historic value, that it is necessary to make high demands upon the manner in which the mending has to be carried out.

This, however, should not lead to the conclusion that every valuable textile which has been damaged by some cause should be mended. In fact there exist two conflicting opinions, which spring from the same root, namely, the conviction that the style and the character of the object concerned must be preserved.

The first opinion is that if mending has to be done at all, it should be as invisible as possible. It is carried out on the condition that all repairs are documented by photographs and detailed reports, for the information of specialists at least. This method may mean reweaving tapestries, knotting a new pile in rugs or darning according to design in other fabrics. There remains, of course, a certain degree of insincerity towards the unsuspecting visitor, who finds himself confronted with a textile object, of which absolute authenticity is suggested, because there is no mention of restoration having been carried out. This objection, however, can be partly removed by providing schematic drawings or photographs with every restored object on which the restored parts are clearly marked.

The second opinion is that honesty, with regard to the observer and with respect to the artist who created the textile, requires that the repairs have to be carried out in such a way that the mended parts can easily be distinguished from the authentic, without disturbing too much the effect of the original work of art on the observer. This can be attained, for example, by sewing fabrics with structure and colour slightly different from the authentic object behind the holes and tears. In other words, all possible measures should be taken to preserve what has been left at the moment of conservation and to avoid further degradation. This opinion has gained much support.

To summarise, then, there are two important groups of preservation methods:

1. Restoration methods which, in principle, are directed towards restoring the original state, and
2. Conservation methods which aim at preserving the *status quo*.

It will be clear from the above that what is often understood to be restoration is, in fact, conservation. The following example will illustrate this.

A textile object consists of a plain woven material on which a number of pictorial representations or motifs are sewn in appliqué technique. When the basic fabric is badly deteriorated, but the appliqué work is still in good condition, the latter is often removed and sewn on to a new fabric identical to the original base fabric. This method of working can be classed under conservation methods, because the replaced plain fabric functions only as a carrier, whereas the preserved appliqué work determines the art historical value.

The choice between restoration and conservation depends on different rational factors, apart from irrational ones such as aesthetic and other feelings. When a textile has a representative function, as is often the case with tapestries and rugs which cover the walls of rooms in palaces, town halls, and comparable dwellings, one is more apt to decide on restoration. In museum collections items do not generally have a representative function and conservation methods should be considered very carefully. In general, conservation starts with cleaning, because dirt is considered to be a very harmful agent. Sometimes, however, the demands of conservation may conflict with the requirements of a particular specimen. Blood stains are considered especially dangerous to leave in textiles, because blood contains traces of iron, which is a catalyst of deteriorating chemical processes. A blood stain in a shirt of a murdered important historic person, however, is of such historical importance that it is not permitted to remove it.

This example could be amplified by others from, for example, the field of ethnographical textiles, where mud may be an essential part of the specimen and may not be removed. In the following chapters there will be mention of some other specific problems of different types of textiles, which complicate decisions.

10.2 CONSERVATION

The conservation of textiles can be attained:

1. By taking measures which eliminate or reduce the harmful effects of outside factors such as light, too high relative humidities, polluted air, etc. (see Chapter 7).
2. By treatments which are carried out with or on the textile objects.

The latter can be divided into three groups:

(*a*) Application of needle techniques.

(*b*) Application of natural and synthetic adhesives.
(*c*) Combinations of (*a*) and (*b*).

10.2.1 THE APPLICATION OF NEEDLE TECHNIQUES

For the conservation of textiles by mending with thread and needle different methods can be followed, the decision as to which one to choose being made according to the form, condition and the historical and aesthetic value of the object.

Form

The treatment of a flat textile (or textile fragment) will generally be different from the treatment of a dress, where 'drape' decides the style to an important degree. With flat textiles, supporting fabrics can be used when the loss of suppleness is not too great. In the case of a dress made of a supple material, however, the application of even a very thin material will greatly harm the drape. Ecclesiastical garments are rather stiff and can be spread out flat, so, in this case, the methods for flat textiles can generally be applied.

Condition

The line between 'good' and 'bad' conditions in specimens is obviously not clearly defined, but depends on the subjective impressions of the person judging. A more objective view is to say that whether a textile is judged to be in a good or bad state depends on what is to be done with the restored object. It may be in a perfectly good state to be kept either lying in a drawer, or fixed between glass plates, but not suitable at all to be exposed hanging in a representative room.

In general, an object is considered to be in good condition if this condition does not vary widely from the original, i.e. the object can be fairly well handled and does not show too many worn spots. When this is the case, it will suffice only to fasten the frayed edges and the loose threads round the holes with a fine, regular stitch. If the structure of the textile allows it, and a hole is not too large, then darning the object can be considered, according to fabric weave. If this is not possible, a piece of fabric, similar in structure and colour can be sewn behind.

If the textile is in poor condition, a supporting base must be considered. This may mean only that it is put on a stiff base, e.g. a linen-clad wooden plate and covered with a glass plate.[1] In many cases fixing it on a flexible supporting layer will be preferred. This can be done either by fastening it at the edges with fine flat stitches or buttonhole stitches, or by fastening very weak, badly worn spots following the 'laid and couching' technique. Where there are loose threads these become the 'laid' threads and the thread chosen for repair is the 'couching' thread. This technique can be applied, for example, in repairing gold brocade.

If it is necessary to fasten pieces of fabric which are in danger of coming loose, threads can be laid across and fixed with stitches made with the same thread as they are laid (self-couching) (Figure 10.1).[2] It is also possible to first lay some threads at smaller or greater distances on the fabric and then to fasten them with another thread, the couching thread (couching proper) (Figure 10.2).[3]

In some cases one may want to affix a fabric not only at the face, but also at the back. The fastening of the three layers (two layers of supporting fabric,

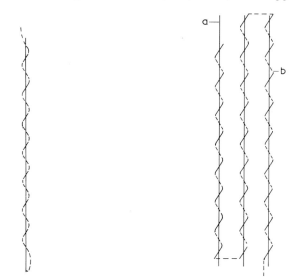

Figure 10.1. Self-couching

Figure 10.2. 'Couching proper': (a) laid thread, (b) couching thread

with the object in between) can be done with tacking stitches. They should not be applied over great lengths, for example, across the full length as well as the full breadth, because in that case the layers will not remain in position and rumpling will occur along the rows of tacking. Alternate rows of tacking, 140–200 mm in length, has from experience been seen to yield the best results (Figures 10.3, 10.4 and 10.5). Mentioned above are some stitches that might be used for fastening threads and fabrics. When embroidery is to be repaired the choice of stitch will naturally be decided by the technique used in the object. It is then necessary, in some way, to give visible indications of what spots are repaired, as has already been stated in the introduction.

As any restoration should also be aesthetically justified, the restorer should be master of all needle techniques, and should also have the artistic feeling to maintain the balance of the work of art. The correct thickness of needle and the right yarn (material, colour, number) should be chosen for each object repaired. Thus, silk fabrics must not be restored with mercerised cotton yarns; first, because the difference in material will remain visible however beautiful the gloss of the yarn may be; secondly, because the yarn will always be too thick, even after splitting; and thirdly, because the simple thread obtained by splitting twined yarn is too hairy, a disadvantage which may be partly removed by paraffinising. So silk yarns will have to be used which, because of the great length of the fibres, are easier to split. These yarns are becoming more and more difficult to get, and synthetic filament yarns (nylon, polyester) may often have to be used instead.

Sometimes it is feared that split silk or synthetic filament yarns may be too weak for this work. It has been found, however, that in museum objects

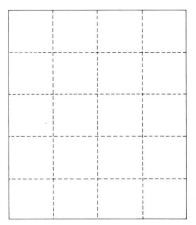

Figure 10.3. Tacking over the full length as well as over the full breadth will cause rumpling along the rows of tacking stitches

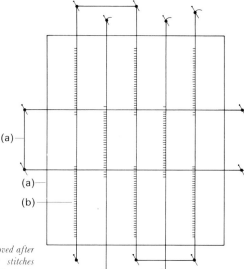

(a)—

(a)—

(b)—

Figure 10.4. (a) Auxiliary threads to be removed after tacking; (b) alternate rows of tacking stitches (14–20 cm in length) only over the length of the fabric

the forces per stitch are so small that very thin yarns can be applied without any risk. In any case it is thought by some people that yarns used for repair should wear sooner than the fabric. This proposition is derived from the clothing industry which uses yarns that, in case of forces exercised at the seams, will break ahead of the threads of the fabric, thus avoiding irreparable holes. With museum objects this problem generally plays no part, except when costumes and uniforms are worn for shows. However, fairly great forces might also be exercised when textiles are fastened on a supporting fabric under considerable tension. In this case it is desirable that the tacking threads should break.

When the yarn is thin enough, the restoration is almost invisible. Moreover, no holes are made in the object, as is the case with thick yarns.

Value of the Object

The time factor, which also involves cost, often plays a great part in the choice of needle technique. Working with thin yarns, with regard for

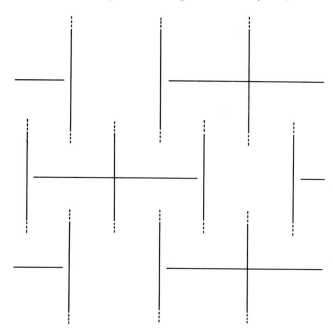

Figure 10.5. Alternate rows of tacking stitches over the length as well as over the breadth of the fabric

aesthetics, takes considerably more time than working with thicker yarns, and consequently raises the cost of the conservation work. The historical and aesthetic value of the object must determine such great expense is justified.

In general, serious objections must be raised to proceeding with a less aesthetic method of restoration owing to limited funds. In that case it is better to simply clean the object and to store it under the right surrounding conditions (see Chapter 7).

Supporting Fabrics

The supporting fabrics to be applied should be chosen to correspond with the object. A first requirement is that they should be as transparent as

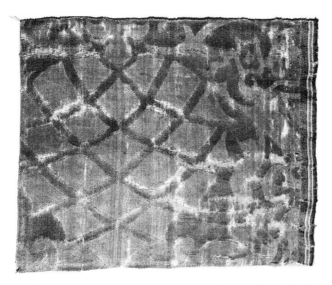

Figure 10.6. The silk fabric has been sewn on to a thin cotton fabric, dyed in a matching colour. The technique is as in Figure 10.4

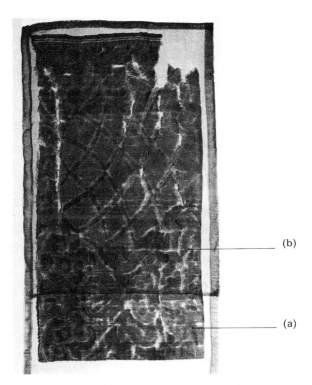

(b)

(a)

Figure 10.7. The silk fabric has been sewn (a) on a silk crepeline fabric; the couching can be observed, (b) between two silk crepeline fabrics

possible, so that the object can be clearly studied from face and back, e.g. in order to analyse the structure of the fabric. This requirement can only be partly complied with, for no matter how transparent a fabric may be, it will always veil the structure and the colours to some degree (Figures 10.6 and 10.7).

Most transparent fabrics on the market are also too stiff for this purpose, having been treated with stiffening agents. There are, however, some factories which still deliver thin fabrics to special order. (Note: Owing to great changes in the various branches of the textile industry it cannot be certain that the fabric available at present will also be obtainable in some years' time, and restorers are advised to apply for information to the first author of this chapter).[4]

A note of warning is sounded here against coarse canvas fabrics, as used for cushion slips, or thick tulle fabrics. Their texture becomes imprinted into the thinner material of the objects to be restored. Moreover, there is the risk that the hardness of their yarns will cause further wear of the restored object when it is handled.

10.2.2 CONSERVATION METHODS USING ONLY NATURAL AND SYNTHETIC ADHESIVES

Natural Adhesives

The methods of this category may not have been applied as long as methods using needle and thread, but they have been in use much longer than is usually supposed. At the end of the last century, and in the beginning of this century, many flags and banners were preserved by glueing them on or between textiles by means of a kind of starch paste, e.g. rye-flour and wheat-flour, gum arabic or some animal glue.

In many cases the results of this glueing were anything but satisfactory, for several reasons. First, the adhesives were easily deteriorated by mould and bacteria, when the textiles were exposed to humid surroundings, or wetted by leaking (filtering) water and condensation. Secondly, in the course of time the glue between the old and new material became very brittle and/ or hard, and the flexibility of the textile was diminished greatly, a great disadvantage. especially for those objects where the suppleness was an important feature.

Often smaller fragments of fabrics, such as samples or small pieces of Coptic and Peruvian textiles, etc., were stuck on cardboard by means of some natural glue. In these cases perhaps the decrease in flexibility was not so important, but a much more serious disadvantage was that the glue often became visible at the front as dark spots.

Although this way of conservation can be severely criticised, it must be realised that the greater part of these objects would have been lost, if they had not been preserved in this manner. Nowadays the application of glues of vegetable or animal origin for the conservation of ancient textiles has almost completely been abandoned. In Russia, however, particularly in the Hermitage Museum in Leningrad, they still preserve textiles by sticking them on a textile support with wheat-flour paste. During his visit to this museum in 1961, the first author established that the results with this paste were excellent, and it may be useful to mention their methods in some more detail.[5, 6]

Three recipes (see Table 10.1) have been developed because of the different textures and thicknesses of the fabrics which have to be treated. The different compounds in the recipes have a specific function. Wheat-flour is the glue. Gelatine serves to improve the properties of the glue by increasing the sticking power and making the adhesive film more transparent. Glycerine has the property of binding water, so that the glue never dries up completely. It will

Table 10.1 THREE RECIPES FOR CONSERVATION ADHESIVES

Composition	Recipe 1 low viscosity %	Recipe 2 medium viscosity %	Recipe 3 high viscosity %
wheat-flour 30% (1st quality)	1–2	3–4	18–20
gelatine (pure)	0·25	0·25	0·25
glycerine (chemically pure)	2	3	3–4
ethyl alcohol (96%)	10–15	10–20	10–20
benzoic acid or thymol (chemically pure)	0·1–0·2	0·1–0·2	0·1–0·2
add distilled water to 100%	to be calculated	to be calculated	to be calculated

always contain some percentage of water and keep a certain suppleness and elasticity even when the surrounding atmosphere has a low relative humidity. Alcohol has a double function: first it reduces the viscosity to some extent, and secondly as it is more volatile than water it accelerates the first phase of the drying process. Benzoic acid and thymol are pesticides, which prevent the development of moulds and bacteria.

Recipe 1 has such a low viscosity that the textile is impregnated by it, although after drying there is hardly any perceptible influence on the appearance and the handle. Only with dark coloured, natural silks with a damask pattern have colour differences been established.

Recipe 2 has a distinctly higher viscosity than recipe 1, so that in general, no impregnation will take place, except with fabrics with very open textures.

In Recipe 3 impregnation is totally excluded. A close film of adhesive forms between the old textile and the supporting fabric, creating a 'sandwich' structure. This paste is recommended for coarse, thick and heavy textiles, such as tapestries.

Whereas recipes 1, 2 and 3 are primarily applied to fix the textiles on a support, recipes 4 and 5 (Table 10.2) are meant as reinforcing agents. The fragile textiles are impregnated with them, and loss of fibres at the front will be avoided. Recipe 6 (Table 10.2) is in use for the improvement of the suppleness of stiff fabrics, also by impregnation.

About 20 years ago the development of conservation methods by means of synthetic resins started independently in various laboratories. In the beginning, more often than not, the results obtained were not at all satisfactory, for several reasons. First, the properties of synthetic resins available at that time could not satisfactorily meet the demands of a good conservation of textiles. Secondly, there was not enough experience in a proper application of these products, and thirdly, the main cause of the only very moderate success, was that the scientific researchers who worked on these methods were not sufficiently aware of the specific demands of this particular field of application. Owing to frequent contact made by these researchers with art historians, who are specialists in the field of museum textile objects, they are

Table 10.2 ADDITIONAL RECIPES FOR CONSERVATION ADHESIVES

Composition	Recipe 4 %	Recipe 5 %	Recipe 6 %
wheat flour 30% (1st quality)	0·25–5	1	—
gelatine (pure)	—	0·25	—
glycerine (chemically pure)	2	2	10
ethyl alcohol (96%)	15–20	15–20	30
benzoic acid or thymol (chemically pure)	0·1	0·1	—
add distilled water to 100%	to be calculated	to be calculated	60

now better known. Moreover, in industry various types of synthetic materials are manufactured whose properties can now be used satisfactorily.

Properties of Synthetic Resins

To understand the properties of the synthetic resins and their behaviour in the course of time, it is necessary to enter into a discussion on what resins are, and the main principles of their manufacture.

According to the definition given in reference 7, a resin is 'an amorphous substance or mixture, of intermediate or high molecular weight, which is insoluble in water but soluble in some organic solvents, and which at ordinary temperatures is either a very viscous liquid or a solid which softens gradually on heating. All solid resins are thus thermoplastics, and thermoplastics obeying the solubility criteria just mentioned are resins'.

These thermoplastic resins are composed of large linear molecules (linear macromolecules), which are formed from small molecules (base units) by the process of polymerisation. When in these macromolecules only one type of small molecule takes part, or different types in *regular* sequence, these polymers are called *homopolymers*. Where different types of small molecules in *irregular* sequence take part, they are called *copolymers*. Often a certain polymer can only be attained by a chemical transposition of another polymer. So polyvinyl butyral has to be prepared from polyvinyl acetate via polyvinyl alcohol. The procedure is as follows:

H H
| |
C = C   POLYMERISATION
| |
n H   O
|
C = O
|
CH$_3$

VINYL ACETATE

H H
| |
—| —C — C — |—
| |
H   O
|
C = O
|
CH$_3$
n

POLYVINYL ACETATE

SAPONIFICATION

H H
| |
—| —C — C — |—
| |
H OH
n

POLYVINYL ALCOHOL

ACETALISATION
WITH BUTYRALDEHYDE

H   H   H   H
| | | |
—| —C — C — C — C — |—
| | | |
H   O   H   O
\ /
CH
|
CH$_2$
|
CH$_2$
|
CH$_3$
$\frac{1}{2}$n

POLYVINYL BUTYRAL

The saponification and acetalisation reactions are obviously not 100% complete, so polyvinyl alcohol will always contain a number of acetate groups and polyvinyl butyral a number of acetate and hydroxyl groups. The physical and chemical properties of the resins are dependent on:

1. Average degree of polymerisation (average number of base units per molecule).[8]
2. Distribution of the degree of polymerisation.
3. Presence of different groups as a result of incomplete transposition reactions.
4. Pollution by chemicals such as initiators, inhibitors, reaction accelerators, etc., which were necessary for the polymerisation process.
5. Presence of plasticisers, chemicals which may have been added to increase the flexibility of the solid resin. When they have been added after the polymerisation process it is called external plastification. In the long run a reduction of the flexibility and an increase of the brittleness of the resin film may appear, because these plasticisers are more or less volatile. It is also possible that they have been built into the molecule during the polymerisation process, which is, in fact, a kind of copolymerisation. In this case there is an internal plastification, and evaporation of the softening component will never take place.

Requirements for Conservation

Synthetic resins are only useful for conservation purposes when they have no noticeable influence on the appearance (visual and tangible), the colours and the flexibility of the textiles. It is evident, however, that these requirements can never be met completely (see also Chapter 2).

Another very important demand is that the resins are not subject to degradation under the influence of light and the surrounding atmosphere. This means that a film of the resin:

1. has to keep its solubility in its solvent;
2. must not yellow;
3. must not give noxious compounds on decomposition;
4. must not show a decrease of sticking power;
5. must not have an ill effect on the ageing of the textile material or on the fading of dyes;
6. must keep its flexibility.

There have been plenty of experiments with plastics with regard to their usefulness in textile conservation, but only a few members of the family of polyvinyl compounds and the acrylates derived from them meet the demands in an acceptable manner.

Polyvinyl acetate in the form of an aqueous dispersion is mainly used for glueing on a support. It is, however, less suited for impregnation, because it has, even in low concentrations, a clearly noticeable effect on colour, gloss and character of the fabric to be conserved. However, when it is necessary to impregnate a textile which is entirely or partly degraded to such a degree that a nearly continuous loss of fibres takes place, then this can be done with polyvinyl butyral. With low concentrations, say 0·5–1·5% in ethyl alcohol, dependent on the thickness and the porosity of the fabric, no noticeable effect on colour and gloss occurs, and there is only a slight effect on the flexibility. Another agent for impregnation is soluble Nylon in a 1–5% solution in methyl alcohol which also gives very satisfactory results.[9, 10] Yet another is Modocoll E.[11]

Description of Conservation Methods with the Aid of Synthetic Resins

The application of synthetic resins can take place in three ways:

1. Adhesion on a supporting base and impregnating simultaneously.
2. Impregnating the fabric without fixing on a base.
3. Adhesion on a supporting base without simultaneous impregnation.

1. This method, where adhesion on a support and impregnation take place simultaneously, often yields an insufficient result. The concentrations of the glue solution minimally required (5% or more) to guarantee good adhesion between the two layers are so high that the appearance is unfavourably influenced.

Among methods in this group is the Sieders method, in which flat textiles such as flags, banners and textile fragments are glued on to a stiff transparent base with the aid of 4–5% solution of polyvinyl alcohol in water.[12] As a base, glass or a sheet of polymethylmethacrylate (Plexiglas, Perspex) is used. Polyvinyl alcohol, however, which in fresh condition is soluble in water, has a too low adhesive power even in these concentrations. The objects easily become detached from the base, especially if the fabrics still contain tensions as a result of the weaving process, or unequal tensions as a result of locally occurring painted parts. Moreover, a flexible base is preferable to a stiff one, and for this the sticking power is far too low. Finally, it appears that polyvinyl alcohol becomes insoluble in water over the course of time, so that one of the attractive properties of this synthetic substance has been lost.

Another polyvinyl compound soluble in water, polyvinyl pyrrolidone, appears subject to change and, moreover, is an easy prey for fungi and bacteria in damp surroundings. In the end polyvinyl butyral soluble in alcohol was found to give most satisfaction, although even here in concentrations of 5% or more colour, gloss, suppleness and touch are influenced disadvantageously.

From this it can be concluded that glueing and impregnating should never be done at the same time.

2. The polyvinyl compound, polyvinyl butyral, which appeared to be most suitable for simultaneous adhesion and impregnation, is also best suited for impregnating textiles which have become so brittle and fragile that a reinforcement is necessary to prevent further loss, by breaking of textile fibres. The concentration should not be high (0·5–1·5% is suitable).

It is a well-known fact that in the case of wall hangings, very serious wear occurs where the combination of a woollen weft, dyed dark brown with the aid of iron-containing dyes, and a silk warp are used. To prevent further deterioration the tapestries can be sprayed with a 1% solution of polyvinyl butyral in ethyl alcohol. The applied quantity is sufficient for the adhesion of the fibres, but on the other hand so small that the colours, the appearance and the touch will not change, while possible later restoration will not be hindered in any way.

This treatment was adopted in the Netherlands in 1961 for wall hangings in a very bad state of repair. Up to now they appear to be safeguarded against further loss of fibre.

3. It is possible to glue a textile object to a base without it being impregnated at the same time. First the support is impregnated with the glue solution. After the glue has dried, this fabric is sprayed with the solvent used for the glue with a mistspray. By this means the adhesive layer in the supporting textile becomes sticky, and the old textile can then be laid on the support, which results in the adhesion of the two textiles without the old material being impregnated. In actual practice this method is very difficult to carry out. Even if the glue layer is moistened only slightly too much, there is a great risk that the glue will become liquid to such a degree that it will ooze through the fabric, producing unsightly dark spots on the face. When too little solvent is used to moisten the glue layer, it does not become sticky enough and insufficient adhesion takes place. A great disadvantage is that it is necessary to execute the mounting of the old material quickly and directly in the right way, as displacement of the fragments on the base is impossible.

This lining method is theoretically attractive, but in practice it is very difficult to perform owing to the complexity of execution and the resulting risks.

The method considered most suitable so far for adhesion on a base, is the so-called 'heat sealing' method. Polyvinyl acetate resin, which possesses a low melting range, about 70–120°C, is used. In the Netherlands, a mixture of two types of aqueous dispersions is used successfully, namely, Mowilith

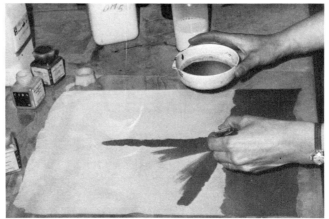

Figure 10.8. Impregnation of the supporting fabric

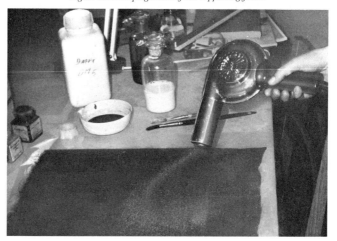

Figure 10.9. Drying of the impregnated fabric

Figure 10.10. The polyester foil is drawn off the fabric

DM5 and Mowilith DM VI.[13] After being spread out on a flat polyester foil, such as Melinex, the supporting fabric is impregnated with a mixture consisting of 1 part Mowilith DM 5, 1 part Mowilith DM VI and 3–4 parts distilled water (Figure 10.8).[14]

When drying of the polyvinyl acetate layer is complete (Figure 10.9), the polyester foil is drawn off the impregnated base (Figure 10.10) and the latter is spread out, glossy side up, on a new foil. Next, the old textile is spread out in the right position on this base in such a way that weft and warp of the two fabrics lie parallel. Then, with the aid of a warm iron (temperature of about 80°C, because the polyvinyl acetate film becomes sticky at this temperature) the two textiles are joined together. It is necessary to put a piece of Melinex foil between the iron and the textile that is to be lined, so that sticking of the polyvinyl acetate film to the iron on such spots where the old textile shows holes is prevented. The lined fabric is stripped off the Melinex foil only after it is perfectly cool.

With very thin, flexible fabrics the flexibility decreases too much when using this lining method and in such cases, it is certainly advisable not to impregnate the base entirely with the polyvinyl acetate dispersion, but only locally, for example, using a square pattern or a dotted diagonal pattern. Consequently, there are less fixing points between the two textiles, flexibility increases, but the result from a viewpoint of conservation decreases. The same holds good in the application of a needle technique for conservation of old textiles, for as the density of the stitches made becomes lower, the conservation quality becomes poorer.

It is evident that where the old textile is put on a supporting base without being impregnated simultaneously, the result is only partial conservation. The old fabric itself, and especially the front which catches most light, is in no way safeguarded against further deterioration. It is often necessary to spray the front of the old textile with a solution (1–1·5%) of polyvinyl butyral (Mowital BH 10) in 96% ethyl alcohol after lining.[15] In this case the liquid should always be sprayed on, because the polyvinyl acetate would be dissolved and would ooze through to the front of the fabric if applied with a pencil.

10.2.3 CONSERVATION METHODS WITH COMBINED USE OF NEEDLE TECHNIQUES AND ADHESIVES

When confronted with the problem of conservation of an old textile, a choice of conservation method will have to be made, according to the nature of the object and the condition it is in. If several methods are possible, a sewing method should nearly always be preferred to an adhesive method, as sewing methods are more natural to a textile. Yet there are many cases where the use of sewing alone no longer allows a satisfactory conservation to be attained. If this is so, there is no need to decide immediately on a complete adhesive and/or impregnation technique, for often a combination of several methods can be the best solution to the problem. This is particularly true for those textiles consisting of different materials, such as costumes, fans, parasols, shoes, uniforms, etc. There are also cases, especially where there is much local wear, where one section of material is locally lined, and the rest sewn on to a supporting layer.

The function of the textile also plays a part in the choice of methods to be used. The decision to line a chair covering will be arrived at sooner than the decision to line a tapestry wallhanging, because the chair covering demands less flexibility but greater strength.

From the above it appears that good execution of conservation and restoration work on old textiles depends as much on a skilful choice of method as on the way in which the method is actually executed. It is, therefore, important that the restorer should possess a thorough knowledge of various textiles, a feeling for style and aesthetics, and most of all wide experience in the field of textile conservation. When complete mastery of all the techniques available has been attained, good results can be achieved.

This chapter cannot be and is not intended to be more than a guide to the methods mostly used in conservation of old textiles. The results reached by the use of these methods depend, largely, on personal skill and achievement.

REFERENCES

1. LEMBERG, M., 'Beispiele der Textilkonservierung am Bernischen Historischen Museum', *Jahrbuch des Bernischen Historischen Museums in Bern*, **37/38**, 133–138 (1957, 1958)
2. EMERY, I., *The primary structures of fabrics*, The Textile Museum, Washington, D.C., 247 (1966)
3. BOSER, R. and MÜLLER, J., *Stickerei. Systematik der Stichformen*, Museum für Völkerkunde, Basel 77, 78 (1969)
4. Central Research Laboratory for Objects of Art and Science, Hobbemastraat 25, Amsterdam, Netherlands
5. SEMENOVITCH, N. N., *Restavratzija I iss ledovanije Khoudogestvennyck pamjatmkov*, The Hermitage Museum, Leningrad (1955)
6. LEENE, J. E., 'Restauration des tissus de Musées', *Bull. de Liais. du Ciéta*, No. 14, 22–28 (1961)
7. 'Report on nomenclature in the field of macromolecules', *J. Polym. Sci.*, **9**, No. 3, 265 (1952)
8. Reference 7, p. 264
9. LANDI, S., 'Three examples of textile conservation in the Victoria and Albert Museum', *Stud. Conserv.*, **11**, 143–159 (1966)
10. Soluble Nylon—'Maranyl Nylon D.V. 45', made by I.C.I. On the European continent available under the name 'Callaton'
11a. GEIJER, A., 'Modocoll as a preservative for textiles and other fragile materials', *Svenska Museer*, No. 1 (1961)
   b. Modocoll E Mo och Domsjö Aktiebolag. Chemical Division. Strandvägen I. Stockholm Ö, Sweden
12. SIEDERS, R., UYTENBOGAART, J. W. H. and LEENE, J. E., 'The restoration and preservation of old fabrics', *Stud. Conserv.*, **2**, 161–169 (1965)
13. Farbwerke Hoechst, Frankfurt am Main, Germany
14. I.C.I., London, Great Britain
15. Farbwerke Hoechst, Frankfurt am Main, Germany

FURTHER READING

CZERWINSKI, A. and WLAZNIK, Z., 'Experimental conservation of historical flags by glueing methods', *Muzealnictwo Wojskowe*, **2**, 41–51 (1964)
GEIJER, A., 'The conservation of textile objects', *Museum Unesco*, **14**, 161–168 (1961)
JAQUES, R., 'Textil-Restaurierung in Krefeld', *Museumskunde* No. 3, 163–175 (1961)
LEENE, J. E., 'Restaurierung und Konservierung von Kostümen', *Waffen und Kostümkunde*, **9**, No. 1, 55–69 (1967)
LEHMANN, D., 'Die Konservierung brüchiger Textilien', *Der Präparator*, **9**, 185–192 (1963)
LEHMANN, D., Conservation of textiles at the West Berlin State Museums, *Stud. Conserv.*, **9**, 9–22 (1964)
LEHMANN, D., 'The restoration and preservation of historical fabrics', *Palette*, **24**, 17–23 (1966)
MÜLLER-CHRISTENSEN, S., 'Textilrestaurierung', *Ber. Bay. Landesamt f. Denkmalpflege*, No. 15, 63–71 (1956)

11
Tapestries

JOHANNA M. DIEHL
Workshop for Restoration of Ancient Textiles, Haarlem
F. VISSER
Chief Restorer, Workshop for Restoration of Ancient Textiles, Haarlem

11.1   INTRODUCTION TO THE PROPERTIES OF TAPESTRY WEAVING

For the execution of a correct conservation and/or restoration of a tapestry, a knowledge of the properties of this type of weave is essential. A woven fabric (see also Chapter 2) generally consists of a warp which runs the length of the cloth and a weft which covers the full breadth. Where the weft turns, the selvedge is formed.

In weaving tapestry, however, several wefts are worked in at the same height over a comparatively short distance, i.e. along a limited number of warp threads. This means that a selvedge is formed at the edges and, in principle, also at each turning-point of the various wefts. By using different coloured weft threads, it is possible to weave patterns. By strongly beating-up the weft (the warp threads being concealed from sight) a rep-weave is obtained, where the reverse side is a reflected image of the front.

When, in the course of weaving, two weft-shuttles carrying different colours meet, they can return round two adjoining warp threads and a very small opening is made. If the next pick makes its turn after one or more further warp threads, this also results in a small opening slightly offset from the first one. In this case the borderline of the two colours proceeds slantwise over the material. If, however, the borderline proceeds parallel to the warp direction, and the openings lie in a straight line one above the other, an elongated opening or slit is the result. If these slits are more than a few millimetres long, they are sewn up in an overcast stitch afterwards. Another way of avoiding long slits is to weave a number of weft threads turning the shuttle at a particular position, and then to let the shuttle travel one more warp thread before turning. The other shuttle turns after one less and this is repeated two or more times. In this way, over a short distance, the slit is moved up one warp thread and there is no need for sewing afterwards.

When this weaving method is used, the colours interlock like the teeth of cogwheels. As shown in Figure 11.1 there is a variety of possibilities in form as well as in distance and width. These are often seen in older tapestries, for example, in the series 'Hunting Tapestries' from the middle of the fifteenth century, in the Victoria and Albert Museum (London). It is also possible to twist the two weft threads at the meeting of the shuttles so that the two colour patches are connected.

These different methods of colour transition influence the appearance of the borderline prescribed by the pattern. If the connection has been made,

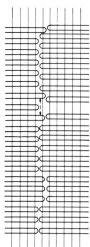

Figure 11.1. Diagram of tapestry weaving without long slits

the two colours are in an equal plane. When, however, there is a slit, even if it has been closely sewn up, there will always remain a slight opening, accentuating the borderline to a small degree. The teeth, of course, have an effect of their own on such a borderline. The tapestry-weaver intermingles these methods to give the best expression to the cartoon from which he works. These cartoons are full size copies of the original design.

Over the entire weaving-breadth of a tapestry, a great number of colour variations occur, so at a certain height the weft is interrupted several times. The result is that the weft direction of a tapestry is always considerably weaker than that of a woven fabric which has an uninterrupted weft made of the same yarn.

For a great number of years, fabrics woven using the tapestry technique have been made in different parts of the world, for example, the Coptic weavings, similar products of South American culture, the Kelims from the Middle East; and although diverging in origin and style, these all have a comparatively simple ornamentation in common. They have either geometrical patterns or more or less stylised figures, which can be obtained with the help of the methods of colour change described. From the Middle Ages until the present day, very extensive tapestries were made in Western Europe using this technique.

It has, however, always been the aim to create a spatial, realistic reproduction of the object depicted. This aim could not be reached by the above methods of colour change, because shading was non-existent in those. This disadvantage could be overcome by hatching, which gave an effect comparable to shading in a drawing. An example of a hatch—all sorts of variations of which are possible—can be seen in Figures 11.2 (a) and (b). The hatchings are carried out according to the demand of the cartoon, and follow a simple course.

A second peculiarity of West European tapestry is that the warp runs across the breadth of the object (giving rise to a noticeable 'rib' across), as do the slits, and the hatches are perpendicular to the warp direction. This is not only the case with wall hangings, but also with smaller tapestry objects, such as cushion-covers, tablecloths and shabracks. There are a very few exceptions to this rule mainly dating from the nineteenth and twentieth centuries. It is difficult to trace what reasons led to the use of this transverse warp. It may have been an aesthetic reason, because the rib gives a very peculiar shading, although the suggestion that the reason was purely technical is not to be excluded. Most West European tapestries were destined to cover the walls of vast halls and the lengths of these walls naturally differed very considerably, although there was far less difference in height. It must, therefore, have been the simplest solution for the tapestry-worker to retain as weaving breadth, the least variable measurement, i.e. the height of the tapestry, and to warp at this width. With such a warp, pieces of different

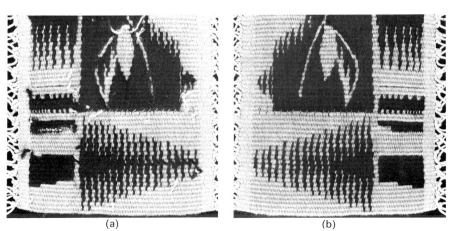

(a)   (b)

Figure 11.2. A piece of fabric in tapestry technique, showing a few types of hatching: (a) back, (b) front

length could be woven; short lengths for the panels, long ones for the larger wall surfaces.

In non-European tapestry there seems to be no special preference for a horizontal or a vertical warp, with regard to the subject represented. A number of textiles which were shown at the exhibition 'L'Art Copte', in Paris in 1964,[1] may serve as examples. In part of the so-called 'Coptic Fabrics', the warp runs horizontally, and in another part, vertically.

11.2 LOOMS

It is, in general, difficult to trace what looms were used in making the different sorts of tapestry of non-Western European origin. Horizontally placed, so-called 'basse lisse' looms were generally used in weaving West European tapestries. However, part of the products of the Manufacture des Gobelins in Paris, established in 1663, were made, continuing a local tradition, on a vertical loom, the 'haute lisse' loom. Fenaille mentions which products were woven haute lisse and which basse lisse.[2]

The techniques of the two types of loom are not explained in this chapter, but references are to be found in the eighteenth century *Encyclopédie ou Dictionnaire des Sciences, Art et Metiers*.[3] It suffices to note that in the horizontal loom, the warp is led through shafts moved by the feet, so that the hands remain free for inserting the weft. Odd and even warp threads are stretched alike in this way during weaving.

The vertical loom has no shafts and the moving of the warp is also done by hand. This has the advantage of making it easier to see what the work looks like on the reverse side. In fact, in both cases the weaving is performed 'at the back'. When the work lies horizontally, it is not so simple to check the piece in the course of manufacture, which may result in mistakes such as inverted letters.

A disadvantage of the haute lisse loom is that only one of the two groups of warp threads is stretched during manufacture. This may sometimes be noticed by a somewhat undulating lie of the fabric. However, this should not be mistaken for the frequently occurring phenomenon where every other warp thread in a tapestry seems to lie a little higher. This occurs with haute lisse as well as with basse lisse products and is caused by the fact that the weaver, who handles the shuttles with the right and the left hand alternately, does not stretch the weft to the same degree with each hand.

As far as conservation or restoration is concerned it makes no difference on what kind of loom the tapestry was woven or whether it has a horizontal or a vertical warp.

11.3   THE MATERIALS

Generally, wool is used for the warp of tapestries. In more recent tapestries, linen has sometimes been used for the purpose, and in modern ones, cotton. The weft is mostly wool or wool and silk. Only rarely was a tapestry made entirely in silk, but occasionally linen was used. In very costly weaves, gold, silver-gilt or silver thread was used. Linen yarns were used for sewing up the slits and nowadays we also use cotton yarns.

11.3.1   THE CONDITION

Wool is generally in fairly good condition, and in most cases only the dark brown shades are entirely worn. Silk is often entirely worn, although in the finer weaves, the silk parts are still well connected, and the design can be distinctly made out. Handling the fabrics often causes the silk to pulverise. Linen becomes very brittle in the course of time. Because the warp in Western tapestries is mostly horizontal, very large and heavy pieces often hang from the weft. Owing to the weight the fabric sags and this makes the slits between different weft threads draw apart. This imparts an increased tension to the linen sewing yarn of the slits and eventually they snap. The adjoining warp threads are pulled sideways, which causes tear, especially of the silk which is in a delicate state. In the course of time the warp threads will also break. Resewing the slits regularly can, of course, greatly retard this breaking. In early times this happened regularly, but during the last few centuries, when the large hangings were often hammered to the walls along the borders, it was not done, although the sagging went on just the same.

The tapestries absorb much damp and dirt from the walls and the apertures behind them, and on the front, smoke from woodfires, nicotine, etc., is collected. Besides this, normal wear and tear, and damage of all kinds play a part in the condition of the tapestry. Nail holes, openings for doors, beams, light switches and doorknobs are encountered. Often rats have eaten away pieces, and insects also play their part in the damage. Repairs done with the best intentions, but executed injudiciously, can do much harm.

11.4   CLEANING

Working on a dirty object is unhygienic and disagreeable for the restorer. Moreover, the insertion of new yarn (which would probably get soiled) is more difficult in dirty and less supple fabrics, and it is hard to find correctly matching shades. If at all possible an object should always be cleaned. It is essential to have it photographed before cleaning, as documentation, and as an aid to the subsequent repairs. It is also advisable to have the object photographed after cleaning.

11.4.1   WASHING IN WATER

An object can be cleaned thoroughly in water only, or in water with a synthetic detergent which reacts neutrally, or with soap of Marseilles. A very careful investigation will have to be made beforehand to see if the fabric and dyes can withstand washing. This may be done by careful local moistening of several different parts of the fabric. It may happen that one yarn of a sparsely occurring colour bleeds strongly, while all the others are washfast. It is also important to consider that the original yarns may have a good wash fastness, but that those used for later repairs may not.

Should these tests be successful, wetcleaning can be started. The fabric should be kept as flat as possible. For very small pieces, plastic developing basins as used in photography and available in all sizes, can be used. For larger pieces, basins of stainless steel can be made to order, or temporary basins may be set up for each object using polyester or polyethylene foil and wooden frames. Large wallhangings give most trouble. These, too, must be washed in a horizontal position, and handling in a wet condition must be avoided, if possible. If their measurements render handling necessary, it will have to be done in such a way that no force is exerted on the delicate weft, which is even more vulnerable in a wet condition than when dry.

It is possible to clean a tapestry by putting a net in a basin and laying the tapestry over it. After washing, the tapestry can then be hauled up with the net, and the water can drip out, thus speeding up the drying process. The net must be stretched tightly and evenly, and be supported along the edges in several places to prevent the tapestry from sagging in the middle and drying unevenly. This could cause difficulties later when stretching it for restoration.

11.4.2   CHEMICAL CLEANING

Should it appear impossible for a fabric to be cleaned wet, either because of its bad condition or because the fabric is so delicate that the risk of loading it by absorption of water and weakening it cannot be taken, then a chemical cleaning process, though less effective, may be used. Once again, tests must be made beforehand to discover the fastness of the colours in the drycleaning fluids. The objections that grease is removed from the fibres can be overruled by adding lanolin to the final rinse. In practice, petroleum distillates show better results than other organic detergents.

11.5   RESTORATION AND CONSERVATION

A tapestry can rarely be left at the cleaning stage; measures should be taken to conserve it in the best possible way. There are a number of ways of achieving this.

11.5.1   CONSERVATION

In this process, pieces of cotton or linen lining are fastened behind loose warp threads and weak spots. The colour of the lining should be chosen so as to match the surroundings. The tapestry should obviously remain face down on the worktable during treatment, otherwise the lining cannot be fixed smoothly. A simple smooth board on legs or trestles can be used.

Annoying old repairs may be removed, and all slits must be sewn up anew. Lastly, a strong linen or cotton lining is placed behind the whole fabric, sewn not only along the edges, but fastened to the tapestry in vertical panels 0·4–0·5 m (about 2 ft) apart, so that the weight of the tapestry is taken for the most part by the lining. The lining, as well as the smaller pieces loosely placed behind, should be washed in very hot water beforehand, so that no shrinkage is possible later.

If a tapestry contains large worn silk parts, then it may be desirable to impregnate them with a 1% solution of polyvinyl butyral in ethyl alcohol. After the alcohol has evaporated, worn fibre material will have stuck together and will not pulverise so easily. This treatment remains invisible. All colours, however, must be tested beforehand for resistance to alcohol.

In some cases where the object has become extremely vulnerable, the tissue can be glued to a support by means of a synthetic glue. This method can be used for small wallhangings, cushion covers and the like, woven on a linen warp which has become very brittle. It must be remembered, however, that only a small part of the comparatively thick material (the ribbed back) rests against the supporting fabric. If the weft is very worn, it may happen that the glued threads tear away from the front. Great care has to be observed here.

11.5.2   TOTAL RESTORATION

Theoretically, it is possible to mend tapestry, or any rep, in such a way that it is restored to its original condition. All the old repairs can be removed, all missing parts filled in, and all worn materials replaced by new

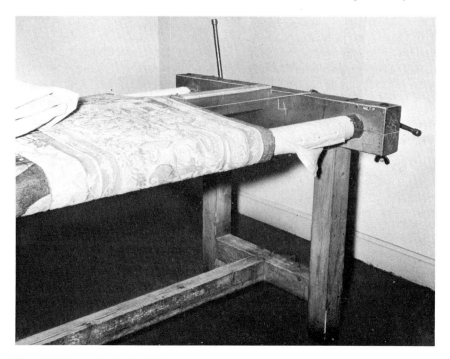

Figure 11.3. Conventional work-table for restoration of tapestries. (Rijksmuseum, Amsterdam, Netherlands)

ones, while the original design and the methods which were formerly used by the weaver are taken into consideration. This drastic and lengthy method will sometimes be the only one to guarantee the preservation of unique, often very large and heavy wallhangings for an indefinite period of time.

It is advisable not to make darns in worn parts, as old material surrounding the darn will soon tear, and the old design, and its method of execution will be lost.

It will be clear that for such restorations, yarns of the same nature as the original ones must be used. For inserting new warp threads, however, cotton may be used instead of wool. For the weft, wool and natural silk are needed and sometimes metallic threads. As a great number of the shades needed are not available commercially, they will have to be dyed by the restorers. Synthetic dyes can be used for the purpose as they are simpler to handle than the natural ones. It is imperative, however, that these dyes when used on woollen and silk yarns, possess at least the same fastness as those on the fabric in which they are to be inserted, otherwise after a short time the darn starts to differ from the surroundings.

For the animal fibres, wool and silk, it is best to use acid or direct dyes, which can be shaded in the bath till the right shade is reached. The most practical way is to work with yellow, blue and red dyes; all colours lying between these three components can be obtained by mixing in the right proportions. Mordants or vat-dyestuffs are not suitable for this purpose.

Since the restored fabric will probably be subjected to cleaning in the future, it is necessary to give attention to the washing fastness of the new yarn. Perspiration fastness must also be considered in connection with the handling of yarns during repairs.

For restoration work, worktables consisting of an oblong frame of strong beams, one of which is placed at a higher level than the others, are often used. The tapestry is placed with the weft direction along two long beams, and fastened to them with drawing-pins or clamps. In this way, the work is slightly tilted towards the restorer (Figure 11.3). However, he must still bend right across the foremost beam and the fabric. He can work over a height of about a foot, after which the work must be stretched anew. It is better, therefore, to use tables with two beams at the same height, between which a third movable beam is placed. A tapestry can now be placed across the high beam and on either side of this the fabric lies more or less vertical. This is a far better working angle for a restorer, as it enables him to stay in an upright position and work over a greater height. This reduces stretching, which again means less wear, while the tapestry can be worked on from two sides (Figures 11.4 and 11.5).

Figure 11.4. (Right) Diagram of the work-table, as developed at the Workshop for the Restoration of Ancient Textiles, Haarlem.

The work-table consists of a rigid framework, on which are mounted the standers 6 and the crossbeams 5. Between the two standers the heavy beam 7 is fixed with the bolts 8. By means of the holes in the standers beam 7 can be adjusted in height. On beam 7 a half round beam 9 is mounted, which can be moved up and down in relation to beam 7 by means of screwspindles 10. The tapestry is hung in over beam 9, and is fastened to the beams 2 in the front and the back of the table. Beams 2 are fixed to the crossbeams 5. The fastening of the tapestry (see inset) is done by means of clamping between two narrow laths 3 and 3a (divided into parts of 1 m length), which are clamped by braces 4 (4 braces per pair of laths of 1 m). The laths are backed with felt to prevent damaging of the tapestry. The tapestry can be tensioned by moving upwards beam 9.

To support the tapestry during the work the supports 11 are mounted, which are adjustable by means of the slotted laths 14 and the bolts 15. The supports are fixed to beams 2 with crosslaths 12 and hinges 13. The laths 17 are mounted as a support for the arms during work. The part of the tapestry that is ready is loosely rolled up upon the pole 16, resting with its ends on crossbeams 5.

In case the height of the tapestry is large the worktable has to be wide (see Figure, width nearly 4·5 m). Now it will be necessary, to prevent bending of beams 2, to mount a third crossbeam (like 5) in the middle of the table. Besides, extra crosslaths (like 12) and slotted laths (like 14) will have to be mounted to the middle of supports 11. These can be fixed to the third crossbeam and to beams 2. Then it is no longer possible to rest pole 16 on crossbeams 5, but the pole might now be hung with cords to supports 11. For clarity this third crossbeam is not shown in the figure

161

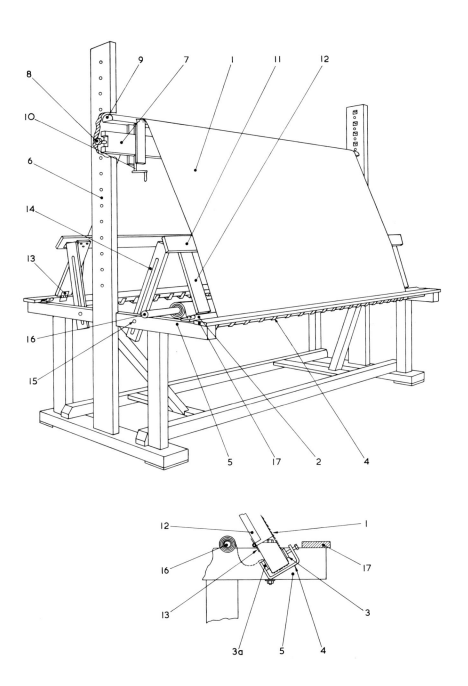

Figure 11.5. Work-table for restoration of tapestries (Workshop for the Restoration of Ancient Textiles, Haarlem, Netherlands)

11.6 CHOICE OF REPAIR METHOD

When making a choice of the best method of repair from the methods already given, all factors will have to be carefully weighed. A particular procedure to cover every case cannot be given. Total restoration is extremely expensive. The alternative is conservation, which is considerably cheaper but yields less satisfactory results. Generally speaking, the destruction of the fabric will be delayed for a short time only, while all the damaged spots, missing parts and suchlike remain completely visible. It should be realised that bad spots or missing parts, repaired from behind by a piece of material of a totally different nature (as advised by Böttiger[4]) may be eye-catchers, which can have a great influence on the aesthetic impression created by the whole.

The method chosen will depend on the relation between the cost and the value of the tapestry, while the art-historical and historical value, and the personal value to the owner play a great part. It might be that total restoration is being considered but that the cost is an objection. A temporary conservation may be a substitute but it is advisable to have such a tapestry photographed, in detail, with a view to later restoration. For tapestries where a linen warp was used, total restoration is out of the question because of the breaking of the warp threads. Conservation is the only way to keep such a tapestry in existence for some time.

11.7 CONCLUSION

It will be clear that in restoration as well as in conservation of a tapestry, everything that might lead to lasting damage of the old fabric must be avoided.

Under no circumstances should the tapestry itself be touched up with paint. Naturally, there is no objection to continuing a pattern interrupted by a hole on the fixed lining. A serious warning must be given against cutting up one tapestry of a series for use in repairing the others by sewing or sticking pieces of it into the holes.

Advice is sometimes given to reverse tapestries, because the colour at the back is much brighter. This method seldom gives an agreeable result. In figural tapestries, especially, an unnatural effect appears in that all the persons depicted appear lefthanded. In any case these bright colours have no great light fastness so that even if the most stringent precautions are taken, the colours will not last forever.

REFERENCES

1. Catalogue of the exhibition 'L'Art Copte', Paris (1964)
2. FENAILLE, M., *État général des tapisseries de la Manufacture des Gobelins, depuis son origine jusqu' à nos jours*, Paris (1903–1912)
   SCHMITZ, H., *Bildteppiche*, Berlin (1919)
3. DIDEROT, D., *Encyclopédie ou Dictionnaire raisonné des Sciences, Arts et Métiers*, Paris, 1751–1772, Supplement 1776–1777, Index 1780
   GOEBEL, H., *Die Wandteppiche, Part 1, Die Niederlande*, **1,** Leipzig (1923)
   SEVENSMA, W. S., *Tapestries*, Bussum (1965)
4. BÖTTIGER, J. und KÖHLER, J., 'Über die Pflege gewirkter Tapete', *Museumskunde*, 205 (1907)
   BÖTTIGER, J., *Les tapisseries des Châteaux Royaux de Suède, Expériences et Conseils*, Uppsala (1937)

12

Carpets

DORA HEINZ, Ph.D.
Head of Textile Collections, Austrian Museum of Applied Art, Vienna

12.1 DISPLAY

In many respects, the conservation of carpets involves the same problems as the preservation of textiles, in general. It is self-evident that carpets kept in a museum should, in the first place, be sheltered from direct sunlight and protected against moths. This is relatively easy, but preventing damage through dirt and dust is a far greater problem. To display all carpets behind glass would present great technical difficulties; nor would it be acceptable on aesthetic grounds, especially for pieces that are shown lying on the floor. It is absolutely necessary to provide effective dust protection during the hours in which the museum is closed to the public, and this is best achieved by covering up the carpets with some closely woven material. These covers have, moreover, the advantage of serving as light screens in addition to the window curtains, which are essential in any display of textiles. To facilitate the covering and uncovering so that the covers can also be used during daytime when there are only a few visitors, it is advisable to attach the covers to rollers. They can then be drawn across the carpets in one pull. These rollers are made to rest on the frames of the show-cases and should keep the cover well stretched so as not to touch the carpets. Occasional cleaning of the carpets will, however, be necessary in any case.

12.2 CLEANING

Woollen carpets that still have a relatively sound structure may safely be treated with a vacuum cleaner, but the suction should be adjusted so that no loss of pile substance is sustained.

The problem of cleaning is entirely different with objects that have been collecting dirt for decades, where the dust and soot adhere not only to the surface but have penetrated to the foundation threads. In all old collections even very costly pieces have been found in this condition, the reason being

164

that formerly the washing of old textiles was rejected as harmful to them and even likely to destroy the old yarns. Experience, however, has shown the contrary to be true and that even very worn textiles may be subjected to wet treatment.

A thorough cleaning of the entire carpet beyond the surface is to be recommended not only for aesthetic reasons, because the finer points of the pattern and the shading have become invisible, but also out of purely conservational considerations. Hard crusts that form on the back of the carpet are apt to make it hard and liable to break, and the small but sharp dust grains destroy the threads themselves. Particularly when the carpet is moved or rolled up, as may be necessary from time to time, there is the danger of the breaking of the foundation threads causing very bad or even irreparable damage.

Before washing a carpet it is essential to make sure that the colours are fast. The risk of colours running is greatest in restored parts, since the natural dyes used for the old parts are, as a rule, fast enough. There are cases, however, of well-preserved carpets that would not stand wet treatment, as fine details of the pattern had been traced later in colour, or whole parts at one time redyed with cold dye. It is, therefore, essential to test all the colours in different parts of the carpet before the washing is undertaken.

Technical problems increase with the size of the carpet to be washed. It is not only necessary to provide large enough basins but also an appropriate place for drying afterwards. As important as the washing itself is the proper rinsing of the fabric, and every care should be taken to avoid remnants of washing aids being left in the foundation threads. These threads should be thoroughly cleaned as any dirt or dust grains left behind would become hard on drying, after drenching, and would consequently cause more harm.

Fifteen years ago nearly all carpets on view in the Austrian Museum of Applied Art were submitted to a thorough cleaning. The silk carpets were washed in distilled water only. For the woollen carpets soap flakes which contained no alkali were added. Synthetic detergents were not used at all in the absence of reliable information about their effect upon old textiles. As carpets soak in so much water they must be dried lying flat and never hanging, where they might tear because of their weight. Very thick carpets, e.g. Savonnerie carpets, require many days to dry properly. The best method is to use a grating, which gives access to the air from both sides. Wiping the carpets to remove excessive moisture should only be done from the back as it would leave lasting imprints on the pile.

12.3   RESTORATION

The cleaning and proper care of carpets introduces numerous technical problems, but few theoretical ones. These, however, are the main problems when it comes to restoration. There can be no general rule as to whether the existing condition is to be preserved, and any further deterioration prevented, or whether replacements should be attempted.

Individual decisions must take into account not only the nature of the damage but also the general condition of the carpet in question. As the field of rugs and carpets is very wide, ranging from the precious archaeological find to the industrial mass product, there must also be different standards for restoration. In an ordinary carpet in use, eventual damage will always be repaired, as far as possible, in order that it may further serve its purpose as a decoration and floor covering. The museum, of course, does not deal with such cases, but with the other extreme, that is pieces that are of historic interest as specimens of a certain period or technique, regardless of their state of repair. These carpets must, as a rule, be preserved as they are.

Most carpets in the possession of museums have been damaged with time. Two opposing concepts are involved here. On the one hand, the criterion of successful restoration is supposed to be the preservation of the existing condition and, on the other, restoration is meant to achieve an all-over effect that comes as close as possible to the original appearance of the piece. It will, therefore, be necessary to weigh both points of view against each other in every individual case. Extremes should always be avoided, as they would only lead to unsatisfactory results. Replacements should generally be considered only if it is a question of small lesions in an otherwise complete piece. Where there are only fragments left, museum restoration should never attempt a complete reconstruction, replacing large parts to restore the original size of the carpet. Even if the pattern were known such a procedure could not be approved of. The carpet should be regarded as a work of art, realising an underlying artistic concept, which is to be preserved as clearly as possible. This means that replacements should be attempted where simple conservation would spoil the over-all impression, e.g. when holes are mended with a neutral one-colour support, and that it must be dispensed with where the original condition is open to conjecture, and especially where replacements would have to be made at the cost of original parts.

12.4   PRACTICAL EXAMPLES

A few practical examples from the carpet collection of the Austrian Museum of Applied Art, may serve to illustrate these theoretical considerations. First, there is a Persian carpet which was originally in the imperial collection (Figure 12.1). This is a case where restoration went much too far. Large parts were replaced, badly impairing the general impression. The new knotting is very dense and, since the original pile is worn away, is much too high. Therefore, it stands out awkwardly, setting wrong accents and ruining the impression of the design. The new parts have now become even more conspicuous as the colours have changed, especially the red of the new ground, which has turned brown. The restoration was carried out by a carpet firm, whose method may be justified for a carpet of everyday use but does not apply to a museum piece.

In the museum itself missing parts in several Anatolian carpets were replaced. Here the foremost aim was to preserve the general character of these carpets which were otherwise in good condition. As it was a matter of repairing numerous but very small holes (Figure 12.2), the insertion of new knots to fit the pattern was no great problem. Simply putting a piece of material underneath would, on the other hand, have rendered the holes in the pile the more conspicuous and would thus have impaired the impression.

Figure 12.1. Detail of a Persian carpet from the seventeenth century with annoying replacements (Courtesy Oesterreichisches Museum für Angewandte kunst, Vienna)

Figure 12.2. Arabesque holbein carpet, the light filtering through, after removing the old darns, and before starting the replacements (Courtesy Oesterreichisches Museum für Angewandte Kunst, Vienna)

Figure 12.3. Detail of silk hunting carpet from the sixteenth century, before restoration (Courtesy Oesterreichisches Museum für Angewandte Kunst, Vienna)

Figure 12.4. The same cutting after restoration (Courtesy Oesterreichisches Museum für Angewandte Kunst, Vienna)

Plate 12.1. Detail of East Persian tendril and animal carpet from the sixteenth century, with old darns

As these were wool carpets of a coarse weave, the insertion of new warp and weft threads where missing was justified. The aim of a restoration like this is to execute the repairs in such a way that they are invisible on the face of the carpet.

The case of the silk hunting carpet was entirely different (Figure 12.3). This time it could only be a matter of conservation for the damage this carpet showed was only partly due to time and wear. Crude, inexpert repairs such as darning or simply stitching together of holes with strong yarn and twine had had a destructive effect upon the carpet. New rents and holes formed along the edges of the darns, small parts of foundation threads were altogether ripped out and the patches of every sort of material which had been sewn on to the back of the carpet caused baggy places and folds which threatened to break the silk warp. A replacement of the missing parts was quite out of the question from restorative considerations, as the insertion of new warp and weft threads would have endangered the already very weak and injured parts of the silk fabric around the old darns. When all of the old repairs had been removed the back of the damaged parts was overcast with silk to which the edges and loose threads were fixed. To render these neutral parts less conspicuous, silk rep was used which resembled the structure of the carpet foundation, and the individual pieces were dyed to match the surrounding original parts. As the pile of this carpet is very low and contains metal brocading the parts where the underlay shows do not differ in height too much from the intact surface, and the general impression of the carpet, with its rich pictorial design, remains (Figure 12.4).

The conservation of the famous East Persian tendril and animal carpet (Plate 12.1) will be carried out according to the same principles. This carpet also comes from the imperial collection. At present, its back is still covered by a patchwork of coarse repair patches which have been sewn to the carpet with rows of interlacing stitches, which even go through the pile. The removal of these coarse stitches will without doubt greatly improve the appearance of the carpet. However, because of the great injury the silk foundation threads suffered through being stitched with thick yarn, it will also be necessary in this case to overcast the back of the damaged parts for support.

13

Flags and Banners

JOHAN LODEWIJKS

Director of Central Research Laboratory for Objects of Art and Science, Amsterdam

13.1 INTRODUCTION

In this chapter the methods in which flags, colours, guidons, standards, ensigns, banners and drumbanners can be restored and conserved will be discussed.[1] As the methods used are the same for all types, in this chapter they will be indicated by the common name 'flags'.

Flags can be distinguished into different types, according to their structure:

1. Flags, consisting of one sort of material, mostly wool, silk or linen, and made by sewing together various colours of the material in a certain pattern. The materials used are dyed beforehand in the piece, or as yarns. Flags made according to this system can be of considerable size, e.g. ships' flags. These are mostly made of wool, but sometimes of linen.

2. Flags consisting of one or more colours of cloth, entirely or partly painted, the paintwork differing in consistency and structure. Here we distinguish two main types:

(*a*) Paintwork applied by using a paint paste, which contains a so-called thickening agent. This thickening agent, of animal or vegetable origin, prevents the colour from running into the fabric. Afterwards, the thickening agent is rinsed out entirely or partly, mostly with the aid of water at 80–100 °C. This results in paintwork which does not form a close layer, but which leaves the textile structure fully visible and barely alters the porosity of the cloth. Flags of this type are usually made of wool or linen.

(*b*) Paint applied with the aid of a paint paste, where particles of colours, the pigments, are suspended in a binding agent mostly of animal (tempera) or vegetable (linseed oil) origin. This type of paintwork is more or less identical with the method used for ordinary painting, entirely covers the fabric, and is sometimes coated with varnish. Because the paint used here does not penetrate through the cloth, the flags are often painted on both sides, sometimes with the same, but often with a different representation. As the binding agent, especially with thinner fabrics, penetrates through the cloth, it was necessary to apply the paintwork at the same height front and back. Flags with this type of paintwork are mostly made of silk, but sometimes of wool or linen. Smaller flags are usually of double cloth, with a firm lining inserted between; consequently, totally different representations are usually found on each side.

3. Flags consisting of one or more shades of cloth, to which embroidery is applied. In this type, three groups are distinguished:

(a) Flags where the cloth is embroidered directly with certain representations or ornaments. Here one always finds two pieces of cloth, embroidered separately, silk being the material mostly used. Often one or two linings as strengthenings are found, especially with heavy and compact embroidery. Here the embroidery is stitched wholly or partly through the lining. The materials used for the embroidery are mainly silk, metal threads and, to a lesser degree, yarns of wool or linen.

(b) Flags where separately manufactured embroidered appliqués are sewn on to the cloth. With this type a heavy lining is practically always found between front and back, as these appliqués are too heavy to fasten them to a thin material. The appliqués, consequently, are always sewn to the lining. They may locally be 10 mm thick or more, and are generally made round a core of cotton, kapok, paper or wood. The embroidery mostly consists of silk and metal thread (gold and silver).

(c) Flags with a combination of (a) and (b).

4. Flags of less frequently occurring fabrics, ornamented with textile materials, sometimes also with other materials. These objects often present special problems in conservation, and are further discussed at the end of this chapter.

13.2 THE CLEANING OF FLAGS

Before washing a flag it is necessary first to check whether the colours will run. This can be determined by placing the spot whose colour fastness has to be determined, over a wad of cottonwool, which is covered with one or two layers of filter paper. Next the face of the spot is moistened periodically for a minimum of 20 min with a detergent fluid, at a temperature of about 50°C, containing two or three times more detergent than is actually used when washing. Then the underlying paper and the cottonwool are checked. If no colour from the fabric has penetrated into the paper, the fabric is washable, at least in this spot. It goes without saying that all colours, and especially the restored spots, should be submitted to the washing test. This is extremely important, because in the restorations which took place at the end of the last, and the beginning of the present century, materials with a low washing fastness were often used in appliqués. If all the colours prove to be washable, it does not mean that the flag can be washed unconditionally, as this also depends on the construction of the object and of the materials used. Each object has to be considered individually, and firm rules cannot be given.

For silk flags, embroidered and double, with one or two linen or cotton linings, no fixed procedure can be given. When such a complicated object is washed, the lining may show a different reaction to the water from the silk front and back. If the lining was not washed originally, it will shrink considerably during the washing process, which will cause the front and back of the flag, which show much less shrinkage or none at all, to bulge, while the materials round the embroidery will rumple. If the lining is very strong, its shrinkage can be prevented by stretching the flag on a frame prior to washing. The object should not be removed from the frame until it is perfectly dry. In many cases, however, stretching is no longer justified and washing such flags is a risky thing. The best plan then is not to wash the object at all, but to find out first if careful removal of loose dust in dry condition, as with the help of a vacuum cleaner, the suction opening of which is covered with a fine gauze, would not be sufficient. If this would not suffice, there is a possibility of drycleaning the object by immersion in perchloroethylene or trichloroethylene, after first having determined the fastness of the colours with regard to the chosen chemical detergent. Drycleaning hardly ever entails any shrinkage.

Where a flag is composed of two separate cloths with one or more linings between, and large appliqués are sewn on separately, these appliqués can be unstitched, causing the fabrics and the lining(s) to come apart before washing. The different fabrics and the appliqués can then be cleaned separately. Metal or textile fringes and other sewn-on ornaments should also be removed before washing.

For washing flags a flat washbasin made of stainless steel or plastics, such as P.V.C. may be used. The size of the basin has to be about 2–3 m square, which makes it possible to wash almost all flags, except very large ships' flags, at one go. It is advisable to place the basin in a slightly slanting position with an outlet in the bottom at the lowest point, which promotes a quick removal of washing and rinsing water. The basin should have an upstanding brim all round 8 to 12 cm high, and a mixer tap for hot and cold water should be fixed over the washbasin. Both the hot and the cold water should be softened, although demineralised or distilled water is better. A flexible hose, connected to the mixer tap is useful for rinsing. For washing objects which are fairly strong, it is sufficient to spread the flag on fine polythene gauze, like screen-gauze, before it is immersed in the previously prepared washing fluid. The fluid should fill the basin to a height of 3–4 cm. When washing very fragile flags it is necessary to sew two fine polythene gauzes together, both round the flag and wherever there are holes or pieces missing, so as to prevent shifting of the flag between the gauzes. It has been found that the meshes of the gauze must not be too small, as with polyester or silk crepeline, because then the larger particles of dirt and dust gather between the gauzes and cannot be carried off. The gauzes should not be too coarse in structure either, for if they are too profiled, an imprint of the gauze structure will be visible in the fabric of the flag after drying. This applies especially if the flag is of a fine silk fabric.

Flags which are larger than the bottom surface of the washbasin can be washed in parts. For this purpose tables should be placed against the basin, either on one side, or, if possible, on two opposite sides of the basin. The flag is now washed in stages and subsequently moved across the basin from one table to the other over a distance equal to the washed part. The use of a screen gauze as a support over the whole length of the flag offers an extra advantage, because if this gauze is fairly stiff, it keeps the flag from cracking on the edge of the basin, at the same time allowing it to bend easily.

For the cleaning of flags the following prescription yields good results:

1–2 g neutral soap chips,[2]
1–2 g sodium tripolyphosphate,
0·2 g carboxymethylcellulose (C.M.C.),
1 litre water.

The above cleaning fluid has a pH of about 9. If a somewhat lower pH is desired, sodium metaphosphate can be used instead of sodium tripoly-phosphate. The phosphate acts, among other things, as a cleaning activator, whereas C.M.C. prevents the redeposition of the released dirt on the textile material. The sodium tripolyphosphate, moreover, allows the use of tapwater instead of distilled water, because this compound acts as a water softener at the same time, so that there is no risk of a calcium precipitate on the textile material.

Washing takes place at a bath temperature of about 30°C and lasts about 20 min. Next the fluid is allowed to drain and the object is rinsed till all soap residues have been removed. To the last rinse is added 0·5 g acetic acid per litre of water.

13.3   CONSERVATION OF FLAGS

For the conservation of flags various methods have been developed, which can be distinguished in three groups:

1. Sewing methods.
2. Methods where glues are used.
3. Combinations of 1 and 2.

These methods are described in Chapter 10.

The method used for conserving flags depends on many factors. A first consideration is that conservation must not influence the material or any possible aesthetic qualities of the object. (In Plate 13.1 and Plate 13.2, it can be seen how coarse tulle fabrics and coarse stitches influence the appearance.) This, of course, does not only concern the textile materials, but also all added materials, such as metal thread and paintwork. A matt paint-work will never have the character of a shining oil-painting.

Another factor also decisive in the choice of the conservation method to be used, is the historical or art-historical value of the object. It certainly makes a great difference, in practice, whether we deal with a very important or rare object, or whether it is our task to conserve one out of many identical flags, the historical and art-historical value of which is only slight.

In the first case a method will be chosen exclusively based on the importance of the object, factors of time and cost not being considered. In the second case, however, there is often a necessity to choose a less time-consuming method, otherwise the cost entailed by conservation far exceeds the importance of the object. Besides it will generally be undesirable to spend, say, six months on the conservation of a fairly unimportant flag, while at the same time more important and rare objects are waiting for conservation treatment. From this it should not be concluded that it is only the important objects that should be conserved, as less important objects do certainly form part of the historical and art heritage.

All these considerations have led to the development of conservation methods, where glues are used (heat-sealing, *see* Chapter 10) and which, compared with the earlier applied methods, are greatly labour-saving and consequently time- and cost-saving.

This, however, does not mean that the sewing methods should be abandoned altogether, for the glueing methods are meant as alternatives only to be applied in those cases where objects of no great historical or art-historical value are concerned, or where the textile material is already disintegrated in such a way that conservation by sewing is no longer feasible. An advantage of the heat-sealing method is that the front of a flag is not covered with a thin supporting fabric, such as crepeline, as happens when the object is sewn between two thin fabrics, or with couching stitches, when the object is only fastened to one support.

Flags that have frequently flown in the wind, like ships' flags, usually have only small fragments left. When conserving such fragments, the first problem is whether the supports on which they are to be fastened should be the original size of the flag, or whether they should be just large enough to hold the fragments concerned. A general rule is hard to give and an individual decision will have to be made for each conservation.

For large flags it is advisable to choose a support of a size equal to the remaining fragment of the flag, if this remaining part is only 75% or less of the original, and if the missing part has a close geometrical shape. This often is the case with ships' flags, where it is usually the part farthest from the staff which is missing through wear.

Where restored fragments of flags on display are concerned, the public can be given an impression of the original object in various ways. If sufficient room is available, a dummy can be fastened behind the conserved fragment of the original object, an imitation made of crepeline or some other thin material. The conserved fragment should be sewn on with large stitches to the proper spot on the imitation. The imitation of the flag is made with the same seams and stitches as the original, and the fabric is dyed beforehand in the required colours.

The manufacturing of an imitation in a thin, transparent fabric is preferable to a true-to-nature copy in a fabric identical to the original flag-cloth, because the imitation in a thin fabric shows the original size and design in colour in a way that does not distract the observer's attention from the original fragment. If sufficient space is not available, it is preferable to hang the conserved fragment as it is, placing a small-scale copy next to it, so that the public can form an idea about the original size and design of the flag.

When mounting flags, it is most important that heraldic laws should be considered to determine what is front, back, right or left of a flag. To prevent major mistakes being made, it is advisable to consult the heraldic literature.[3]

13.4 METHODS OF CONSERVATION

A variety of conservation methods for the different types of flags will now be dealt with in succession.

13.4.1 FLAGS CONSISTING OF SINGLE FABRIC WITHOUT EMBROIDERY, APPLIQUÉS OR PAINTWORK

Conservation of this type generally gives little difficulty. If the condition of the fabric allows it, these flags can be sewn on or between polyester or silk crepeline. The crepeline can be dyed in the colour(s) of the flag beforehand, which renders the supporting fabric less obvious. With flags consisting of various coloured fabrics, the support can be painted in the colour design by hand, by covering the old flag with a glass plate and spreading the crepeline over it. The design of the flag can be copied on the crepeline. A paint with a

Figure 13.1. Algerian flag. Silk. Late eighteenth or early nineteenth century. Before restoration (Courtesy Rijksmuseum, Ansterdam)

thickening agent should be used to prevent the edges from running. If the fabric of the flag is in a bad condition, preservation of the flag by means of the heat-sealing process should be considered (Figure 13.1 and Plate 13.4).

13.4.2 PAINTED FLAGS CONSISTING OF SINGLE FABRIC

Flags consisting of single cloth and which are painted, can be treated by the same methods as above, the difference being that it is not possible to imitate the painted design on the supporting fabric. Therefore, supports are generally used that have been dyed homogeneously in the basic colour of the flags (Figures 13.2, 13.3, and Plates 13.5–13.7).

13.4.3 COMPOSITE FLAGS

With composite flags (flags consisting wholly or partly of several layers, with or without embroidery or appliqués), it is far less simple to lay down a method of conservation. However, it is a general rule that a composite flag should not be taken apart except under exceptional circumstances, because the construction is an essential part of its identity and authenticity. Other methods should be used if possible, even if they appear to be less effective. In many cases, however, taking the flag apart cannot be avoided, because otherwise no conservation at all would be possible.

When choosing the conservation method to be followed, the main aim is to conserve objects in their existing condition, and one should take care not to give these objects a so-called 'face-lift', subjecting them to an artificial rejuvenation. All parts of the flag's identity should be kept, for far from reducing the value of the flag, they contribute to it. An uninteresting,

Figure 13.2. Spanish flag. Linen. Early seventeenth century (probably c. 1620). Before restoration (Courtesy Rijksmuseum, Amsterdam)

aesthetically ugly flag should remain ugly, and a bullethole in a flag should be carefully accepted as a historical datum.

Possible conservation methods to be used for a number of composite flag types will now be dealt with.

1. Flags consisting of one or more layers of cloth, without embroidery or appliqués can be washed without being taken apart, only if the flag is still strong enough to be stretched on a frame to prevent the expected differences in shrinkage. If this can no longer be done, the flag should be taken apart before cleaning, and conservation can then take place in this state. Now each part of the flag can be treated, according to the requirements and con-

Plate 13.1. Flag covered with coarse tulle. At the bottom the fabric is removed

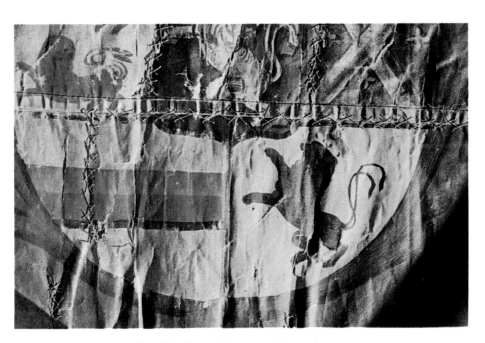

Plate 13.2. Coarse stitches are applied to mend tears

Plate 13.3. Gilt thread with silk core. Between the windings of the gilt strip of silver the silk core can be seen. Both metal and core are damaged

Plate 13.4. Algerian flag, 'heat-sealed' on a polyester supporting fabric (Courtesy Rijksmuseum, Amsterdam)

Plate 13.5. Spanish flag, heat-sealed on a polyester supporting fabric (Courtesy Rijksmuseum, Amsterdam)

Plate 13.6. Flag of the Southern Low Countries. Heat-sealed on a polyester fabric. Front (Courtesy Rijksmuseum, Amsterdam)

Plate 13.7. Flag of the Southern Low Countries. Heat-sealed on a polyester fabric. Back (Courtesy Rijksmuseum, Amsterdam)

dition of the different fabrics, as explained for the conservation of single-cloth flags.

Mounting the parts should always be done by hand in a sewing technique identical with the original. For this reason, all sewing techniques should be carefully registered in the form of descriptions, drawings and/or photographs before taking the objects apart. A synthetic material, such as polyester thread, may be used as sewing thread, if this matches the original thread in colour, thickness and gloss.

2. Flags consisting of various layers, with sewn-on appliqués, but without other embroidery. As mentioned before, it is usually necessary to unstitch the appliqués beforehand. The various fabrics now lie loose from each other, and the 'mere' flag can be treated as stated under 13.4.1.

If necessary, the appliqués are conserved separately from the rest. Loose threads can be kept in place with the aid of couching stitches, perpendicular to the thread direction. Appliqués in a very poor condition can be covered with silk crepeline or polyester crepeline, dyed the right colour. Apart from one of the above mentioned methods, in many cases it is advisable to spray the front of the appliqués with a solution of 1·5% weight polyvinyl butyral

Figure 13.3. Flag of the Southern Low Countries (?). Silk. Early nineteenth century (?). Before restoration (Courtesy Rijksmuseum, Amsterdam)

(Mowital B.H.10) in 96% ethyl alcohol, as this prevents the brittle fibres from breaking further.

3. Flags consisting of several layers of cloth with embroidery and without appliqués, may be divided into two types, those where the embroidery has been done on one layer of fabric only, and those where it has been stitched through the lining as well.

Flags where the embroidery is on a single layer of fabric, have a different front and back, which may or may not be separated by a lining. If there is a lining, front and back of the flag can be sewn in small stitches with thin thread, the same colour as the fabrics, to the lining, which then serves as a support. Naturally this only makes sense if the flag, and particularly the lining, is in fairly good condition. If the whole flag is in a bad state, then the object can be sewn between two layers of silk or polyester crepeline, dyed to match the object. If one does not want to affect the outside, then the flag can be taken apart and new linings can be added to the front and back. To protect the embroidery against further deterioration it is advisable to spray front and back with a solution of 1·5% weight polyvinyl butyral in ethyl alcohol.

Flags where the embroidery has been stitched through the lining cannot be taken apart without ruining the embroidery entirely. Therefore, such a flag can only be conserved by applying a layer of crepeline on front and back or by further fixing to the lining. The embroidery can sometimes be protected by fine couching stitches. Again, spraying with polyvinyl butyral prevents a rapid deterioration.

4. Flags consisting of several layers of cloth, with embroidery and appliqués, generally offer no extra difficulties, because, after unstitching the appliqués, a conservation method, as mentioned above can be applied.

13.4.4   FLAGS CONSISTING OF UNUSUAL MATERIALS

This section includes flags of less frequently occurring fabrics, ornamented with textile or other materials. Some flags, and particularly banners, make use of velvet or velour. Covering this sort of pile fabric with crepeline destroys much of its appearance. These fabrics can, however, be treated very well according to the heat-sealing method, if at least the following precautions are observed.

Before applying the support, the velvet or velour is put face down on some other pile fabric, the pile of which is longer than that of the original. Next the impregnated supporting fabric is spread over it, and after covering with Melinex, is joined to the original fabric with the aid of an iron heated to about 80°C. It is now possible to exert a slight pressure on the fabric, with the iron, without damaging the pile of the original fabric, because the upstanding fibres will grip the underlying pile of the velvet or velour. This treatment, of course, also works for fabrics which consist only partly of velours, such as some brocades.

When ribbons, galloons, cords, fringes and tassels are present, it is often better to treat them separately. Here, too, the original situation should be accurately registered beforehand by way of notes, drawings and/or photographs. Only the cleaning of metal threads consisting of a metal strip, wound round a silk core will be discussed here (Plate 13.3). There are several cleaning methods.

Mechanical Methods

The most widely used mechanical method employs a brush made of glass fibre. When viewed under a binocular magnifier, the threads appear to have suffered severely under this treatment. The metal strip shows a great number of scratches, while the silk core is also seriously damaged.

By scratching the metal band an increased shine is obtained, first because the corrosion layer is removed, and secondly because the light reflecting surface is enlarged. An added objection against this method in the case of gilded threads is that the gilding is scratched off, and the underlying metal, often silver, appears. This means that after treatment gold (gilded) braid looks like silver braid. Furthermore, the metal is again unprotected against surrounding influences, and it will easily soil and corrode again.

Chemical Methods

At this point, treatments with ammonia and thiourea should be mentioned. Ammonia has the disadvantage that it is strongly alkaline, and therefore detrimental to the silk core, while the cleaning effect on silver thread is very poor.

Thiourea cleans silver excellently, but only in strongly acid surroundings. Thiourea is found in 'Silverdip', a fluid which, besides thiourea and a non-ionic detergent, contains 8 g of hydrochloric acid per litre (see also Chapter 16). This hydrochloric acid is the active component which dissolves the black silver sulphide. The thiourea then binds the liberated silver in the form of a complex compound. 'Silverdip' has a pH of about 1, which is generally detrimental to the silk core, and more so, as the hydrochloric acid cannot be entirely rinsed out it will thus remain active for a long time. It has been shown that on decreasing the percentage of hydrochloric acid the activity of the 'Silverdip' quickly decreases. However, little is known about the influence of thiourea on the silk core of metal thread. An investigation has shown that in silk yarn (as contrasted with wool) no increase of the sulphur percentage was observed after thorough rinsing. From this it may perhaps be concluded that thiourea can be completely rinsed out of silk, if the metal threads are entirely open to the rinsing water.[4]

It appears from the above that there is not a single method for cleaning metal threads that is without risks. It is, therefore, advisable to first consider whether the cleaning of metal threads is absolutely necessary. If it is, then a treatment with soap and water or with ethyl alcohol and a piece of cotton wool can be tried and perhaps a good result achieved. If after all, it is decided to use 'Silverdip', as this has the greatest effect, then after treatment, the metal threads should be protected against repeated corrosion, as it is unwise to perform the treatment repeatedly.

Genuine gold thread, which, however, is not often found in old textiles, is generally cleaned sufficiently by means of soap and water or alcohol.

Corrosion products can often be adequately removed from copper threads by using diluted ammonia.

The cleaned metal threads of cords and galloons can be protected by varnishing with a solution of 2–3% polyvinyl butyral (Mowital BH 10 from Farbwerke Hoechst, Frankfurt am Main, Germany) in ethyl alcohol. For fringes the concentration of polyvinyl butyral must not be any higher than 1–1·5% otherwise the fringe becomes too stiff. Cords and galloons are usually stiff by nature. If there is no intention of performing this protecting treatment, the cleaning of metal thread made of silver, gilded silver, of gilded copper is useless, as a rigorous treatment yields merely a temporary result.

13.5 FINAL CONSIDERATIONS

The conservation of flags does not imply that they can be treated as new objects afterwards. In many cases they will stay fragile and their ultimate length of life will be determined by the way in which they are handled. A few guiding-lines in this field may be useful.

1. When flags are hung, the best way to do this is on a horizontal staff, which is inserted through a case of woven material sewn on to the top of the flag.
2. They should never be hung directly against a wall, because salts from the wall might penetrate into the object, and outer walls can, moreover, be distinctly moist. A layer of Melinex (polyester foil) should be placed between wall and object, or the object should be hung away from the wall.
3. They should never be placed over heating elements such as radiators, because besides extreme drying, serious pollution will develop owing to the rising airstream.
4. They should, if possible, be hung in places where no draughts can occur.
5. They should never be hung in places where they are exposed, for short or long periods, to direct sunlight.

If these guiding-lines are observed, a well-conserved flag may form part of a museum collection for many decades.

REFERENCES AND NOTES
1. EDWARDS, T. J., *Standards, Guidons and Colours of the Commonwealth Forces*, Gale and Polden Ltd (1953)
2. Neutral soap chips have to meet the following specification:

Moisture and volatile matter at 105°C (221°F)	10·0% max.
Sum of free alkali, total matter insoluble in alcohol, and sodium chloride	4·0% max.
Free alkali, calculated as NaOH	0·2% max.
Matter insoluble in water	1·0% max.
Titre of the mixed fatty acids prepared from the soap	39°C min
Anhydrous soap content	85·0% min.

3. GERARD, R., 'The heraldry, conservation and restoration of flags', *Bull. S. Afr. Mus. Ass.*, **4**, No. 8 (Dec. 1948)
4. LEENE, J. E., Private communication

14

White Linen Damasks

C. A. BURGERS

Assistant Keeper, Department of Sculpture and Applied Art, Rijksmuseum, Amsterdam

To give linen a smooth lustrous surface after washing and cleaning, the common methods of beating, mangling and pressing are not suitable at all for valuable and usually frail museum objects, such as sixteenth or seventeenth century white linen damasks. For these the slightly adapted approved household method of spreading the material upon a smooth surface seems more advisable.

A sheet of clear Perspex somewhat larger than the size of the piece of linen in hand, covering a sheet of ruled paper of about the same size and set out in exact squares should be placed on top of a solid flat table. It is an advantage if the table has a frosted glass top with light underneath, although this is not essential, and if designer's ruled paper, in which the squares in thick lines are subdivided both horizontally and vertically is used.

The clean linen is spread, face down, on top of the Perspex, the warp and the weft following more or less the lines of the ruled paper. Next, the linen is sprayed with distilled water until it is almost soaked through and any air-bubbles between linen and Perspex are removed by carefully pressing the material with a wetted sponge (distilled water). The wet linen is easy to handle, and it is not difficult to direct the threads of warp and weft along the vertical and horizontal lines of the ruled paper, using a damp sponge, starting from the outer edges. When working with badly worn linen one will find that the use of finely subdivided ruled paper will also make it possible to adjust loose threads in the right direction.

Whilst dressing the fabric with the sponge, the sponge will have already absorbed some of the water taken up by the threads and as a result the material may already adhere to the surface underneath. After the cloth has been arranged with all the threads in the right direction it is necessary to press the linen carefully but firmly, either directly with a dry sponge or with blotting paper and a dry sponge. The purpose of this is to press the face of the cloth as closely as possible against the smooth surface of the Perspex sheet, leaving absolutely no air-bubbles in between. Special care has to be taken at the hems and repairs where air-bubbles are most fre-

182

Figure 14.1. Napkin, white linen damask. Conquest of Barcelona (1705) by Charles III (later VI) of Hapsburg. Collection C.A. Burgers, Amsterdam. Before treatment

Figure 14.2. Napkin, white linen damask. Conquest of Barcelona (1705) by Charles III (later VI) of Hapsburg. Collection C. A. Burgers, Amsterdam. After treatment

quently trapped. After pressing, most of the unevenness in the weave, such as thick threads, knots or repairs, will show on the reverse, and the face of the cloth will be almost completely smooth. (Figures 14.1 and 14.2).

If the linen is allowed to dry slowly when the process is finished, it will regain more of its natural firmness than if dried quickly. Once completely dry the cloth usually adheres to the Perspex from which, however, it may be easily drawn off with some care. At this point a fragile cloth may be stuck, if necessary, on a supporting layer.[1,2]

Although the cloth can be stored folded, rolled or laid flat, it is better not to fold it, as it will ultimately crack along the lines of the folds. If stored on a roll, the cloth should be wound together with a thick layer of paper to prevent any unevenness (hems, knots, darns) making impressions on the cloth at every turn of the roll. The surface should be on the outside, and the hems parallel to the length of the roll.

The temporary adhesion of the linen to the Perspex when dry may be utilised. It should, for instance, replace the ironing of linen damasks before they are photographed.[3] Also, by preparing the cloth in this way, using the Perspex from an exhibition frame, the backboard (covered with a non-slippery fabric such as flannel) may be easily fitted behind the cloth without any danger of creasing the material.

NOTES

1. As an adhesive is recommended a mixture of aqueous dispersions of polyvinyl acetates: 1 part of Mowilith DM 5, 1 part of Mowilith DM VI in 3 to 4 parts distilled water
2. As a supporting layer is recommended a thin polyester fabric, e.g. polyester crepeline
3. Ironing is suggested in an otherwise most useful article by Marta Claréus 'Fotografering av vit damast', Fataburen, Nordiska Museet och Skansens, Aarsbok 239 sq (1967)

15

Historic Costumes

GUDRUN EKSTRAND

Keeper at the Kungliga Livrustkammaren (The Royal Armoury), Stockholm

15.1 HISTORICAL BACKGROUND

The costumes and textiles of the Royal Armoury (Livrustkammaren) in Stockholm form the major part of a unique historical collection dating from the early seventeenth century to the present day. As the museum has a long history, the collection has been housed in many different places. The first storage was the Royal Palace 'Tre Kronor' (Three Crowns) which was burnt down in 1697. Since then, the collections of the Royal Armoury, the Royal Wardrobe and parts of the Royal Stables have been stored in many different places. They are now in the building of Nordiska Museet (Nordic Museum).

Because the collections were moved several times during the centuries, some damage was inevitable. However, the worst injuries have been caused by moths in storerooms that were too small and too warm, by mould in rooms that were too damp, and by dust, soot and light to items on permanent display. All these injuries are in fact irreparable, and it is very sad to see the faded fronts of the costumes that have been on show for a considerable time.

When Baron Rudolf Cederström was director, he was a passionate pioneer in the restoration of textiles, such as costumes, flags, embroideries, etc. As early as the beginning of this century, he started a programme of restoration and issued written reports, describing the procedures and the types of materials used. Since then there have been few opportunities to pursue research work in the field of conservation, on a scale corresponding to the value of the collections.

15.2 CONSERVATION

When restoring a brittle textile, a costume, or a similar item, one has to bear in mind its history. Furthermore, if an object is two-dimensional, such

Plate 15.1. Coronation robes of Queen Sophia Magdalena (1772). Same pattern as that of the robes in Figure 15.1. Front

as a flag, a standard or a curtain, one should be able to study it from both sides. In the case of costumes, which are three-dimensional, the problem is still more complicated, because they should be able to undergo examination from all angles.

One of the leading principles for the conservator is to be honest, i.e. never to disguise the restoration so that it cannot be traced. Of course, there is no need to emphasise the restoration, but there should not be an imitation of the original material. In case another generation finds a better method, the applied material should be easily removable, for it is impossible to reach the point beyond which no better treatment can be devised.

It is always possible to clean the item in a careful way by removing as much as possible of the dust, soot and other additions that have changed the original character of the object. This helps to prevent further deterioration.

The so-called drycleaning or solvent method is hardly ever used in the workshop. One hesitates to add any solution that might give rise to future change. If a costume consists of only one material, it is preferable to wash it in distilled water. Very often, however, the item consists of a number of materials of different colours.

Superficial dust could interfere with the wetcleaning process and it has to be removed from the front and back of the object. This can be done by using a hand vacuum-cleaner with a medium-sized mouthpiece, in front of which is mounted a small frame covered with tulle, which forms a screen. The mouthpiece with the frame is moved carefully over both sides of the object. Subsequently, the surface is cleaned by rubbing it lightly with soft chamois leather, or a moist brush, which is a laborious method demanding a delicate touch as well as patience. When the whole chamois is dirty, it can simply be washed in soapy water.

If the surface of the object is not flat, e.g. when embroidered parts are present, some places may be difficult to reach with the chamois leather. Then it will be necessary to use a tiny brush of short marten hairs, barely wetted by dipping it into cold or lukewarm distilled water (if necessary containing some liquid detergent or ammonia), and wiping the excess water off on a piece of blotting paper. This process has to be repeated till the item is cleaned. When a detergent has been added to the water, it is necessary to 'rinse' the item afterwards, using distilled water and a clean brush.

As a special point, it should be mentioned that this museum considers it very dangerous to use a hot iron to make any surface smooth or even. The same results can be achieved by careful flattening after washing.

15.3   EXAMPLES OF RESTORATION

To give some information about the various costume restoration problems, a series of examples has been chosen.

One of the most evident proofs of successful cleaning results from washing white (or silver) costumes that will stand water treatment. The appropriate parts of some of the queens' dresses have been treated by this method. The coronation robes of Queen Louisa Ulrica, dating from 1751 (Figure 15.1) are made of silver brocade with gold crowns. The court train (328 cm long), lined with white taffeta silk, was well suited for washing in view of its plain shape. So was the elliptical skirt, mounted on a narrow hip-panel and having no lining apart from a 12 cm high lining at the hem. The robes were very dirty, especially at the front.

After vacuum-cleaning, the skirt and the court train were soaked for just long enough to make them completely wet (i.e. not more than a few hours), and then washed twice in distilled water with sponges. They were rinsed three times, and blotting paper was used for drying. Distinct dark or oxidised spots had to be treated with a brush and water containing some ammonia.

It was found that trains are best treated when lying flat, as the wrinkles can be smoothed out in water, by delicate and careful treatment with sponges. What must be emphasised is that the object should not be moved from the washbasin or oilcloth on which it has been treated before it is entirely dry. When the material is wet it is much heavier than when dry and the strains on the old and brittle material are, therefore, greater.

The bodice is made of double layers with metal stays between them, and had to be cleaned by using dry chamois leather and a damp brush, as

Figure 15.1. Coronation robes of Queen Louisa Ulrica (1751). Side view. Silver brocade interwoven with gold (crowns). Lace trimming on the court train (Courtesy K. Livrustkammaren, Stockholm)

described above. The court sleeves had been removed, probably long ago, because of their very brittle character. A pair of them was now washed by means of distilled water and brush, and they were attached to the bodice.

The court sleeves and the cuffs and lace strips, belonging to a formal dress of Queen Sophia Magdalena, dating from 1772 (Plate 15.1 and Figures 15.2, 15.3) had to be cleaned after being detached. The very thin and delicate silk material had evidently attracted much more dirt and dust from the fires than had the other materials. When unfastening the sleeves, every single stitch was exactly marked so that it could be sewn back again. The cylindrical sleeve was drawn over a cylinder so that it was not flattened during washing, and put into a basin specially made to fit it. The sleeves had to be soaked overnight, and the water was changed as many times as was found necessary. Finally, the water was soaked up with sponges. The sleeves were treated carefully, using a small brush and the fingers to arrange the delicate rows of folds.

Another example of conservation of a costume is the black velvet coat of Gustavus Adolphus, who died in 1632. This black coat can be traced in various descriptions in the inventories (Figure 15.4). In 1707 it was said to have been cut; in 1661 it was described as old-fashioned, but in 1628, when the King was still alive, it was said that the lining was of sable and the decoration

Figure 15.2. Coronation robes of Queen Sophia Magdalena (1772). Rear view (Courtesy K. Livrustkammaren, Stockholm)

consisted of five rows of black lace-work. Before the restoration it looked rather ruined, although the pattern of the black velvet still showed Italian-looking flowers (Figures 15.5, 15.6).

It was considered wise to moisten the very brittle and dry black velvet which was no longer in its original condition. It needed support as it had suffered from an anonymous restoration long ago, when a thick lining of coarse black cotton was attached. This material had evidently caused new cracks. Now the cotton had to be removed, and with a pair of tweezers the old stitches were pulled out after being cut. The original front piece was unpicked from the back, as there were no original threads left in the side

Figure 15.3. Sleeves of thin white silk veil for Queen Sophia Magdalena's coronation robes (1772). The right sleeve has been removed and washed. The upper visible threads indicate points for replacing the sleeve (Courtesy K. Livrustkammaren, Stockholm)

Figure 15.4. Coat of black velvet used by Gustavus Adolphus. Outer front after restoration. A new silk lining has been attached (Courtesy K. Livrustkammaren, Stockholm)

seam, and it was put into a basin and sprinkled with distilled water. After soaking all night the superfluous water was absorbed by sponges. The front piece (still lying in the same position) was left for a couple of days at room temperature till it was entirely dry. Then it was removed with the help of a sheet of paper to avoid wrinkles.

The same procedure was undertaken with the other pieces. In their case, however, the basin was filled with distilled water to a height of 10 mm before the pieces were placed into it, in order to avoid damaging the flossy surface of the velvet with spraying water. The pieces were then lowered into the water on a glass plate in such a way that only the back of the velvet was wetted. These pieces also were left in the same position until fully dry; the glass was put underneath to make their removal easier.

A new piece of Chinese silk was dyed in a grey-black colour, matching the coat and was cut and shaped to fit the big triangular pieces, but a little larger. It was attached to the inside of the velvet by sewing at equal intervals all over the surface to strengthen the brittle material. The only piece with the original seam left was the back, and here the original silk thread was

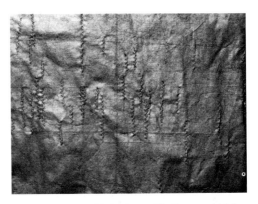

Figure 15.5. Coat of black velvet used by Gustavus Adolphus. Detail showing the brittle velvet from inside on back (Courtesy K. Livrustkammaren, Stockholm)

Figure 15.6. Coat of black velvet used by Gustavus Adolphus. Detail showing the coarse lining with seams (Courtesy K. Livrustkammaren, Stockholm)

re-used. The new silk lining was folded along the lower-edge and made as soft as possible.

Another interesting case was the restoration of a man's cap (Figures 15.7, 15.8 and 15.9) which was required for an exhibition in 1959. As this had lost its original inventory number which might have registered it among the costumes of Charles X (died 1660), its origin was no longer known. Because of its soft material and insignificant character, it had not been considered especially interesting and worth treatment. The cloth was dirty, faded and moth-eaten. The shape was the traditional one for a man's cap, cut into four triangular gores, with flaps for the ears and the neck and a peak in front. When this cap was examined, it was found that in the crown of the cap another lining was attached on the inside. And this 'lining' appeared to be another skull- or helmet-cap.

This small cap had traces of rivet-holes, indicating its use as padding in a

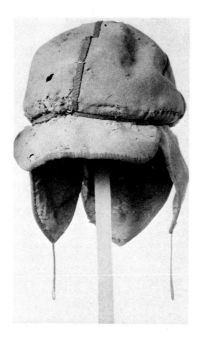

Figure 15.7. Man's cap, mid seventeenth century. Grey cloth and yellow taffeta lining. Front view (Courtesy K. Livrustkammaren, Stockholm)

Figure 15.8. Man's cap, mid seventeenth century. Inside before restoration; inner helmet cap visible (Courtesy K. Livrustkammaren, Stockholm)

Figure 15.9. The small padded helmet cap found inside man's cap (Courtesy K. Livrustkammaren, Stockholm)

helmet. (A test with a fluorescent lamp made traces of metal visible on top of the cap). An anonymous restoration of the original cap had evidently been made long ago. It was recognisable by coarse patches of linen which had to be removed. At that time, the inner skull-cap may have been added. When this helmet-cap was removed, the yellow silk taffeta lining of the other cap was fully visible.

The corresponding points on the skull-cap and the outer cap were marked with small red silk stitches. Pieces of new cloth dyed in the appropriate

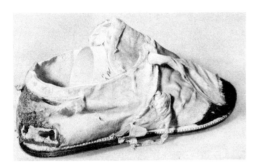

Figure 15.10. One of a pair of child's shoes (for Gustavus III as a small boy about 1748), covering of white and black silk. Heel part badly damaged. Before restoration (Courtesy K. Livrustkammaren, Stockholm)

Figure 15.11. One of a pair of child's shoes (for Gustavus III as a small boy about 1748). Heel part after restoration (Courtesy K. Livrustkammaren, Stockholm)

colour were sewn beneath the exterior cloth, after it had been cleaned and softened. The silk lining was cleaned by brushing with water, and restored by silk of the correct colour put beneath the original material. Finally silk tulle had to be attached above the torn flaps.

The helmet-cap was stitched together and padded with woollen cloth; the inner lining was yellow silk satin and the surface next to the helmet was made of linen. It also had remnants of a leather sweat-band. From this restoration two objects were thus obtained.

The child's shoes, from the ceremonial costume of Prince Gustavus III (about 1748), for a member of the Order of Seraphim show the various restoration problems to be encountered in our museum (Figures 15.10 and 15.11). The materials consisted of white and black satin and leather; the toe-caps being of black satin, and the lining of white leather braided with white silk ribbon. The shoes were dirty and deformed, with pieces missing as if eaten by rats, especially on one heel.

The treatment started by wiping off the dirt with a chamois leather on the outside as well as on the inside. The white satin was also carefully brushed and then dampened by using a brush dipped in distilled water. The ribbons

Figure 15.12. The complete admiral's uniform of Charles XIII (d.1818) on mannequin (Courtesy K. Livrustkammaren, Stockholm)

were laid on a piece of blotting paper and cleaned with a brush dipped in water. The white leather was carefully cleaned by applying colourless shoe-polish with a pencil covered with a piece of linen. The heel was treated in 'steam' at about 35°C, and given the right shape. It was then filled with tissue-paper and the shoes were left to dry for some days at room temperature. The fragments of the ribbons around the edge were covered by a strip of silk tulle. On one shoe, double layers of dyed tulle had to be sewn on the toe-cap and near the leather sole, the tulle had to be tucked in and wrinkled to follow the shape of the shoe. Beige-coloured silk satin (white would have been too striking) was sewn over the heel and put beneath the damaged silk of the sides.

The dress-coat of the admiral's uniform used by King Charles XIII (died 1818) had been restored previously, but the matching trousers of blue woollen tricot were left, probably because of their state. In 1964, it was desirable to make the costume more complete for display (Figure 15.12). By this time, however, only the upper part and the vertical embroidered gold stripes from the waist to the feet of the trousers remained, owing to further destruction by moths (Figure 15.13). The lining in the waist, and the embroidered strips showed the pattern, however, so a reconstruction of the pattern could still be made after the remaining pieces had been

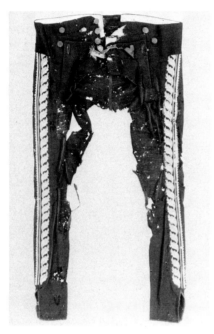

Figure 15.13. Remains of trousers of blue woollen tricot for admiral's uniform of Charles XIII (d.1818) (Courtesy K. Livrustkammaren, Stockholm)

dampened and stretched. A cotton cloth, dyed to the corresponding blue colour, was cut to the original shape of the trousers and the pieces were attached accordingly. The gold embroideries were cleaned by brushing with distilled water (with some detergent added).

As the accompanying hat could not be shown in its existing condition, it was decided to restore it (Figure 15.14). It was made of black felt with high brims at the front and back, and with a golden cord and a bullion tassel on each side. The decoration in front also included a button, a white plaited silk rose on the upper edge of the brim, a braid, and a plume of blue and yellow feathers. The lining was of white silk. Beneath the beige-coloured leather sweat-band was a padded string.

First an appropriate block was made of light-weight expanded plastic to give the hat the right shape during the treatment. Because of the sharp fold the brims had almost entirely lost their connection with the top (particularly in front of and above the heavy tassels). The outer parts of the hat were cleaned by means of a brush dipped in distilled water. Pieces of cloth were then added underneath to strengthen the damaged parts. As the original sweat-band was still left, it was cleaned by wiping with a chamois. The old fastenings had disappeared, but the holes were re-used for the new strings. Several cracks in the felt were treated by inserting felt strips. The 53 cm long black silk ribbon which originally fixed the standing brims (it being drawn through the crown and the brims), was now washed and partly strengthened

Figure 15.14. The hat for the admiral's uniform of Charles XIII (d.1818). During restoration (Courtesy K. Livrustkammaren, Stockholm)

by a strip of selvedge of tulle. The coloured feathers were carefully cleaned with a marten hair brush and distilled water (using blotting paper).

A frock-coat of the uniform used by Charles XIV (died 1844) as Field Marshal (Figure 15.15) was also restored. The smooth and even surface of cloth made this material very difficult to restore without the treatment being too obvious. The materials in this case were blue cloth, padding (Figure 15.16), black and white silk lining and gold embroidery on collar and cuffs (Figure 15.17). The damage came from moths and the embroideries were dark from oxidation. The lining was cleaned, as described before, with a chamois and a moist brush. The decoration of the Order of the Sword (a small silver sword) was cleaned by using water with some liquid detergent (berol) added. The upper edge of the collar and the right front were edged with double layers of tulle, dyed to the right colour, in order to keep the fragments of cloth in position. The centre parts of the back were strengthened by new cloth supports. Small patches were attached beneath some small holes (as described above). On the turned-up cuffs, new braid of thin cloth had to be sewn as the old braid was very fragmentary.

Figure 15.17. (Above) Frock-coat of Charles XIV. Before restoration: damage on sleeve (Courtesy K. Livrustkammaren, Stockholm)

Figure 15.15. (Left) Frock-coat of Charles XIV (d.1844). After restoration (Courtesy K. Livrustkammaren, Stockholm)

Figure 15.16. Frock-coat of Charles XIV. Before restoration: damage close to collar (Courtesy K. Livrustkammaren, Stockholm)

16
Uniforms

P. M. MÄDER

Textile Restorer and Manager of the Department for Conservation of Military Textiles, Swiss National Museum, Zurich

J. G. KERKHOVEN

Conservator of the Collections of Uniforms, Flags, Medals, etc. on Military History at the Netherlands Army Museum, Leiden

In general, the same rules apply to the restoration and conservation of uniforms as to other textiles. The first thing is to establish what materials they are made of, the particular weave of the fabrics, the nature of the damage and the soiling, and what the behaviour of the textiles and the dyes will be during washing and drycleaning. The results of this preliminary examination should be recorded in a report, to which a minute description of the restoration activities, with illustrations and naming the materials used, i.e. fabrics, yarns, detergents and dyes, should be added at a later date. It is advisable to enter the recipes for the preparation of restoration and conservation agents and their range of application in an alphabetical card-index, so that they can easily be referred to.

16.1   CLEANING

One of the greatest problems in the restoration of textiles is cleaning. This problem is even more serious for uniforms, because they generally consist of widely different materials, which are often connected in such a way that it is impossible to separate them without serious damage. Greatcoats, trousers, waistcoats consist of wool, linen, silk, cotton, or a combination of these materials. Coats have breast- and shoulderpads, laces, braids, wool, gold, and silver embroidery, paintings, leather facings, and to the uniforms belong leather bags, metal buttons, caps made of different materials, felt hats, etc. A considerable part of the uniforms and equipment is so seriously polluted by sweat, dust and stains that complete cleaning cannot be avoided. A choice can be made between washing and drycleaning.

For most of the uniforms washing is not advisable, because the leather facings, the thick pads and painted parts behave differently from the rest as to shrinking, swelling and drying. Moreover, the colours are by no means always fast. Washing is to be preferred only when the uniforms, or their component parts, are made of the same material or of some materials behaving in a similar way. It is common knowledge that stains can be removed·more easily and cheaply in this way than by the drycleaning method.

The great advantages of drycleaning are, however, that the risk of shrinking of the material is smaller, and dyes which are not fast in water often are

Figure 16.1. Epaulet of gold embroidery, the right half cleaned by 'Silverdip', the left half untreated

fast in drycleaning solvents. Another advantage, with thick woollen material and paddings, is that there is no risk of fungi and bacteria developing when drying.

After extensive tests it appears that white spirit to which the cleaning activator Tempo D.C. has been added provides good cleaning power. The high flash grade 60°C (140°F) white spirit, having a boiling range of 180–210°C (674–770°F), is best suited to the purpose. Moreover, it contains about 15% aromatics which give it excellent cleaning power (*see* Chapter 4). Tempo D.C. Super (Firm–Stockhausen, Krefeld, West Germany) consists of sulphonates and organic phosphor compounds, and is a cleaning activator with a softening effect. The liquid is practically neutral and free from ammonia, and can take proportionally large quantities of water and afterwards be dissolved in white spirit.

The uniforms are placed in a swillering-swingbath in which they are very carefully subjected to a general cleaning. After this cleaning, persistent stains can be removed with soft brushes by careful spotting. They are then hung on a coat-hanger and dried in the open air.

This manner of cleaning is specially suited for woollen uniforms and leatherwork. Linen and silk uniforms, shirts, plumes, etc., can be cleaned in demineralised water to which either the non-ionic detergents Tinovetin N.R. (J.R. Geigy AG, CH–4000, Basel) or Sandopan K.D., (Sandoz AG, CH–4000, Basel), or Hostapon T. (Farbwerke Hoechst AG, Frankfurt am Main, Germany) have been added.

For leather objects, such as bags, belts, trousers and facings, the leather dressing agent (BML Dressing) can be used (see Chapter 23). By massaging the leather with soft brushes, or with the balls of the hands, its suppleness and softness is recovered. To avoid stickiness after treatment, the pieces are packed in polythene foil for about 1–2 h, and hexane is inserted through a narrow opening. In this hexane the sticky matter on the surface of the leather is dissolved. The leather can then be polished with a soft cloth, although in the case of dyed leather, only the back can be treated. In this way missing spots in the paint or lacquer can be touched up.

Another difficult problem is the cleaning of fabrics and embroideries made of silver and gold thread. They seldom consist of pure gold and silver, but generally of gilt and silvered strips of brass, wound round a core consisting of textile fibres. The corrosion layers consist of basic copper carbonates containing a detergent and silver sulphides, and good results can be reached with a diluted ammonia solution. Only if the corrosion is very severe should 'Silver-dip' be used. This is available in two compositions:

Recipe 1* (J. Goddard and Sons, Ltd, Nelson Street, Leicester, England)

Non-ionic wetting agent	0·5%
Demineralised water	86·4%
Hydrochloric acid	5·1%
Thiourea	8·0%

*A similar product is supplied by Chem. Fabrik, Aarberg, Switzerland.

Recipe 2 (Research Laboratory, Swiss National Museum):

Non-ionic wetting agent Pluronic L 62	0·3%
Demineralised water	86·7%
Phosphoric acid	5·0%
Thiourea	8·0%

The mechanical cleaning is done with a soft brush or a pencil (Figure 16.1). Neutralising by rinsing thoroughly must take place afterwards (control with pH-indicator paper). The use of glass pencils is highly unwise (see Chapter 13).

To prevent oxidation and corrosion after cleaning, the metal thread must be degreased and sprayed, or coated with a thin layer of Paraloid B 72 (Rohm and Haas, Company Export, Philadelphia, U.S.A.). Paraloid B 72 (15%) is an acrylic resin and must, for this purpose, be diluted with sulphur-free toluene. Metal parts of uniforms (buttons, hat-shields and buckles made of silvered and gilt brass) can be cleaned in the same way and provided with a protective layer.

Formerly in this museum, many of the uniforms were folded lengthwise and only partly shown. By being exposed to daylight for years, this half has faded, and in some cases even lost its colour altogether. The fibres, too, have greatly deteriorated. When it was decided to show these uniforms in full, it appeared necessary to touch up the faded half so that no difference was noticed. After various tests the following formula was found to give most satisfaction:

Per litre solution:
  12 g Cibalan dyestuff
  1·5–2·5% acetic acid (60%)
  200 ml methylene glycol.

The dyestuff (the quantity is dependent on the desired depth of the colour) was added to the boiling water and then boiled for about four minutes. After this, the solution was cooled to 40°C, and acetic acid and methylene glycol added.

Before dyeing, the parts to be treated are moistened. With a fine retouching pistol the colour solution is put on layerwise. Next the colour can be fixed by using a cool iron, with a cloth being put over the spot to be fixed. Small spots are retouched with Deka-Permanent-Textilfarben (Deka-Textilfarben AG, München, Germany). These are laid on with a pencil or a wad of cottonwool. Under large missing parts and holes, a fabric dyed in a matching colour is laid, and fastened with fine stitches.

After cleaning, the uniforms and parts of equipment are soaked in a Mitin or Eulan bath against moths and insects. When these products are applied correctly, protection is guaranteed for years. If parts of uniforms do not allow bath treatment, they should be sprayed from time to time with Mitin or Eulan.

When reconstructions are necessary, they take place according to precise drawings and descriptions, made in accordance with pictures and regulations. Fabrics, belts and braidings must be woven and dyed anew.

When the uniforms are to be exhibited, hinged manikins are used. The figure stands free in the glass case without a bottom plate and is only held by an iron rod fixed in the floor (Figure 16.2). The heads of the manikins, made of papier-mâché, are obtainable in four different types. Alterations can be made by simply putting on layers of plaster (Plates 16.1–16.3).

16.2   RESTORATION

Restoration of the available uniform parts in the depot of the Netherlands Army Museum (Leiden, Netherlands) is only considered when they are needed for exhibition.

The decision to restore or not depends on the material condition of the object in question and on the documentation required for restoration. The object may be damaged, eaten, or worn in such a way that there is no sense in restoration. However, it keeps its value as a model for reconstruction or as material for study.

Documentation by way of regulations, journals, quartermasters' lists, accounts, diaries, pay-books, and memoirs, also such things as drawings and prints, can be too conflicting to be used as supporting evidence for a restoration. In this case restoration must be abandoned, especially when the original object itself has changed beyond recognition because of former attempts at restoration, or through alterations for the stage or carnival.

If an object is considered suitable for restoration, it may be reversed without objection, as this has also been done in the past. The colours of soldiers' old uniforms are recovered in a surprising way by reversing the garments. Officers' uniforms, generally of a superior quality material, hardly ever need this treatment when being restored.

First the uniform is entirely taken apart, laces and facings are unstitched, then the separate parts are washed individually. This is done by rinsing them between two nylon-covered frames, in a detergent.[1, 2] By washing the parts separately, there is no risk of the running of colours, and at the same time tensions produced by the swelling of threads in the fabrics and of the yarns in the seams, are prevented. Each washed part is then left to dry on filter paper, and ironed to reduce the drying process to a minimum, for the sake of preservation of the colours.

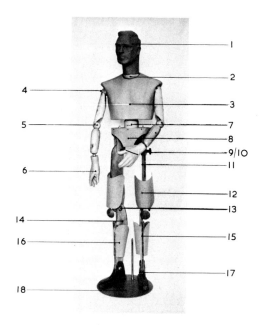

Figure 16.2. Movable man's figure made of wood and papier-mâché. (1) Head: Material papier-mâché. (2) Neck piece: Consists of a wooden rotating disc which enables the head to be moved in any direction. (3) Breast torso: Made of papier-mâché available in 3 different sizes; an opening in the back makes it possible to adjust the arms and the middle part with handscrews. (4), (5), (6) Arm: Consists of three parts, of which the upper and fore-arm made of wood, and the hand of papier-mâché. The arms can be adjusted in any direction by ball-and socket joints. The hands are available in three varieties. (7) Connecting joint to put the upper part of the body in any required position (ball-and-socket joint). (8) Hip: The hip consists of a wooden rotating disc, lengthened downwards by cardboard. There are three hipwidths available. (9), (10) Connecting piece for the thigh: Consists of two parallel wooden planks in which the upper part of the thigh can be inserted. The joint is fixed with a handscrew. (11), (12) Thigh: Wood with bent cardboard. (13) Knee joint: Wood. (14) Shin: Wood. (15), (16) Calf: Consisting of two sideways bent pieces of cardboard. (17) Foot: Black hardwood with a joint that can be fixed by means of a handscrew. Shoes can be easily fitted on the wooden feet. However, a hole is to be bored in a shoesole, so that the whole figure gets a better foothold by a metal rod which can be fastened in the floor. (18) Bottomplate: Iron.

Before putting the articles of dress on the figure, the different spaces, e.g. the waist, upper and lower parts of the legs, knee joints, can be filled in with cottonwool or paper. For exhibitions of longer duration the various joints are fixed with a second screw by way of precaution (By courtesy of Swiss National Museum)

Plate 16.1. Uniform of a grenadier captain, 1818, Canton Zürich, Switzerland. All parts are original, except for the shoes

Plate 16.2. Hussar, period of Republic Helvetie, 1798–1803. Only the coat is original, the other parts of the uniform are reconstructed. A moustache and wig have been added to the head of the manikin

Plate 16.3. Artillery uniform from 1825–1830. Canton Schaffhausen, Switzerland. All parts of the uniform are original except for the shoes. A moustache and beard have been added to the head of the manikin

Plate 16.4. Hussar of Willem Boreel (1814–1815). Shako and trousers reconstructed. Dolman and equipment restored (1968)

Plate 16.5. Drummer of the native infantry of the former Dutch East Indies' Army (1870). Practically total reconstruction of uniform and equipment (1967)

Plate 16.6. Bazooka-team of the Chinese People Volunteers during the Korean War (1950–1953). Wintercap restored (1966)

In cases where the part shows tears or holes, a fabric of the same material, if possible, is stuck behind. The glue for the purpose is a polyvinyl acetate which retains its suppleness.[3] The holes or rents are then darned on to the affixed fabric with silk yarn of the same colour as the uniform.

According to the condition of the material, buttons are bronzed, brassed, silvered, gilded, or provided with a new cloth covering. Laces and facings made of gold or silver thread (or gilt or silvered yarn) are cleaned with a solution of ammonia, rinsed in lukewarm water and dried as fast as possible with a hairdrier. If necessary they are afterwards bronzed with goldspray or silvered with silverspray. Laces and brandenburgs can be reversed and if necessary, slightly tinted with gouache paint. This paint which can be washed in water, does not attack the material and always retains its suppleness. Consequently, it does not crack.

Finally, the parts are put together with the same kind of threads, if possible, as were used in the original before restoration, and this is done by hand. The restored uniform is now pressed with a cool iron, taking into consideration the shape and manner of wearing formerly in fashion. For instance, the trouser-legs of uniforms dating from before 1900 never have a crease.

For the reconstruction of missing uniforms or uniform parts, pieces of originals unfit for restoration are of the greatest importance as models. If no such models are available, documentation of the kind listed earlier, provided it is consistent and complete, may provide enough information. With the data derived from it, working plans on millimetre paper with precise mention of scale and sizes can be made for the tailor, the leatherworker and the gunsmith. The gunsmith usually replaces missing shako parts and reconstructs brass and iron parts of equipment, which are then joined by the leatherworker. A first requirement for reconstruction is that textiles and materials similar to the former colour and quality are used whenever possible.

The manikins, heads and hands are also made by the staff in this museum. The guiding principle is that the attitude, face and hands should be entirely in the style of the period from which the uniform to be exhibited dates. They should also be a realistic reproduction (*see* Plates 16.4–16.6). If the uniform concerned has been worn by a historic person it is exhibited on a manikin with neither head nor hands.

REFERENCES AND NOTES

1. PAARDEKOOPER, A. C., 'Restauratie Uniformencollectie Koninklijk Huisarchief. Jaarverslag 1963 van het Nederlands Leger en Wapenmuseum', *Generaal Hoefer*, Leiden 21–25 (1964)
2. 'Nonidet' P40, 1 part on 100 parts water. The 1% solution in distilled water has pH 7–8. *Shell, Industrial Chemical Technical Bulletin.* IC: 63: 10
3. A mixture of 1 part Mowilith DM 5, 1 part Mowilith DM VI and 3 to 4 parts distilled water

17
Lace

MARIA JOSÉ TAXINHA

Chief Restorer in Textile Department, Instituto de José de Figueiredo, Lisbon

The art of lace-making dates back to the evolution of handwork. The peoples of antiquity used their fingers to interlace reeds, wickers and vegetable fibres to make baskets, nets and cloths.

Lace may be made with a needle, a *crochet* (or hook) or with bobbins, and to produce fancy laces such tools as barb needles, 'navettes', 'lacets', 'macramés', etc., are used. There are three main types of lace: bobbin lace (also known as pillow lace), needlepoint lace and lace embroidered on tulle.[1-5]

17.1 BOBBIN LACE

Bobbin lace owes its origin to an improvement in passementerie, when thick braid trimmings, originally woven, gradually became indented and lace-like. It was first executed on a pillow using pins and a constant number of threads. This is probably the beginning of bobbin lace, with a continuous thread, which prevailed throughout all the lace centres until the middle of the seventeenth century. This technique was maintained in the Binche, Valenciennes, Lille and Malines laces. Each type had its own definite characteristics and, although distinguished by technique, was still known by its place name.

> Binche lace is recognised by its 'Fond de Neige', a slightly tight cloth stitch in the flowers made with an extremely fine thread.
> Valenciennes lace is distinguished by its simple but uniform mesh, its very solid work and yet by its very close cloth stitch.
> Lille lace is composed of a mesh with two slightly twisted threads, thus forming a clear and transparent net. It is narrow, usually no wider than 7 cm and is characterised by its simple patterns.
> Malines lace is recognised by its fine but resistant net known as 'Fond de Glace'. The mesh is particularly tight at the corners, as the lace maker

does not use any pins. The flowers are outlined by a slightly twisted linen thread.

All these laces are made of linen.

The material used is a deciding factor in Chantilly and Blonde laces, which are worked with a black or ivory silk thread. The mesh is fine, hexagonal and always has a cordonnet winding round the motifs. The evolution of this epoch-making style brought about some changes in the working methods. This was the origin of the cut-thread technique which gave lace makers the opportunity to increase or decrease the number of threads according to their patterns. Decorations were worked individually and joined by 'Brides Picotées' or by a round mesh net. With this method, wider laces could now be executed, together with more precise patterns.

Amongst the types of lace which followed this technique, mention must be made of the Duchess of Bruges lace, only made in Flanders, the variety known as Rosaline with its ground of 'Barrettes Picotées' and the Duchess of Brussels, a finer and lighter lace, the difference being partly due to the use of an extremely fine thread. Brussels was the main lace centre which specialised in this technique.

At the beginning of the eighteenth century, lace makers in Brussels first used a net of hexagonal meshes called 'Droschel'. It was particularly light and made with an extremely fine linen thread. This resulted in a further change in technique, whereby instead of joining the net directly to the motifs, narrow strips of net were made into which the decorations were inserted and sewn with needle stitches. This new process was named appliqué. With the adoption of this new technique, whereby the execution of the decoration became independent from that of the ground, the contrast between the values of decoration and the lightness of the ground was emphasised, and it became possible to give Brussels lace an almost ethereal effect.

17.1.1   RESTORATION

The lace in the restoration process which will be described has all the characteristics of the eighteenth century Brussels lace. Its composition consists of medallions alternating with fruit baskets and bunches of flowers tied with bows, placed on a mesh Droschel ground, as well as various floral decorations interposed between the medallions on a 'Fond de Brides' (Figure 17.1). All the decoration elements are worked individually, according to the cut-thread and appliqué techniques, and linked to the net ground by an almost invisible needle stitch.

This lace was executed with a wide variety of stitches: cloth stitch, half stitch, 'Point de Neige', 'Jours'—many kinds of 'Point Esprit', relief outlining the flower decorations and picots sewn with needle stitches to the indented extremities. The lace is seamless; it is an alb flounce measuring 3·82 m in circumference and 34 cm in breadth. It was executed with an extremely fine linen thread of one end with an S twist.

Lace washing is the first and most important part of the restoration treatment. The lace is placed in a basin full of distilled water which is changed after 20 min. The water must be changed as the old layers of dust come off the lace, and in the first hours, the water is almost black. In these immersion baths, the water must be changed until it is fairly clear. Only now can the lace be really washed by placing it on a washing table over a piece of plastic, so that it may be freely moved without being forced against the pressure of the water. Lace must be washed with a natural sponge; a few drops of Nekanil detergent (5% solution) should be added to the water.[6]

When the top surface of the lace has been washed, a second piece of plastic must be placed over the lace, then, holding the two strips, it is turned over to wash the other side. It is rinsed several times until the foam of the detergent has completely disappeared. The lace is then exposed to the sun for bleaching, preferably in the early hours of the morning, and has to be constantly dampened.[7] This whole procedure can take several days.

For the drying process, the lace, when still wet, is placed carefully on a soft-topped table, covered with plastic.[8] The lace is gently extended with the finger tips, arranging the motifs to be in the right position and the right size, always starting from the selvedge. Pins are placed at the edges to avoid

Figure 17.1. Brussels bobbin lace, first half of the eighteenth century. Detail before restoration, showing the torn part of the lace

shrinking. A circular lace should be dried on a table with a movable top so that the worker can easily pin it by sections. It is also possible to dry the lace in another way, by overlapping sections, pinning them, and then carefully adjusting the motifs, one upon the other. The drying process is carried out in a normal indoor atmosphere.

A binocular magnifying glass (Majora Nachet) was used to execute the second part of the work, because the lace was so fine that it was otherwise impossible to link the loose pieces without altering the size of the lace (*see* Figure 17.2). The restoration work was done with a No 16 needle (Agujas para bordar ilusion—DOSCO) and a cambric linen thread with two ends (No 600 D.M.C.) which was later frayed and used with only one end, so that it would become even thinner than the thread used in the lace itself. The introduction of the needle into the original thread should be made with a magnifying glass, so as to be sure that the old thread has enough

Figure 17.2. Brussels bobbin lace, eighteenth century. Restoration process of the lace. Work done with a magnifying glass

resistance for the needle and the new thread to pass through.

All broken bars and meshes were joined by the edges to link the broken parts and wherever elements were missing, new ones had to be made. The bobbin lace technique was not used, as the lace maker works with several threads whereas this repair was made with only one thread. In the holes, cloth stitches and half stitches were remade by using the existing threads.

The enlarged photos show the work half done and after completion. It will be noticed that the restoration is slightly thicker, although it has been made with a thinner thread than the original one (Figures 17.3 (a) and (b)). This is an extremely delicate process of restoration and may only be carried out with the most soft and gentle movements.

17.2 NEEDLEPOINT LACE

Needlepoint lace is the most artistic of all feminine handwork. It derives from embroidery and has an oriental origin.

Oriental needlepoint lace differs from the European in its characteristic points, as it is worked with a silk thread, white or coloured. Its decoration has small floral or geometric motifs. Oriental laces are easier to work than the European ones and three main types can be quoted, oriental lace worked in coloured silk, Armenian lace made in white silk and with an oriental slipknot, and Palestine lace with its characteristic points.[9] European needle-point appeared first in ancient Greece. It expanded in Italy and the Nether-lands during the fifteenth and sixteenth centuries.

It has been said that needlepoint originated from embroidery. Cut-work was the name given to drawn work made with cut and drawn threads on a cloth which was later embroidered with a needle. In general, the old cut-work was characterised by its geometric designs, rosettes, foliage, characters and its symbolic or conventional subjects. The process was simplified throughout the ages and developed eventually into a new technique of sewing threads on to a parchment or paper base, on which was the outline of the pattern. Although the work of drawn or cut threads may be qualified as embroidery, by the time the technique of using sewn threads alone has

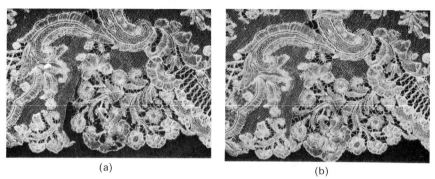

(a)   (b)

Figure 17.3. Brussels bobbin lace, eighteenth century. (a) During work: part of the fragment joined to the lace at the right hand, (b) the lace after restoration

developed, the word *lace* must be used, for this work is done entirely in the air (*Punto in aria*, as the Italians call it). From this process derives Venetian lace in all its varieties.

Venetian 'Reticella' is the name given to those laces with a pattern of a fenced-in shape resembling a net. The Venetian lace of Cyprus and other islands, with its geometric designs, differs from other laces, as it is worked with a cotton thread of a low grade. The Venetian lace in relief was the out-come of a technical need in evolution during this period and may be quoted among the most artistic needleworks. Its motifs are outlined by a high well-shaped relief. These laces have a rather luxurious aspect owing to the variety of points such as Ivory Point, Mat Point, 'Nervure', 'Brides Picotees', 'Jours', 'Brodes'. A word must be said about the pearled Venice lace, a Rosaline lace needleworked with rose points (Point Rose) which is much admired. This lace is characterised by its innumerable Brides Picotées, which form a ground with a minute rose pattern.

Still within the Italian type laces, there are the 'Argentella' points known for their fancy needleworked net called Eye of Partridge (fond diamant), which is unsuitable for a light decoration. Fine Burano points may be recognised by a net of square and rectangular meshes worked in parallel lines with a very fine cotton or linen thread. The pattern has large flowers executed on a mat cloth with a slightly raised outlining cordonnet.

Under the influence of Colbert, French points, imitating the Venetian style, were created. The patterns were, however, conceived in a French way with a mesh ground of Brides, Fine and Picotées, laid out in a hexagonal shape. The motifs were adorned with an outlining thread in relief. This 'Point de France', as it was known, then gave way to several other points: the 'Point d'Alençon, recognised by a fine regular net with small, sober and precise patterns in relief; the 'Point d'Argentan', characterised by large closely-placed flowers with varied Jours and a wider net of twisted threads;

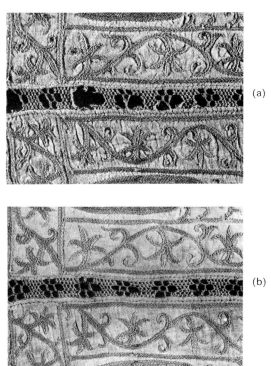

(a)

(b)

Figure 17.4. Needlepoint lace. Oriental work of the seventeenth century. (a) Detail of the lace before restoration, (b) same detail after restoration

and the 'Point de Sedan, distinguished by a special floral design with pine-cones and elongated fruits executed in a festoon stitch. Very fine threads are generally used for French points.

Finally, the Flemish 'Point de Gaze' should be mentioned. It is worked on a very fine net of two simple, twisted threads, and the ornaments are made individually before being placed on the net. They are determined by a more openly worked outline and a particularly fine and transparent ground.

17.2.1 RESTORATION

The restoration work now described was executed on an oriental needle-point lace (Figure 17.4(a)). It is an insertion which decorates a seventeenth century Indo-Portuguese embroidery. This embroidery was worked with a natural coloured Tussah silk thread on a ground of cream cotton (taffeta). It is believed that this embroidery, belonging to the National Coach Museum in Lisbon, was a piece of a garment.

The insertion is worked in needlepoint with the same Tussah silk thread used for the embroidery. The decoration is made up of small motifs of rosettes in an open stitch, and geometric figures in a closed stitch. It is undoubtedly an oriental lace, for it is worked with very specific materials, and is part of the decoration of a garment which has all the characteristics of a certain type of embroidery made in India under Portuguese influence. The stitch used in the lace resembles the knotted festoon stitch of the European needlepoint lace. The lace insertion to link the embroidered cotton strips is worked on the edge of one strip and is sewn with a fine cotton thread to the edge of the other strip.

The whole garment was washed, as described in the previous restoration. It was dried in a normal indoor atmosphere, on a soft table, after having been carefully spread out to its right position and size, and pinned at the edges to avoid shrinking. A binocular magnifying glass was used to check the resistance of the original silk during the repair of the lace. The work was carried out with a No 16 needle and an untwisted natural silk thread in the same colour as the original silk, and worked with only one end. All points and broken *barrettes* were linked, and the ends were caught in order to join up the parts and broken points. Like the first restoration mentioned, this process had a satisfactory result. The use of the magnifying glass to check the resistance of the threads, in both cases enabled a better result to be achieved than could otherwise have been obtained (Figure 17.4(b)).

17.3   EMBROIDERED TULLE

Old embroidery on tulle was worked on a fine needle-made net of simple, regular meshes. The most fashionable lace patterns of the eighteenth century were made in this way at Tulle in France. They were very popular at the French court, because they looked very splendid, although cheaper to produce than the other kinds of lace.

Machine-made tulle first appeared in 1810 and embroidery worked on it was soon popular. Machine-made tulle is easier and faster to work with than the old type, so a wide variety of needle stitches is used.

17.3.1   RESTORATION

The restoration process now described was performed on a black nineteenth century mantilla embroidered in silk on a machine-made tulle. The decoration is composed of floral motifs with garlands hanging from volutes and a rose bouquet at the centre. With this kind of machine-made silk tulle, the first damage always occurs on the tulle itself, as it is so fragile. The following process was therefore adopted.

Nylon tulle with the same dimensions as the mantilla was pinned on a soft-topped table. The mantilla was then carefully spread out over the tulle, the motifs were gently placed in the right positions and the mantilla was basted to the tulle with wide stitches to avoid any displacement. With the garment pinned to the table, the borders of the motifs were sewn on to the tulle with an untwisted thread of natural silk and small needle stitches which would bind the cordonnet to the border. When the silk tulle was not completely torn, tiny stitches were given to link the tattered pieces to the nylon tulle. Where it was torn, the tulle was cut close to the motifs, making sure that the mantilla is well stitched to the base. The outer border was button-holed with a natural silk thread after removing the mantilla from the table.

REFERENCES AND NOTES

1. CARLIER DE LANTSHEERE, A., *Trésor de l'Art Dentellier*, G. van Oest & Cie, Bruxelles et Paris (1922)
2. OVERLOOP, E. VAN, *Dentelles Anciennes*, Musées Royaux des Arts Décoratifs et Industriels de Bruxelles et Paris (1912)
3. RISSELIN-STEENEBRUGEN, M., *Dentelles Belges, 19ᵉ-20ᵉ Siècle*. Musées Royaux d'Art et d'Histoire, Bruxelles (without year)
4. SCHWETTER, BERTHE, *Enciclopédia de Trabalhos Manuais*, Globo (Brazilian translation), Rio de Janeiro (1950)
5. POWYS, MARIAN, *Lace and Lace-making*, Charles T. Branford Cy, Boston, Mass. (1953)
6. Detergent before commercialisation
7. This work was carried out in Lisbon, Portugal
8. Karlite, a Swedish material indicated by the Textilkonserveringen Historiskamuseum, Stockholm, Sweden
9. Reference 4, p. 315

18
Beadwork

K. S. FINCH

Former Member of Conservation Department, Victoria and Albert Museum, London

Beads are defined as small perforated bodies which can be strung together to form necklaces and decorative articles, or sewn upon various fabrics. Their history can be traced back to the earliest men, and they have been made from such varied substances as glass, precious and semi-precious stones, amber, wood, metals, pottery, ivory, pearls, shells, bone, feathers, straw, teeth, stalactites, marble, seeds and plastic.[1] For this reason, before embarking upon the conservation of an article in which beads have been used, it is essential to determine the nature of the beads and their method of manufacture, in addition to understanding the technique employed in the making of the beadwork object itself.

Glass beads can be made in several ways. The molten glass can be wound around a wire, which gives the bead a smooth straight perforation with little danger of sharpness at the ends, or the glass can be drawn into a tube and cut up into small cylinders, which are mechanically tumbled to polish off sharp edges. They can also be made by pressing into individual bead moulds or by the technique of glass blowing.[1] Glass beads should be tested for colour fastness in the same way as textiles, for often, especially from the nineteenth century onwards, fugitive stains or improperly applied dyes have been used to colour beads, and washing could make the colours run or disappear altogether.

Imitation gold and silver beads are made by blowing gold or silver dust into hollow glass beads, or by placing the beads in a rotating drum which contains a gilding or silvering solution which adheres to the insides of the beads.[1] Beads thus treated can be recognised by holding the work sideways to the light, when they will be seen to be made of glass. It may be found, after suitable tests have been applied, that the beads can be lightly and quickly sponged and dried but care must be taken not to allow the water to penetrate inside the beads.

In glass beads the perforation is a natural result of the method of manufacture, but stone beads and pearls have to be perforated by drilling.[1] This is usually begun from both sides to avoid splitting, often making the two parts of the channel meet at an angle. This can cause some difficulty in the stitching.

During the nineteenth century steel beads were very fashionable.[2] They must be treated with great care, as they are not stainless and can cause a great deal of damage because of rust. Sometimes they rust the thread that is holding them in place without showing signs of rust on their own exterior, so it is not advisable to wash them unless they are part of a very strong fabric. Washing is not recommended either for beads made of wood, straw, lacquer, papier-mâché or seeds, as any colouring matter on them might suffer in water.

Imitation pearls can also be very difficult to handle in conservation. Sometimes they are made of very thin, blown glass which is coated on the inside with a pearl-like substance, and this may dissolve when it comes into contact with any liquid.[1] The so-called Roman pearls, however, are some-what different, and are in fact beads of alabaster saturated with hot wax and then dipped in a pearl essence made from carp scales.[3] They are affected by heat and, of course, by any grease-dissolving chemicals, even soap and water.

Beads made from rolled-up beetle wings can, however, be washed. If they are surrounded by gold sequins or embroidery which may need treatment, it is useful to know that the wings are not affected by weak acids or alkalies. Their colour may change to brown during the treatment, but they will revert to their original colour on drying.

Apart from the handling of the beads themselves, conservation treatment of beadwork depends largely on the techniques used in the making of the article.

18.1 BEADWORK TECHNIQUES

1. Beads can be strung in order on to a single length of thread, according to a pattern drawn out on graph paper, and then be woven, knitted, plaited or crocheted into the fabric itself as it is being made.[3-5] For example, North American beadwork is often woven or plaited with the beads threaded on the weft or plaiting fibres. When these techniques have been used, all threads must be made secure before any other treatment is begun.

2. Tambourwork (Figure 18.1) is a technique which is often used for beading on costumes.[3] Seen from the inside of a garment, this looks like chainstitching, but it is done on a tambour frame with a crochet hook or chainstitch machine, and the yarn which holds the beads can be unravelled like a crochet chain. As in the techniques mentioned above, all loose threads must be secured before starting any other treatment.

3. Stitched beads with no background (Figure 18.2), worked with a needle and thread, was the technique employed in the making of the jet collars of the nineteenth century, the pearly ones recently fashionable, and the collars such as those used by the Eskimoes in Greenland.[5] The work is started by threading a row of beads on a thread with a needle. The second row is stitched alongside the first, by picking up more beads and securing them by passing the needle and thread through a bead on the first row at regular intervals. The work is regulated in size by increasing or decreasing

the number of beads in each interval. When a new thread is wanted, it is knotted to the end of the preceding one.[4, 5]

4. In folk art the world over, rows of threaded beads are often couched on to leather, skin or felt, the couching stitches never passing through the actual beads themselves.

5. In most European stitched beadwork, each bead is stitched separately into the designs, fitting in with the rest of the embroidery, which is nearly

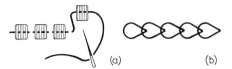

(a)   (b)

Figure 18.1. Diagram of tambourwork. (a) Front (b) back

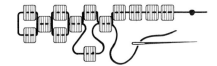

Figure 18.2. Diagram of threading beads

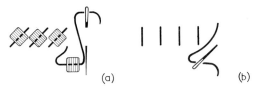

(a)   (b)

Figure 18.3. Diagram of embroidery with half cross stitches on canvas. (a) Front, (b) back

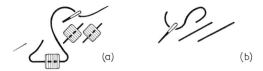

(a)   (b)

Figure 18.4. Diagram of embroidery with tent stitches. (a) Front, (b) back

always done on a textile fabric, though paper and vellum have been used as well.[4, 5]

6. In the seventeenth century, beadwork covering the whole surface was stitched on to strong, closely woven linen, with waxed, silk thread and was used to cover boxes and mirror frames. The beads were threaded and couched to follow the designs in a tightly spaced, irregular manner, which gave to the technique a mosaic-like appearance.

7. In the nineteenth century, beads were much used in conjunction with embroidery in silk and wool on an open linen canvas. The wool often used was a rather fine Merino worsted called Zephyr in Germany, and known elsewhere as Berlin wool, since it was produced there from about 1800 for canvas embroidery.[2] From about 1800, vegetable dyes seem to have been

replaced for the dyeing of green colours by a solid green which is not wash-fast and, unfortunately, runs steadily through the nineteenth century in Berlin wool work, samplers, and many other embroideries and prints. Throughout the nineteenth century new dyes were being used and they must all be tested for their colour fastness.

The beads used with this embroidery in silk and wool were stitched in regular rows according to the canvas (Figures 18.3, 18.4), using a half cross or tent stitch and with a well-waxed cotton or linen thread. This type of work was used mostly for covering chairs and for cushions and bags.[2]

18.2   METHODS OF CLEANING

18.2.1   WASHING

Both washing and drying should, as far as possible, be done with the object lying absolutely flat and straight, for in this way the fibres which have been relaxed by the moisture can be made to set in the most desirable position. Beaded canvas-work will need to be held straight on a board with pins while it dries, as this prevents the direction of the embroidery stitches pulling the work into a diagonal shape. It is best if it can be dried with the right side uppermost, as this tends to improve the colours.

When washing very fragile objects, care should be taken to prevent damage which can occur when the fibres swell and become heavy with water. Sometimes it is sufficient to lay the object on a supporting sheet of polyester, but this is not enough to hold the very heavy costume parts made by primitive peoples, which often have long fringes of beads strung on stapled vegetable fibres, such as hemp or jute. These fringes should be arranged in their proper position on a piece of coarse synthetic fabric and secured with long stitches before washing, in order to keep the beads in place until the work is dry again. The textile part can now be strengthened further while it is still wet by being sprayed with a solution of polyvinyl alcohol in water. This will slide off the clean beads and concentrate in the vegetable fibres. The concentration of the solution may vary from 5 to 10%, depending on the kind of textile, i.e. the lower concentration for heavy material, the higher concentration for light material.

On occasions it is desirable to strengthen the textile before washing, and in these cases, polyvinyl butyral or soluble nylon may be used. For an example of this method, see the account below of the conservation of a seventeenth century mirror frame.

Bead baskets and other objects where wire has been used need very careful treatment. If the wire is silver and in good condition, it should be possible to wash the object but if it is steel, one must be careful of hidden damage caused by rust. Rusted wire has no flexibility and this makes any repair work very difficult.

18.2.2   DRY METHOD OF CLEANING

The method of cleaning with dry sodium bicarbonate is one that will not remove stains but which works very well on objects that are dirty from display rather than actual wear. It appears to work by releasing the grease that is binding the dust. The area to be cleaned should be covered with powder and left overnight in a warm dry place, after which it should be very gently brushed and tapped off. Dry powder falls out very easily of its own accord.

18.2.3   DRYCLEANING

A less satisfactory method is the one using a drycleaning fluid. These fluids are rarely successful in removing old stains and have a degreasing effect; they are also difficult to handle in many work-rooms.

18.3   STRENGTHENING AND REPAIR

When beads occur in combination with woollen embroidery on canvas, the wool attracts damp and this can cause deterioration of the linen in the canvas. It is possible to strengthen the fibres of the canvas with an application of a solution of polyvinyl alcohol (concentration about 5%, according to the fabric). This concentrates in the canvas and the vegetable fibres holding the beads, but has no apparent effect on the wool. Strengthening the original fibres in this way seems preferable to restitching the beads with new yarn.

Repairs to beadwork should be done by employing the technique used when the object was made, otherwise the repair cannot move in harmony with the rest of the piece and will cause more damage. Though it is generally possible to repair the textile, it is not alway possible to replace beads. However, if the beads have come off a rigid object, such as a box, and have been saved, it is possible to replace them by dropping them into position and securing them with a 10% solution of polyvinyl butyral.

18.4   TREATMENT OF A SEVENTEENTH CENTURY MIRROR FRAME

Although general rules exist which can act as useful guides in conservation work, the fascinating and rewarding task of the conservator is the solution of the unique problem posed by each new object to be treated. This was very true of an interesting seventeenth century mirror frame (collection of Lennox Money) of beads couched in silk on a linen ground, where the clear glass beads forming the background to the design were quite black with dirt inside and the design could only be made out with difficulty (*see* Plates 18.1, 18.2, and Figure 18.5).

Some beads fell off with handling, which indicated loose ends apart from those to be seen at the gaps in the embroidery where beads were already missing. Only washing and rinsing could bring out the dirt from inside the beads, but it was clearly necessary first to strengthen and make secure the spun silk thread used in the stitching. The work was therefore painted all over the back with a 10% solution of soluble nylon, and when this was dry it was turned face up and the same solution painted all round the edges, including the edges at the gaps in the embroidery. The washing was done by soaking the object repeatedly in baths of Lissapol N (a few drops per litre of water), to which a few drops of ammonia were added just before the bath was siphoned off. Although ammonia releases the grease quickly and, therefore, shortens the washing time, it should always be remembered that it dissolves the sericin in silk. It was possible to use it in this case because the silk was supported by the soluble nylon. The rinsing was in distilled water and

Figure 18.5. Mirror frame, seventeenth century. Detail of the couching technique in bead embroidery

the result was very good, with clean beads and hardly any loss. Repairs were done by stretching a piece of linen in an embroidery frame, laying the mirror frame on this and stitching in strategic places to hold the two together.

REFERENCES
1. SLEEN, W. G. N. VAN DER, *A Handbook on beads*, Publication of the 'Journées Internationales du Verre', Liège, Musée du Verre (1967)
2. MORRIS, BARBARA, *Victorian Embroidery*, Herbert Jenkins (1962)
3. LARSEN, CAROLINE, *Jeg Broderer Selv*, Politikens Forlag (1959)
4. ANDERSON, E., WANDEL, G., VOGEL-JØRGENSEN, T., Berlingske Haandarbeidsbog. *Naal og Vaev I Leksikon*, Berlingske Forlag (1950)
5. ERLANDSEN, IDA-MERETE, *Sy og vaev med perler.*, Høst og Søn (1957)

19
Gloves

K. S. FINCH

Former Member of Conservation Department, Victoria and Albert Museum, London

19.1 THE WEARING OF GLOVES

From manuscripts, works of art and physical evidence, we know that since antiquity great men have worn gloves. As part of official dress, they were made of knitted silk or of leather, and often lavishly trimmed with fur, jewels, and gold embroidery. Those belonging to Tutankhamun and the Holy Roman Emperors have survived. Embroidered gloves are still part of the ceremonial vestments of some church dignitaries.

Gloves were also worn for protection, and even the Vikings, however hardy, did not brave the North Sea without the protection of gloves or *vanter* with thumbs, but otherwise fingerless. Falconers and soldiers wore gloves of very heavy leather with elbow-length cuffs and articulated iron plates on the back of the hands for armour. Other gloves used for protection were made from stout cloth as well as heavy leather and hide.

Few gloves exist now that were made before the thirteenth century, but after that date they were in greater demand and more have survived to the present day. Ladies also began to wear gloves, and these were always decorative. Some were made from chamois or kid, with gauntlet cuffs or with soft, rather wide wrists. Linen gloves reaching to the elbows were also worn.[1] There would usually be embroidery on the cuffs and on the back of the hand.

Some time about the year 1400, a fashion began for half-gloves or mittens and these are occasionally seen on contemporary figures. At least one pair, very pretty and knitted from crimson silk and gold thread, has survived.[2]

In the sixteenth century, elegant, long-fingered light leather gloves became fashionable. They had stiffened, and nearly always, tabbed cuffs covered with silk satin, that had first been worked with silk and gold embroidery and seed pearls. The motifs were flowers of the Tudor period interspersed with religious symbols, such as pelicans, lions and lambs. Gold pillow lace with spangles was used for trimming the edges and carnation pink taffeta for lining the cuffs. In no other period were such splendid gloves produced. They were worn by both men and women and were fashionable for a long time.[3]

Towards the middle of the seventeenth century, women began to wear close-fitting white gloves and mittens in silk, velvet, or fine soft leather. They were either short or elbow-length, according to the length of the sleeve with which they were worn. Stiffened cuffs were no longer used, and the trimming included ribbons and fringes, as well as embroidery with silk and gold thread. Men's gloves were much heavier and became plainer until by the eighteenth century they were hardly decorated at all. They were worn for protection only, i.e. for riding and by soldiers.

Gloves and mittens worn by women at this time were elbow-length and could be made from any sort of leather and fabric. They were mostly white, though mittens and gloves to match the dress were considered to be very elegant. Embroidery was lighter in design, used over the seams and round the tops. Gold embroidery was confined to evening gloves.[4]

During the nineteenth century and until World War I, fashions regarding the shape and length of gloves changed rapidly. Both men and women wore gloves as a necessary part of dress. Men's gloves were usually short except for riding, but leather gauntlet gloves were also worn. Men too, wore fine pastel-coloured leather gloves. Colours, mostly in pastel shades, were much used for daytime wear and long white mittens and gloves were for evenings. The materials could be of any textile fabric and leather, glazed kid being considered the most suitable for evening wear.

19.2 THE USE OF METAL THREADS

Metal threads frequently occur in the decoration of gloves, and before he can treat them, the conservator needs to know both the composition of the metal and the methods of manufacture of metal threads. Unfortunately, very little has been recorded about the composition of metals used for threads and decoration. A little more is known about methods of manufacture. Even the Bible gives us a reference to the making of gold wire. Exodus, Chapter 39, describes the manufacture of the gold wire used to decorate Aaron's vestments, 'And they did beat the gold into thin plates and cut it into wires, to work in the blue, and in the purple and in the scarlet and in the fine linen with cunning work'.

There are other descriptions in embroidery books and books of reference of how skillets of gold were beaten into thin plate, kept pliable by annealing, and cut into strips which could be brazed or hammered together for continuous lengths.[5-11] If round wire was required, the strips were hammered on an anvil and made circular in cross-section. This wire could be reduced to finer sizes by tension. Later, dies were used to stretch gold that had been shaped into rods for wiremaking. The end of the wire was hammered down to a diameter smaller than the die so that the wire could be pulled through by tongs. The size of the finished wire would depend on the strength of the men pulling. Manual strength had to be relied on until the mid-fourteenth century when water mills were adapted for wire-drawing in Nuremberg. Gold wires like these must have been difficult to work, and a more flexible gold thread was made by spinning flat strips of gold plate or flattened gold wire round a core of silk. This was a very costly process until, in the twelfth century, English silversmiths found a way to gild silver rods which could be drawn into wire, always keeping the same ratio of gold to silver. The resulting silver-gilt wire was extensively used. In the late 1560s an improved drawplate for pulling wire was introduced in England, which allowed the manufacture of silver-gilt wire fine enough to be used in the making of pillow lace. About 1600 gold was also plated on to copper wire. This is not as long-lasting as silver-gilt and, at first, most embroiderers appear to have refused to work with it, except when it was twisted with coloured silk and used, for instance, to represent foliage.

Purl and bullion were made from either round or flattened gold or silver-gilt wire. From the seventeenth century, copper wire has sometimes been used closely wound with coloured silks. Sequins were made from round wire twisted into tiny rings and hammered flat, while variously shaped spangles, which decorate embroidery and the edge of pillow lace, were punched out of plate. The quality of sequins and spangles varies greatly. Pure gold wire was used for making sequins as late as 1700, though copper had been used as early as the sixteenth century.

The quality of gold and silver threads degenerated during the eighteenth century, in spite of legal standards laid down in England during 1698, to decree the amount of copper with which the silver base should be alloyed. In 1732 Christopher Pinchbeck introduced a new alloy, called after himself, that simulated gold but was made from copper with 15% zinc. A simulated gold wire was also made by pulling a copper wire through zinc vapours. Many nineteenth century fringes were made with materials like these. The oriental gold work covering many Asian costumes usually contains a great deal of copper, but it is otherwise made in the same way as European gold thread.

In the 1860s, untarnishable Japanese gold and silver was introduced into Europe. Japanese gold thread is made from narrow strips of gilded paper wound round a core of orange silk. Silver thread is made from silvered paper wound round a core of white silk.

19.2.1   TREATMENT OF METAL THREADS

Care must be taken to identify all metal threads before attempting to clean them. Chemical tests are invaluable, but in some circumstances it may be necessary to identify metals *in situ*, in which case it is nearly always possible to distinguish the different metals by using a microscope. A pocket microscope magnifying 15–25 times is most useful as it is so easily moved to examine each detail.

Metal embroidery of any kind should be touched as little as possible since salts on the skin easily cause tarnishing. If handling is necessary, frequent handwashing should be the rule. Rubber must not come in contact with gold and silver, so rubber gloves should not be used.

Good quality gold and silver gilt does not tarnish easily except in damp or acid conditions. However, over a long period of time, dust can settle on gold and silver embroidery and be very difficult to remove. If the quality of the metal thread is good, very careful cleaning with ammonia is possible and usually successful. Ammonia dissolves dirt very quickly and also evaporates completely. It must be handled with the greatest care, but its use on good quality metals is rewarded by excellent results. However, the ammonia should not be allowed to touch the silk core of a thread since it will dissolve the sericin which gives the silk its strength.

Worn copper gilt and other inferior metal threads should never be cleaned with ammonia. In these cases, the metal can be safely cleaned with sodium bicarbonate, which will release the dust. Brushing with a light 'stroking' motion will help to restore their brightness, but one cannot expect to get startling results from poor quality or worn metals. Rubbing with magnesium carbonate or breadcrumbs has also been known to work. The look of metals can be improved by washing in distilled water with a drop of Lissapol. This is rarely possible, however, except in the case of fringes which can be removed (see also Chapter 13, p. 179 and Chapter 16, p. 197).

19.3   GLOVING LEATHER (See also Chapter 23)

The skins of very many different animals have been used for making gloving leather, but those principally employed over the greater part of 2000 years have been the pelts of domestic (wool) sheep, hair sheep, goat and, to a lesser extent, antelope, pig, calf and horse hides. There are three basic methods of converting raw hides or skins into leather, each of which produces leather of different character from the others:

1. Tanning, making use of the 'tannin' in vegetable matter.
2. Tawing, a mineral process originally employing alum and salt.
3. Chamoising, an oil process employing marine animal or fish oils.

19.3.1   VEGETABLE TANNAGE

For gloving leathers, the most important source of tannin has been sumach leaves. This plant has been employed for thousands of years around the Mediterranean and Middle East, and produces a leather of pale colour and excellent quality, which is less susceptible to 'red rot' than some other kinds of leather. The principal vegetable-tanned leather used for gloves has been 'basil' made from sheepskin tanned with sumach.

19.3.2   TAWING

Over the centuries, this has probably been the principal method employed for making gloving leather, either alone or in combination with chamoising or oil tanning. As tawed leather is rather spongy, for glove work it was usually dressed by a process called 'stuffing' or 'feeding'. This consisted of treading it in tubs containing an emulsion of, for example, egg-yolk, flour, grease and oil with a little water, which must have modified the pure white to a pale cream. The so-called 'kid' gloves of Victorian times were usually made of tawed goat or lamb skins, stuffed and glazed on the surface.

19.3.3   CHAMOISING

In this process a soft, durable, washable leather was produced by soaking the skins in marine animal or fish (usually cod) oil, after removing the natural 'grain' to facilitate entry of the oil from both sides. The skins were then piled up and left until the pressure produced sufficient heat to cause the oil to oxidise and combine with the fibres. After a thorough washing, the leather was a pale yellow colour called 'buff', because in early times the process was used for dressing buffalo hides. The term 'chamoising' probably arose because the process was also used for dressing chamois skins. Thus, chamoised leather is exemplified, both by the kind of leather used for jerkins, doublets and buff coats, and that used for 'wash' leather (or 'shammy') which has been much used for gloves, pouches, bags and many other purposes for centuries. Sometimes alum was also used, producing a leather of composite character, which is often difficult to diagnose.

In modern times many variations of each of the three ancient processes outlined have been developed, of which perhaps the most important is the substitute for alum, in the mineral process, of salts of chromium and other metals, and especially in the making of pure white gloving leather, of titanium. These processes produce soft beautiful leathers which can be fast-dyed and are washable.

Most 'cordwain' leather gloves of the sixteenth to eighteenth centuries were made with the grain side inward, where it remains white or pale cream, the exterior being the flesh side of the leather with a sueded finish and stained, usually a light fawn colour. The ancient vegetable dyes were, in the nineteenth century, gradually replaced by the aniline dyes derived from coal-tar, but all were fugitive and no leather coloured in this way can safely be washed with ordinary soap and water. Surface dust and dirt can be removed with Fuller's earth or with sodium bicarbonate. If white or undyed leather is still very dirty, it may be immersed for a short period in petrol or carbon tetrachloride, but both these solvents are dangerous to the operator and, by dissolving the grease which formed part of the dressing, are injurious to the leather. A modern cleaning agent is Soap B30 now commercially available as the product Vulpex (see note 5, p. 262) of which 2% is dissolved in white spirit. It is non-toxic and although inflammable, has a high flash-point and so is not as dangerous as petrol. Also, it is soluble in water and is, therefore, valuable for cleaning materials which would not be harmed by water.

It is dangerous to rub the surface of leather which might thereby be damaged, but if the surface has already been damaged, magnesium carbonate on cottonwool can be used for polishing. Damage can easily be caused in trying to clean old leather and it is permissible to overlook stains so long as the shape of the glove is right. The best way to achieve this is to remove the surface dust and dirt as recommended above, then put rolled, acid-free, tissue-paper in the fingers and a pad in the palm, just strong enough to support the weight of the leather but soft enough to give the impression that the glove is filled with air. The glove is then saturated with ether and as the leather dries, it contracts where it has been stretched out of shape and thus improves its appearance.

19.4 CONSERVATION OF A PAIR OF ELIZABETHAN GLOVES *(circa 1600)*

On the outside, the alum tanned leather was flattened, crumpled and a dirty buff colour. On the inside the leather was white and glazed. At the wrist the frill of carnation pink silk was edged with gold lace; the silk being

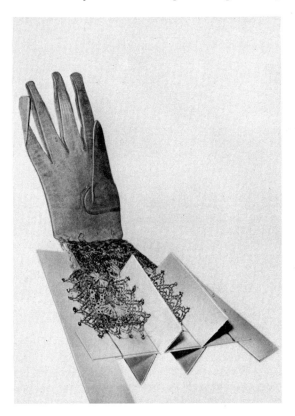

Figure 19.1. Elizabethan glove (c. 1600). The lace edgings have been pinned out for cleaning and drying in shape

in a bad condition, but the gold lace intact. The similar gold lace edging the cuff of good quality silver-gilt wire with a silk core, was also intact. When it was new, this gold lace edging would have stood out stiff and straight, but now it was crumpled and discoloured. The cuff itself was cream satin embroidered with silk, gold and seed pearls. The gold embroidery was silver-gilt wire with a silk core, also purl held in place with a silk thread running through the centre of the spiral. The cuff was interlined with leather and lined with carnation pink taffeta in fair condition. It is important in conservation work to keep the original stitches, but sometimes this is not possible and a considered decision has to be made on the minimum of unstitching necessary for cleaning and repair. In this case it was decided that the frill had to be removed. At several points during conservation, photographs were taken and notes made of exactly how the frill was gathered

Figure 19.2. Elizabethan glove (c. 1600) after cleaning and repair

on to the cuff. It was then possible to clean the main part of the glove, both the leather and the embroidered cuff.

The dust was removed by covering the glove with sodium bicarbonate which, after some time, was gently brushed and tapped off. At this stage, necessary repairs were made before starting to clean the gold embroidery and gold lace edging. The gold embroidery was cleaned first, then covered with tissue-paper to protect it from contact with hands while the cleaning of the gold lace edging was carried out. For this task, the gold lace was pinned out as shown in the photograph (Figure 19.1). This was for two purposes, both for cleaning and in order to let the clean lace dry straight.

The cleaning of the gold was done with ammonia which was not allowed to come in contact with anything but the gold itself. A small sable brush was dipped into ammonia, and wiped on cotton wool to remove all but the vapour. The gold was then brushed with a light 'stroking' motion, to remove the dirt. After each application, the dirt was cleaned off the brush on to the cotton wool. This is a long and delicate task, depending on the resistance of the dirt. When a section was finally clean, it was rinsed with distilled water applied sparingly on a clean brush and immediately soaked off on to cotton wool. The water was never allowed to spread on to the satin background.

Two rinsings were sufficient. The rinsing of the gold lace edging was more liberal as this also served to straighten and dry the lace in shape. When the gold lace edging was completely dry, Ercalene was applied with a brush to protect it against tarnishing as well as to keep the shape.

The frill was pinned out and the lace edging treated in the same way, first with sodium bicarbonate, then ammonia. After treatment with Ercalene, the repairs were carried out by laying the taffeta on to fine silk crepeline, stretched on to an embroidery frame to minimise handling, and couching with a very fine silk thread. The frill was gathered according to the notes and restitched on to the cuff. Finally, tissue-paper was rolled and put into the fingers, and a pad of tissue placed in the palm. The glove was placed on a bottle and the leather saturated with ether to remove the creases and give a better appearance. The end result was as is shown in Figure 19.2.

19.5   CONSERVATION OF A PAIR OF KNITTED MITTENS
(circa 1490)

The mittens were knitted from crimson silk with a gold thread design. The technique can be seen in the photograph (Figure 19.3). They were in very good

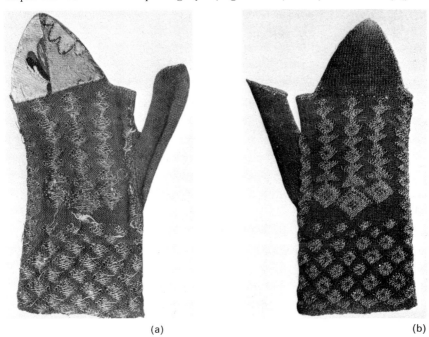

(a)   (b)

Figure 19.3. Knitted mitten (c. 1490), after restoration. (a) The inside showing the knitting technique, which by using a separate gold thread for each pattern detail gives a raised effect to the design. (b) Right side. The raised effect of the design can be observed at the sides

condition and needed only a little repair which was done with matching silk before they were washed in distilled water and Lissapol N. A shape had been prepared beforehand from silicone paper for each glove and these were put inside as soon as each one was washed to help them to dry in shape.

REFERENCES

1. Museo Stibbert, Florence
2. Robert Spence collection at the Guildhall Museum, London
3. Victoria and Albert Museum and Guildhall Museum, London
4.a. CUNNINGTON, C. WILLETT, *English Women's Clothing in the Nineteenth Century*, Faber and Faber Ltd, London (1937)
  b. CUNNINGTON, C. WILLETT, '*English Women's Clothing in the Present Century*, Faber and Faber Ltd, London (1952)
  c. WILLETT, C. and CUNNINGTON, PHILLIS, *Handbook of English Mediaeval Costume*, Faber and Faber Ltd, London (1952)
  d. WILLETT, C. and CUNNINGTON, PHILLIS, *Handbook of English Costume in the Sixteenth Century*, Faber and Faber Ltd, London (1954)
  e. WILLETT, C. and CUNNINGTON, PHILLIS, *Handbook of English Costume in the Seventeenth Century*, Faber and Faber Ltd, London (1955)
  f. PHILLIPSON, BARBARA and CUNNINGTON, PHILLIS, *Handbook of English Costume in the Eighteenth Century*, Faber and Faber Ltd, London (1957)
  g. WILLETT, C. and CUNNINGTON, PHILLIS, *Handbook of English Costume in the Nineteenth Century*, Faber and Faber Ltd, London (1959)
5. HUGHES, THERLE, *English Domestic Needlework*, Lutterworth Press, London (1961)
6. DEAN, BERYL, *Ecclesiastical embroidery*, Batsford, London (1958)
7. LARSEN, SOFUS, *Nordisk Guldspinding og Guldbroderi i den tidlige Middelalder*. Einar Munksgaard, Copenhagen (1939)
8. *Berlingske Haandarbejdsbog naal og vaev i leksikon*, Copenhagen (1950)
9. DIGBY, G. WINGFIELD, *Elizabethan embroidery*, Faber and Faber Ltd, London (1963)
10. SCHUETTE, MARIE, and MÜLLER-CHRISTENSEN, S., *The art of embroidery*, Thames and Hudson, London (1964)
11. *Encyclopedia Brittanica* G. 485.

Plate 18.1. Mirror frame, seventeenth century. Before treatment

Plate 18.2. Mirror frame, seventeenth century. After washing and restoration

Plate 20.1. Tibetan tanghka, front

Plate 20.2. Tibetan tanghka, back

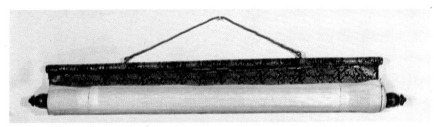

Plate 20.3. Tibetan tanghka, rolled with the back outside

Plate 21.1. Featherhead of Kukailimoku, Hawaii

20
Ethnographical Textile Collections

A. C. VAN DER LEEDEN, Ph.D.

Curator, Indonesian Department, National Museum of Ethnology, Leiden

As a general rule, Western notions of culture and style serve as a frame of reference in discussions of the principles governing the restoration and conservation of textiles. This approach, however, does not take into consideration that for textiles from non-Western cultures, a different approach might be more appropriate, and the use of any other may cause serious errors. With this in mind some basic principles will be discussed, and illustrated with a few examples.

Outside cultural anthropology—the modern and more general name for ethnography and ethnology—the word culture generally means civilisation and quite often those aspects of civilisation that can be termed leisure activities such as music and painting. Within cultural anthropology, the concept of culture takes on a purely scientific meaning and embraces all aspects of life within any community. In this chapter the term shall be used as understood within cultural anthropology.

It is one of the anthropologist's tasks to compare different cultures and try to arrive at an insight into their common, or universal, elements. In order to be able to fulfil this task, anthropology has developed special methods of which textile experts might usefully avail themselves, when making a study of non-Western textile appearances.

Within every community there exists some sort of order or system, but the non-Western cultures are so radically different from the Western that it is imperative to stress this point strongly. First of all, the idea that other nations are primitive must be abandoned. The so-called natural people certainly have a culture and a well-ordered community. It is not right to speak of high and low cultures, to surmise that in non-Western communities prehistory is still alive, or to see them as static.

It is also a misconceived idea that 'primitive' art is anonymous, in other words, that in non-Western communities the individual artist should have neither influence nor an identity of his own.

Anthropologists use diachronical as well as synchronical methods. When the cultures of peoples with no written language are studied, the starting point lies, as in sociology, in a synchronic study of the various elements of the community concerned (economy, technology, art). For this reason, style-dating is a scarcely heard of phenomenon in anthropology, with the exception of countries like China, Japan, etc. In other cases style-dating is only possible in a relative sense, possibly as the final activity of an extraordinarily intensive comparative investigation. But for a great many areas no such investigation has ever been undertaken yet. Not even for, say, Indonesia, although there are publications which have taken a step in the right direction.[1, 2]

It can be concluded from the above that there is no sense in judging non-Western art scientifically from a Western aesthetic standpoint. Another point is that without doubt a strong subjective influence may be exercised by non-Western art on Western artists. It should be taken into account that every community has its own aesthetic standards, and has acquired its own interpretation of art. The study of this subject is one of the most important activities of the museum anthropologist.

20.1 FACTORS AFFECTING RESTORATION AND CONSERVATION

In general, documentation in the field of materials and techniques, their use and meaning in the communities concerned, is scarce. Moreover, documentation is hampered by the large number of different cultures and the enormous variety of weaving and decorating techniques. A mistaken outlook often attends the collecting of ethnographical specimens. Meaningless indications such as 'kris' from Java, 'textile' from Sumba, etc., may serve as examples.

Wherever possible, textile experts should collaborate with museum anthropologists in the investigation of sources, both at home and in fieldwork. In the latter case, the anthropologist should instruct the textile expert on the general methods pursued in fieldwork.

Because of the great diversity in cultures, specimens which have been collected in general ethnographical museums, may not be handled in the most suitable way, and museums in different parts of the world may have widely differing ideas about treatment. There are, for example, widely varying conceptions about storing. When the textile expert advises storing a garment not folded, but hanging, it may not be acceptable from a cultural standpoint. The storage of Japanese silk kimonos is a good example of this. In Japanese museums (e.g. in the 1000-year-old Shoso-in museum at Nara) they are folded in squares and kept in chests of drawers, as in ordinary Japanese homes. This custom is founded on two factors. In the first place, a kimono consists of straight lengths of equal width (33 cm at the most). Consequently, they can be folded in such a way that the front and back seams fall right on top of each other. Secondly, the Japanese kimonos are among the largest-sized costumes in the world, and the general way of life and the arrangement of the Japanese houses do not allow the construction of wardrobes large enough to store the kimono.

Another example is the restoration carried out on a Tibetan tanghka (*see* Plates 20.1–20.3). This tanghka was provided with a support at the back and could be kept rolled up. Expert advice was to roll it up with the back inside, and in this way to save the front. This, however, was absolutely un-acceptable from the Tibetan cultural standpoint. The tanghka was, therefore, rolled with the back outside. If the restorer had been familiar with this aspect, the manner of restoration might have been different.

Undoubtedly, more examples could be put forward. So to sum up, we may say that, when dealing with ethnographic collections, two points are of paramount importance. First, to what degree do non-technical, cultural aspects influence the decision for restoration and conservation; and secondly, to what degree can restoration and conservation methods be adapted.

REFERENCES

1. JAGER GERLINGS, J. H., *Sprekende weefsels, Studie over ontstaan en betekenis van weefsels van enige Indonesische eilanden*, Diss. Amsterdam (1952)
2. KOOYMAN, S., 'Ornamented bark cloth in Indonesia', *Mededelingen van het Rijksmuseum voor Volkenkunde*, Leiden, No. 16 (1963)

21
Ethnographical Featherwork

HAROLD J. GOWERS
Senior Conservation Officer, Department of Ethnography, British Museum, London

Decorations applied by primitive people to those objects which have found their way into ethnographical collections in our museums and art galleries, frequently present the conservator with problems of considerable complexity. Among the most difficult are those concerned with the treatment of objects decorated by the application of feathers, whether they were applied purely to adorn ceremonial objects or to provide the visible surface of outer garments of clothing. But it is particularly to featherwork of the finest quality, such as that from Hawaii and Tahiti, that the most exacting conservation treatment must be carried out if the specimens are to survive in a presentable condition.

Much future laboratory treatment can be avoided if sufficient attention is paid to the routine requirements of featherwork while stored or on exhibition. Considerable damage can occur, especially to some of the oldest and finest specimens, by inadequate or inefficient control. Feathers are among the materials most vulnerable to moth infestation, and the results of attack can be devastating. However, the remedy is comparatively simple if the regular use of an approved insecticide is maintained and the collections are thoroughly and frequently inspected.

Atmospheric dirt can be harmful not only on account of its possible abrasive action, but also because it may contain sulphur compounds which may come into contact with the feathers and be a contributory cause of both decay and fading. It is believed that, for example, the lipochromes usually present in red and yellow feathers can be caused to fade in the presence of sulphuric acid, a process which is accelerated by the presence of ultraviolet light.[1] It is also suspected that para-dichlorobenzene, used as an insecticide, can, in combination with bright light, increase the rate of fading. Owing to the known sensitivity of feathers it is essential to control the lighting used in exhibitions, but if, as may be the case in some countries, harmful light is unavoidable, vulnerable specimens must be protected by the use of filters.[2]

The use of polythene bags or sleeves can be of considerable help in keeping specimens free from dust and dirt and has the additional advantage of making handling safer by preventing the feathers from rubbing each other with the consequent risk of breaking of quills and barbs.

For specimens in need of treatment there can be no standard method to be applied automatically; the requirements of each object must be carefully considered and adjustments made accordingly, but the following descriptions of work carried out in the British Museum may serve as a guide to forming the basic method of treatment for a variety of feathered objects.

21.1 EXAMPLES OF CONSERVATION

Feathered Head Representing Kukailimoku, Hawaiian God of War
(*See* Figure 21.1 and Plate 21.1)

With all objects scheduled to undergo laboratory treatment, a thorough examination is necessary before work can commence. In this instance the

Figure 21.1. Featherhead of Kukailimoku, Hawaii. Partly cleaned

construction of the object was studied and the method of application of the feathers was ascertained.

The Kukailimoku head was built on a cane framework to the shape and size of the finished work, with additional canes and fibres from the aerial roots of the fig tree so arranged to maintain the shape and attitude of the mouth. The lower section of the neck was stabilised and given additional reinforcement by incorporating a basketry weave.[3] An openwork net of vine (olona) fibre twine formed by tying knots at regular intervals (approx. 8–10 per in) was built over the construction to form a skin which served for the attachment of the feathers. Each feather was fixed into position individually, the quill being bent into a 'U' shape around the net fibre and tied securely. The feathers were attached in sufficient numbers so that they overlapped each other and thus completely covered the net except where it was turned under the base of the neck at the point of finishing. The feathers used were small ones, normally about $\frac{1}{2}$ in long, taken from birds found only in limited areas of Polynesia. The red feathers of *Vestiaria coccinea* and the yellow of *Acrulocercus nobilis* were frequently the only ones used, but black ones were sometimes used to heighten the colour effect.[4]

The head had suffered a certain amount of damage; some feathers were missing and others were loose. Also, the colours had lost their original brightness and lustre. The feathers had assumed a distinctly grey overtone which was attributed to a combination of fading and the presence of dirt.

Removal of the surface dirt was the first stage in the treatment, but before this was started it was necessary to remove all obvious loose feathers. The whole surface of the head was then brushed with a soft mop to release loose particles of dirt on the surface and to search for further detached feathers which were not visibly detached before brushing. These feathers were collected together with those previously removed and stored for reattachment at a later stage of treatment. A few were used in experiments designed to test against the possibility of fugitive colours. Remaining surface dirt was removed by applying a foam of dilute aqueous solution of a non-ionic detergent (Lissapol N) with a clean soft mop, except for areas such as the mouth, which were cleaned with small swabs of cottonwool wound round cocktail sticks, moistened with the same foam.[5] This successfully cleaned all surface dirt from the head, but there still remained some more deeply ingrained dirt, the removal of which constituted the second stage of the cleaning operation. Using the mop and swabs described above, in this case moistened with a dilute (about 4%) solution of synthetic soap (B30, Vulpex)[6] in ethylene dichloride, it was possible to remove all remaining dirt. A 2·5% solution is normally recommended for the cleaning operation, but to counteract the slight degreasing action of the ethylene dichloride the amount of B30 soap was raised to 4%, to take advantage of its oily content. The amount should not be too greatly increased, however, as this soap is slightly alkaline and it is known that feathers containing phaeomelanin colouration are liable to suffer some fading in the presence of alkalies. On drying, the colours returned to almost their normal red and yellow, while the sheen which is characteristic of feathers free of barbicels was also seen to return. Although it must be admitted that a certain amount of fading had taken place over the years, the extent of it was clearly less than had been estimated before cleaning.

The final stage in the treatment was the replacement of detached feathers which had been collected earlier. When all of these feathers had been replaced, the whole head was brushed with a dry mop along the line of the feathers to comb them directionally into their desired positions. The head was then mounted on a piece of expanded polystyrene shaped to fit closely up into the neck, the mount being covered with a protective skin to avoid abrasion. This provided sufficient support to allow the head to stand without danger to itself and without the possibility of distortion.

A Feather Gorget from Tahiti, Collected at about the Time of Captain Cook's Voyage

The gorget was constructed in quite a different manner (Figure 21.2). It was built on a flat framework of canes bent into a 'U' shape with radial canes across to hold them rigidly in the form of an almost semicircular band about 5 in wide and about 18 in in diameter. Set upon this were two more bands of cane which followed exactly the shape of the outer canes of the main framework. These were attached so as to leave a gap between them of about $\frac{1}{8}$ in. Through the gap the peripheral fringe of white dog hair was placed. The hair, which was collected into small bundles, was bound at one end with vegetable fibre so that a series of independent bundles was produced, each looking like an extra long haired artist's brush. These were then tucked between the cane frames and tied so as to hide the vegetable fibre and show only the white hair when seen from the front of the gorget. The other main part of the decorated front of the gorget was composed of feathers tied at close intervals along a series of cords which were themselves tied in parallel lines over the cane framework so that the feathers overlapped each other densely enough to obliterate the canes. The feathers were formed into a

Figure 21.2. Two feather gorgets, Tahiti. Right: untreated. Left: after treatment

series of concentric bands, each of which was separated from the next by a row of sharks' teeth sewn into position.

With the exception of the hair which was washed in an aqueous solution of Lissapol N and dried with the assistance of a warm air blower, the treatment of this object was carried out by using the same materials and techniques as described for the treatment of the Kukailimoku head. The feather rosettes which surmount the gorget were removed for cleaning and re-shaping and were later reattached. Because of the considerable overlapping of the main bands of feathers it was possible to remove selected ones and reposition them to cover gaps where feathers had been lost as a result of moth attack. This caused no noticeable thinning or alteration in appearance.

A band of woven coconut fibre plait sewn to the framework formed the inner collar of the gorget. It had become brittle with age, but remained quite strong otherwise. This was treated with a 2·5% solution of Maranyl Soluble Nylon C.109p (Calaton C.B.)[7] in industrial methylated spirit, after it had been washed and dried.

It may be said at this point that there are occasions when the strength and appearance of feathers may be improved by the application of a dilute solution of soluble nylon in industrial methylated spirit, but this must be

Figure 21.3. Japanese feather jacket

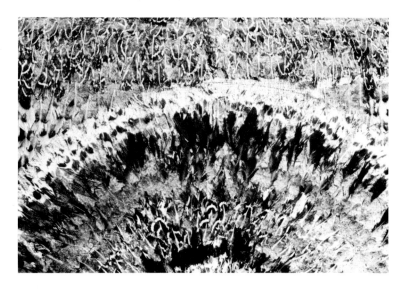

Figure 21.4. Japanese feather jacket (detail)

carried out with the utmost care in order to avoid possible breakage or damage by entanglement of the barbs and barbicels.

A Japanese Feather Jacket

This jacket, thought to have belonged to General Hideyoshi, and dated *circa* A.D. 1550 would have been worn over armour (*see* Figures 21.3, 21.4) It was made by a technique used only up to about the end of the sixteenth century, and presented a rather different type of problem from the previous specimen. It was brought into the laboratory for treatment to prevent the loss of feathers which seemed to have become loose and were in danger of falling if the garment were handled.

The foundation of the jacket was made of woven hemp. The decorative design seemed to have been marked out on the hemp before panels of feathers mounted on their own woven hemp backing were superimposed. The feathers which were from Japanese pheasants and drakes were attached to their backings at the lower extremities of their quills by the use of an adhesive paste.[8] Due to wear and ageing some of the weakened quills had fractured at the point where the adhesive layer terminated, and it was from this point that the danger of breakage and loss seemed most likely to occur.

The treatment necessary was to relax the adhesive and to reset the feathers in a safe position, but although experiments were carried out using a variety of solvents none of them had any softening action. The main ingredient of the adhesive paste proved to be shellac, and any known method of relaxation would have subjected the feathers to conditions from which they would almost certainly not have recovered. It was, therefore, decided that the only feasible treatment would be to reattach each damaged feather by placing an additional spot of a suitable adhesive on the quill above the point of fracture, and to attach it by this to the backing material.

To support the jacket during treatment, a 'T' shaped stand was made to a reasonable working height, in this case about 5 ft 6 in. The bar of the 'T' was amply covered with a layer of plastic foam over an expanded polystyrene former of the correct size to fit comfortably into the jacket.

Each feather was then inspected in turn and all loose or fractured ones were reset with polyvinyl acetate emulsion adhesive (Vinamul N.6515[9]) and held in position during drying by the use of a small square of siliconised release paper (about $\frac{1}{4}$ in square) placed over the feather shortly after the adhesive had been applied; this was covered with a small cube of plastic foam. A pin was passed through the plastic foam to penetrate the release paper and the feather, avoiding the quill, and into the support. This ensured positive adherence of the feather in its correct position without subjecting it to undue pressure.

REFERENCES AND NOTES

1. FOX, DENIS L., *Animal Biochromes*, Cambridge Univ. Press (1953)
2. THOMSON, GARRY, *Stud. Conserv.*, **6**, 49–70 (1961)
3. TE RANGI HIROA (BUCK, P.), *Arts and Crafts of Hawaii*, Bishop Museum Press, Honolulu (1957)
4. BRIGHAM, W. T., *Memoirs of the Bishop Museum*, Vol. 1, Bishop Museum Press, Honolulu (1899)
5. Lissapol N is supplied by I.C.I. Ltd

6. B30 Soap (Vulpex) is supplied by Laporte Industries Ltd, Organic & Pigment Division, Uphill Rd., Ilford, Essex
7. Maranyl Soluble Nylon (Calaton C.B.) is supplied by Picreator Enterprises Ltd, 44 Park View Gardens, London N.W.4
8. JENYNS, SOAMES, 'Feather jacket (Jimbaori) of the Moyayama Period', *British Museum Quarterly*, **32,** No. 1–2, 48–52 (1967)
9. Vinamul N.6515 is supplied by Vinyl Products Ltd, Mill Lane, Carshalton, Surrey

22
Some New Techniques for Archaeological Textiles

HANNA JEDRZEJEWSKA, Ph.D.
Head of Research Laboratory, Department of Antiquities, National Museum, Warsaw

The particular techniques applied to the conservation of textiles depend very much not only on the raw material, but also, generally, on the nature of the specimen. Coarsely woven fabrics need different treatment from the very thin ones, and textiles of great age and historical importance have to be treated in other ways than more modern specimens of purely decorative value.

22.1 BASIC PRINCIPLES OF CONSERVATION

At the Research Laboratory, the main kinds of textile object are woollen articles, either Coptic textiles from the National Museum's collection, or fragments from recent excavations in the Sudan. Their very high documentary importance is the dominant factor in deciding on the method of conservation, which has to comply with the following basic principles:

1. The technique of conservation has to be maximally reversible, and this means that the materials applied or the technical additions can be again separated from the original without causing any detrimental effects.
2. Where chemicals are applied, the quantity used should be kept as low as possible.
3. The actual physical properties of the textiles (pliability, texture, sheen, transparency, colour) should be impaired as little as possible by the applied procedures. The *restoration* of these properties is another, different, problem.
4. The reverse of the textile has to remain open for inspection by specialists studying the weaving techniques.

5. The authenticity of the original must not be in any way impaired by the applied treatments.

22.2   CONSERVATION TECHNIQUES

The techniques at present applied in the conservation of textiles have not been found satisfactory for archaeological specimens.[1, 2] There is no effective method for dealing with frayed edges and loose hanging threads. The back of the textile often remains covered in a permanent way. Also, the necessary reversibility is not assured, for with the removal of the fixing agent (threads, glue) for any purpose, even only for changing the support, the textile is again reduced to its primary state of disintegration, or even worse. The amounts of applied chemical agents also need reconsideration.

Some new techniques have been developed, therefore. First, it was decided to separate the treatment of the textile object into two completely independent groups of operations:

1. Treatment of the textile object itself.
2. Operations of mounting.

These groups were in turn further divided into several particular steps, each serving a limited purpose only and followed by others, all contributing to the final result. Each step has to be carried out by different means, which should not affect the other steps. In this way, a better control of the whole treatment is assured, provided that the particular steps are not cumulated into more universal operations (e.g. consolidation, impregnation and mounting in one single operation). The sequence of the particular steps depends on each individual case. Steps may sometimes be omitted when not necessary.

In the first group, dealing with the textile object itself, there are three basic steps:

1. Consolidation of threads, when there is a continuous loss of fibres, owing to crumbling or to a fluffy condition of threads. The treatment is only local, mostly on threads that will have to be fixed in place, and no reversibility is expected here. As consolidant a 0·01–0·1% solution of polybutyl methacrylate in toluene is applied very sparingly, just to moisten the threads. The extremely small amount of consolidant introduced is without effect on the appearance of the textile.

2. Consolidation of weave, which is the most important operation for fragmentary textiles (Figure 22.1). It is only local, and in most cases is not considered as reversible, even when the fixing agent can be easily removed. The operation has many purposes: repair of tears and broken threads; making up for the loss of warp or weft; returning a dislodged thread back to its original position; joining separate fragments, and immobilisation of weave (for loosely woven textiles). Two basic techniques are used here:

(a) Very minute droplets of glueing substance are put where necessary between threads with a thin dissecting needle (Figures 22.2 and 22.3), or
(b) Thin new threads (silk on wool, linen on linen), are glued on the reverse, but, again, only as many as absolutely necessary.

The glueing substance does not penetrate to the surface and is practically invisible.

In both cases the amount of intervention is extremely small, and is without effect on the original properties of the specimen. But it helps to keep together all precarious threads and separate fragments. As glues, the best yet found are the polyvinyl acetate and polymethacrylate emulsions of well adjusted

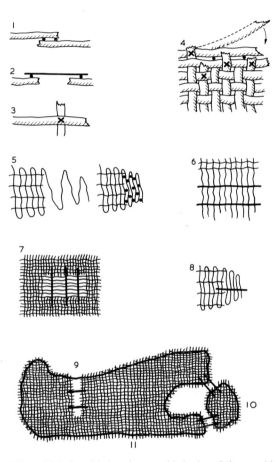

Figure 22.1. Consolidation of weave with droplets of glue, or with new threads glued on the left side of the textile: (1) neighbouring threads are joined together with droplets; (2) new thread is glued over to replace a missing fragment; (3) crossing ends are fixed with a droplet in between; (4) when selvedge is missing, the outer threads are fixed with droplets; (5) when the warp is missing (especially in Coptic textiles), the weft can be fixed with droplets; (6) loose hanging threads are fixed with a few threads put across; (7) loose inside threads are fixed in the same way as in (6); (8) the same as (5). The weft is kept in place with new threads; (9) tears are joined with a few threads glued across them; (10) loose fragments are joined to the main body with new threads; (11) a new thread is glued on the underside, all around the fragment, to protect the frayed edges and to immobilise the weave

238

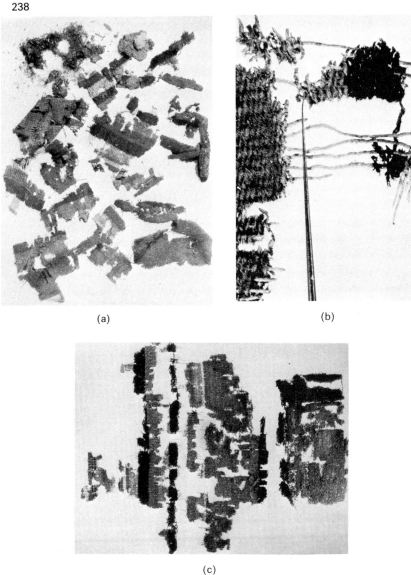

(a)

(b)

(c)

Figure 22.2. Fragments of textile found in Faras[3]. (a) After preliminary separation; (b) in the course of fixing the slipping threads with the help of dissecting needle; (c) after consolidation

thickness, giving small droplets but not allowing deep penetration. The threads have to be air-dry for the operation.

Most textiles also need cleaning. It is, of course, best to clean first, before any other operations are started. If this is not possible, and cleaning (washing) has to be carried out after the consolidation of the fabric, care must be taken to see that the previously applied consolidants are not washed out or harmed by the cleaning agent.

3. Protective impregnation concerns the textile as a whole, and has to be reversible (easy removal of impregnates, without dissolving the previously applied consolidants). Its purpose is to protect the textile against undue desiccation and biological agents. The products applied here can be soluble in water or in aliphatic hydrocarbons. Special attention has to be given to disinfecting agents which while destroying biological pests may be even more harmful to the protected textiles.[4]

In the second group of operations, dealing with mounting, there is no longer any need to do anything substantial to the textile itself, but only to provide a background and support. These are fixed by mechanical means only and can be easily removed without the inconvenience of returning the textile to its initial fragmentary condition. As a rule, the background is prepared as a 'negative' of the original specimen, by cutting in the new material holes corresponding to the original and glueing an open net in these

Figure 22.3. Unfolding a tangle of textile remains: gradually, as the operation proceeds, the threads in the preserved fragments of weave are fixed in position with minute droplets of glue before further unfolding

places (Figure 22.4). When the textile is laid on this negative, all missing parts and the background are filled with the new material when viewing the front. The reverse, however, can be easily studied by looking through the net. The textile is fixed to the negative, in a manner which is invisible, by putting thin nylon threads (or another suitable material) over it. With textiles of not only documentary but also highly decorative value this system of easily removable negative with the necessary reconstructions, may probably solve many problems without the necessity of carrying out reconstructions directly on the original.

The purpose of the support is purely mechanical. It can be rigid or supple, flat or shaped, but it is never fixed permanently. The choice depends very much on the size and kind of textile. As a rule, sandwiching textiles between two transparent sheets has to be avoided. Glass has alkaline properties. Synthetic sheets may give off injurious components, and have, moreover, the disadvantage of attracting dust. Besides, the textiles may become flattened and there is no possibility of adjusting the inner climate.

240

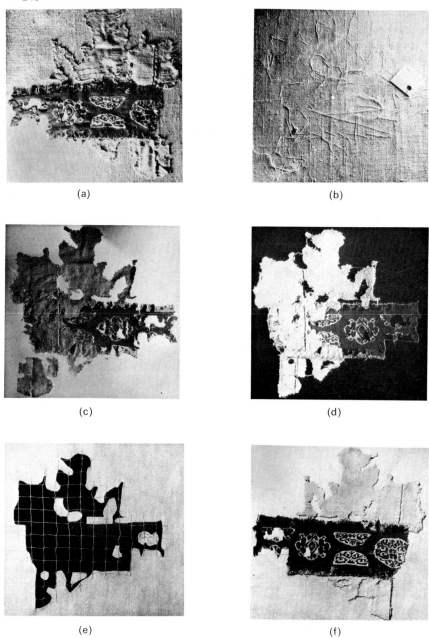

(a)

(b)

(c)

(d)

(e)

(f)

Figure 22.4. Sequence of operations on a fragment of Coptic textile. (a) Before treatment. Stitched to coarse linen support. Creased, frayed. Threads slipping away; (b) reverse, permanently covered by support. The maze of stitches are clearly visible; (c) reverse, after removal of support; (d) reverse, after consolidation. Slipping threads fixed in place with droplets of glue. New linen thread glued all around the textile; (e) a 'negative' background with holes corresponding to the shape of original, and their supporting net; (f) textile after treatment

REFERENCES

1. JEDRZEJEWSKA, H., 'Nowe metody w konserwacji tkanin zabytkowych' (New methods in the conservation of ancient textiles), *Biblioteka Muzealnictwa i Ochrony Zabytkow*, Series B, **9,** 153–164 (1964). Paper read at a Conference in Lodz in 1963

2. JEDRZEJEWSKA, H., 'The "stepwise" treatment of old textiles and other methods of conservation'. Short communication read at the IIC Conference in Delft in 1964. Mimeographed in the preprints from the Conference

3. JEDRZEJEWSKA, H., 'Examen technique et conservation du textile de Faras', in K. Michalowski, Faras 1961–1962, Reports from excavations. Warsaw, 205–212 (1965) PWN

4. JEDRZEJEWSKA, H., 'The damaging influence of disinfecting agents on sensitive ancient materials'. In *Museum Climatology*, IIC London Conference, preprints, 95–100 (1967).

23

Leather Objects

JOHN W. WATERER, R.D.I., F.S.A., A.I.I.C.

Honorary Secretary and Conservator, Museum of Leathercraft, London

It should be unnecessary to say that this article is concerned solely with genuine leather and has no reference to the many materials made in simulation of leather, which have nothing at all in common with it apart from superficial appearance. A warning is necessary because some imitations are so cleverly contrived as to deceive those without specialised knowledge or scientific aids. Objects made of such materials may not yet be found to any great extent in museum collections but are certain to be so in due course. The difficulty of detection has increased since the introduction of fabrics coated with micro-cellular polyvinyl chloride embossed or imprinted with cleverly simulated leather grains or patterns and finishes. Another snare for the unwary which does come within the scope of the present survey, is the simulation of expensive leathers on cheaper ones, such as the finishing of sheepskin to resemble sealskin or of cowhide to look like crocodile or pigskin.

23.1 THE RECOGNITION OF LEATHER

A microscope or even a strong lens will usually reveal when the natural surface of any material, e.g. paper, composition board, or woven fabric, has disappeared beneath a coating of some kind of pigmented finish. With some experience it will also reveal when the natural surface of leather has been tampered with, so that the grain pattern formed by hair follicles and other natural features such as growth-marks and scratches has been buffed away in order to provide an 'unblemished' surface, thereby removing the characteristic appearance of the leather. A lens will also usually serve to reveal whether the surface pattern is genuine or simulated. For example, the holes through which the hairs emerged in pigskin or peccary hogskin go right through the skin (and can be seen also on the flesh side), and the hard scales that form the charm of crocodile can be distinguished from the narrow strip of soft leather that separates them. Such characteristics cannot be exactly simulated. Some imitations, produced on a prepared surface that has been 'painted' are less easy to determine, although this can be done with experience.

Conservators should provide themselves with samples of the principal leathers, approved by experts, which can be referred to in case of doubt. Where doubt exists as to whether the specimen is genuine leather or some other material, the only safe way to ascertain its true nature is to gain access to the under (flesh) side or to a cut edge. Cases have occurred with old material where its true nature could not be detected by ordinary methods. For example, some mediaeval knife handles were covered with fibrous material that 'experts' pronounced to be leather but which microscopical examination proved to be wood in a curious condition after being buried in soil for several hundred years. Determination was achieved by a method perfected by the British Leather Manufacturers' Research Association which consisted of freezing the material, cutting an exceedingly thin slice from an edge and then taking a colour photomicrograph of the section with light behind it. This reveals, by the nature of the fibrous structure, whether the material is leather or some other substance, and if hair follicles are present it is even possible to determine, by the angle at which they lie, from what animal the skin came.

23.2 THE COMPOSITION OF 'LEATHER' OBJECTS

Before proceeding to discuss leather and its treatment, it must be emphasised that many objects regarded as made of leather, incorporate other materials in their make-up, such as wood, composition boards of various kinds, metals, textiles, papers, sewing thread and cotton, adhesives, varnishes and other finishes. The presence of any or all such components will affect the treatment that can, with safety, be applied to the leather itself. For example, a casket may be made of wood (perhaps wormed), covered with vellum originally stuck on with paste or glue, have fittings of iron or brass, and be lined with paper, leather or textile, the ageing of each material possibly being governed by different agencies. The conservator must, therefore, not only be knowledgeable as to what can be done with various kinds of leather, but must also know what cannot be done without harm to the other component materials, as well as how these can be treated without harm to the leather, if they cannot readily be separated. Among the principal agencies that cause or accelerate the ageing or deterioration of materials are the following:

Mechanical Handling or other movement, regular or intermittent. Cleaning too frequently or too vigorously. Stresses imposed by faulty methods of display.

Vermin Attacks by rodents, termites and insects of many kinds.

Microbiological and Biochemical Attacks by bacteria and fungi.

Other natural agencies Relative humidity, temperature, light, dust, chemical compounds.

It is not proposed to treat here all the hazards involved in the first three classes and the modern methods by which they can be avoided or brought under control, except one—fungi, the control of which is by direct treatment of the leather. Avoidance of the other hazards is largely a matter of training and common sense, but their importance should be well known to every curator.

23.3 THE NATURE OF LEATHER

Leather is a manufactured product that can be made from the skin of any living creature by a great variety of methods, the aim of which is to preserve the unique fibrous tissue which forms the middle layer, the *corium* or *derma* of the skin. The outer layer that forms the epidermal system and the bottom layer of adipose tissue are discarded (Plates 23.1 and 23.2). During the last half-century there has been a ferment of development in leather manufacture and it is impossible to describe here all the kinds of leather that are now available.

It is, however, approximately correct to say that the three basic processes that have been used from time immemorial are still employed. These, in ancient terminology, have been known as Tanning, Tawing and Chamoising but today the three main groups are usually called vegetable tanning, mineral tanning and oil tanning, the term 'tanning' being used loosely of all three. There are a few modern processes which fall outside these groups. Beyond these processes which, in general terms, convert raw hides and skins into 'leather', there is a great variety of methods of 'dressing' and 'finishing' which impart particular characteristics to both the qualities and the appearance of leather. The principal methods will be described briefly.

23.3.1 THE PREPARATION OF HIDES AND SKINS FOR 'TANNING'

The preparatory operations are, in principle, the same whatever process is to be employed to convert the raw material, whether *skins* (of small or young animals including calf, pig, goat, sheep and also birds and reptiles) or *hides* (of the larger animals including cattle, horse and buffalo), into leather. Their purpose is to isolate the *corium* and prepare it for the treatment that follows. Some pelts arrive at the tan-yard direct from the slaughter-house, in which case they have to be thoroughly cleansed; others come 'cured' (e.g. sun-dried, dry-salted or wet-salted, or 'pickled') and have to be appropriately cleansed and otherwise treated by immersion in a succession of lime-pits, before the removal of hair and wool.

The removal of hair and wool may be achieved by commencing with old, weak liquors and finishing with new, strong ones, or tumbling the hides or skins in revolving drums with certain chemicals. In the case of sheepskins, where it is desired to preserve wool in perfect condition, the skins may be subjected to the ancient process of 'sweating', that is hanging them in a warm place until the wool is loosened by bacterial action, or the flesh side may be coated with a paste of lime and sodium sulphide which penetrates to the roots within a few hours. The purpose of these processes is to loosen hair or wool and the epidermis so that both can be readily removed by scraping, either by hand or machine, and to bring the pelts into a suitable condition to respond to the succeeding processes. The bottom layer (the adipose tissue) is then cut away and the isolated *corium* is ready for conversion into leather by a method which may fall under one of the following broad headings, or sometimes be a combination of two of them.

23.3.2 VEGETABLE TANNAGE (TANNING)

This process utilises the 'tannin' which is present in varying degrees, in barks, woods, leaves and fruits. In olden times the pelts were laid in pits interspersed with layers of bark, the pit being then filled up with water. From time to time the pelts were lifted out, piled up and then returned with fresh bark to strengthen the liquor, and this was continued for up to 18 months. Today most tanning is performed in revolving drums using liquor prepared from tannin extract, which cuts the time down to a matter of days, or with skins even to hours.

Familiar examples of vegetable tanned leather include full substance (the natural thickness, about 4·5 mm) cattlehide leather used for harness, strapping, footwear soles and certain items of military equipment, and the thinner kinds of cattle-hide leather used for upholstery, travelling bags and cases, briefcases, etc. Originally, this thinner leather was produced by the skilled operation of shaving the hides on the flesh side to the required thickness, but today the use of a band-knife machine splits the hides horizontally into two or more layers, all of which have their uses. Some skins also are vegetable tanned, such as sheepskin intended for 'basil', pigskin, calfskin for certain purposes and goatskin especially when intended for 'morocco' leather. The natural colour of vegetable tanned leather ranges from pale brown, through biscuit, to a nut or reddish brown, according to the particular tanning agents employed.

23.3.3 MINERAL TANNAGE (TAWING)

The original ancient mineral process used a solution of alum and salt and was called tawing. Sheep and goat skins were steeped in this liquor for 10–15 minutes and then dried. The resulting leather was principally used for gloves, women's footwear, bags and pouches, right up to modern times. Tawed leather was pure white, and very amenable to dyeing with the ancient dyestuffs. When freshly made it was stiff and harsh, but was readily softened by 'staking', i.e. pulling backward and forward over a blunt blade set in a stake of convenient height. It was, however, a material of open texture and therefore for many purposes, particularly gloving, was consolidated by 'stuffing' (see *Dressing*). Its character was completely different from that of any other kind of leather. In fact it was not a true leather at all, as by immersion in warm water it could be reconverted into the original raw skin; it could not therefore be washed with soap and water as can true leathers. In later times it was drycleaned but as tawed gloving leather was nearly always stuffed its quality was impaired because the solvents used would remove the oil and grease which were key ingredients.

A new form of mineral tannage was introduced in 1884 when chromium salts were used for the first time. Other metallic salts have been introduced since but chrome tanning revolutionised leather production, resulting in such leathers as box calf and glazed kid which are highly resistant to water and, therefore, largely used for footwear uppers and in beautifully soft 'persian' (hair-sheep) leather for clothing and gloves. Chromed leathers are hard-wearing, stable, not subject to 'red rot' (see p. 251) and will withstand hot, even boiling, water, but their resilient, open texture and their antipathy to the normal adhesives make them unsuitable for some kinds of work including bookbinding. They are generally pale duck-egg blue (prior to staining or dyeing) and cannot be made pure white. Alum tawing, therefore, continued to be used to make white leather until the introduction, in this century, of zirconium salts and the 'synthetic' tannage based on aldehydes, which produce pure white leather that is washable.

23.3.4   OIL TANNAGE (CHAMOISING)

This process, known since mediaeval times as chamoising, probably developed from man's first attempts to make use of raw hides and skins, waste products from slaughter for food, which when dry were hard and horny. Efforts would have been made to restore the original suppleness by treating them with oils, fats or fatty materials such as brains. Certain oils (e.g. seal oil) would undergo oxidation and other changes producing compounds with tanning action, while brains contain 'phosphatides' which also produce a primitive type of tannage.

The chamoising process consists in first 'frizing' the grain surface, that is scraping it to facilitate entry of oils from both sides (this is not necessary when using sheepskin splits from which the grain layer has already been removed). The wet pelts are then liberally sprinkled with cod-liver oil (or other marine animal or fish oil) and subjected to a severe pummelling in the 'stocks'. This is repeated several times and the skins are then either hung in a warm 'stove' or piled up and allowed to heat: this promotes oxidation of the oil and the resulting products combine with the fibres. The skins are then washed and shrunk in a warm soda solution and dried.

Today oil tanned leather is exemplified chiefly by 'shammy' or 'wash' leather, which is now made from sheepskin splits, but in early times was made from antelope skins. It was then used for clothing, bags, purses and pouches and other purposes, and is always distinguishable by its pale yellow colour. The same process was also employed in the making of 'buff' leather and 'doeskin' which was used for doublets, gloves, saddle-seats and other things. Buff leather is little used today but will be found in the museum in the form of military coats and jerkins, strapping and military equipment. Oil dressed leather is tough, washable, extremely durable and not subject to red rot.

23.3.5   COMBINATION TANNAGES

The use of two different processes to produce leather of a specific character is not modern. At least 500 years ago a durable and lasting leather was being made by a combination of tawing and chamoising, but the principle has become more general since the introduction of chrome tanning, e.g. vegetable tanning followed by chrome or vice-versa. 'Semi-chrome' leathers possess important characteristics of both methods as they can, for example, be given the firm structure provided by the vegetable process combined with the suppleness derived from the chroming, and chemical stability.

It must be emphasised that the foregoing merely outlines the basic methods and that although, up to the end of the nineteenth century, most leathers fell within the three main categories, many changes have taken place since and the pace of development is constantly accelerating. The age of an object, if accurately determined as prior to about 1800, is a fairly safe guide to the mode of tannage of its leather—vegetable, alum or oil—but it is becoming more and more difficult to judge the nature of later leathers without scientific aid.

23.3.6   DRESSING

This term describes processes that follow the actual conversion of raw hides and skins into leather and are intended to modify its character to meet specific needs. For example, sole leather is rolled and lightly oiled to render it firm but pliant; harness and strap leather is 'curried', a process that consists in working into the wet leather a mixture of cod-oil and tallow ('dubbin') to make it strong, water-resistant and pliable and to ensure long life. Tawed leather may be 'stuffed' with flour, egg-yolk, oil and grease to give it more 'body' and render it soft and pliable, while chromed leathers, such as box calf, are fat-liquored to make them pliable and water-resistant, and may be further softened by 'boarding', which involves folding the skin grain to grain and rubbing it backward and forward, in two directions, with a cork-covered board. This process produces the characteristic finish of little creases at a right angle to each other producing the tiny 'boxes' from which the name derives.

23.3.7   FINISHING

Finishing processes are those that affect the outward appearance of the leather rather than its character, although there are some, like the 'boarding' mentioned above, that do both. They include:

1. Staining, i.e. the colouring of the grain surface with clear dye, stain that may contain pigment, or pigmented nitrocellulose, using brush or spray.
2. Dyeing, the colouring of leather to a varying depth from the surfaces by immersion.
3. Graining or embossing of a surface pattern that may be of artificial character, or the simulation of a genuine leather grain, originally with small engraved rollers, but now with heated, engraved metal plates in a press.
4. Plating, producing a smooth, glossy surface by means of a heated metal plate in a press.

5. Boarding (see also above), in the case of 'morocco' leather the 'bringing up' of the natural grain pattern into the characteristic granular surface, or the minute creasing of upholstery hide, by folding the leather grain to grain and rolling it backward and forward with a cork-covered board.
6. Enamelling to produce 'patent' leather.
7. The abrading of the flesh side of leather to make a 'suede' finish or the grain side to produce a 'velvet' finish.

There are also many other devices, including the less reputable one of printing patterns in colour on the surface, causing the material to lose its character and charm (Figure 23.1).

23.3.8   UNTANNED HIDE OR SKIN

Under this heading come parchment and vellum, principally used for writing upon but also, at times, for covering boxes and caskets; forel, a type of parchment used for bookbinding, and rawhide, used mainly as a covering for luggage. None of these is 'leather' because no 'tanning' process has been applied. The material is prepared for its purpose merely by liming, scraping and drying, under tension, repeated a number of times. The resulting substance has little in common with leather and cannot be subjected to the same treatment. It is adversely affected by water or damp, in certain circumstances will putrefy, and can be dissolved in hot water, making size. These materials are outside the scope of this book and therefore there is no further mention of them.

23.4   TREATMENT OF LEATHER OBJECTS— ARCHAEOLOGICAL MATERIAL

Generally, leather objects recovered after either long immersion in water or water-logged soil, or long burial in 'dry' soil, will prove to be vegetable-tanned cattle hide, goatskin or sheepskin. Leather recovered from water will be black whatever its original colour, but leather from relatively dry soil may vary from brownish to black. The condition of the former is usually surprisingly good although it will be completely softened; that of the latter will vary according to the nature of the soil and its acidity, but generally it is hard and brittle. Bog water, containing vegetable matter and thereby tannin, will actually tan animal skin immersed in it for long periods, e.g. Tollund man and other corpses recovered from bogs in Denmark, Ireland, etc.

Tawed leathers are not likely to have survived either burial in damp soil or immersion in water owing to their unstable character, but have survived for thousands of years in the dry sand of Egypt. Chamoised leathers appear to withstand either fate reasonably well.

23.4.1   WET LEATHER

If leather recovered from water or water-logged soil is allowed to dry it will be practically valueless, becoming shrivelled and probably disintegrated

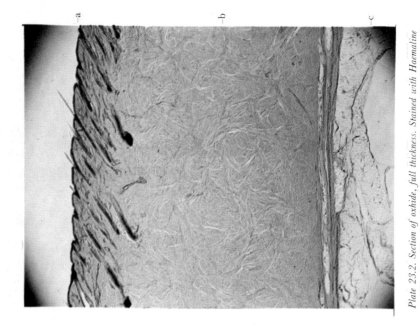

Plate 23.2. Section of oxhide, full thickness. Stained with Haemaline and Phenine. The fat of the adipose tissue is extracted in the course of staining. (a) Epidermis, (b) corium, (c) adipose tissue (× 20)

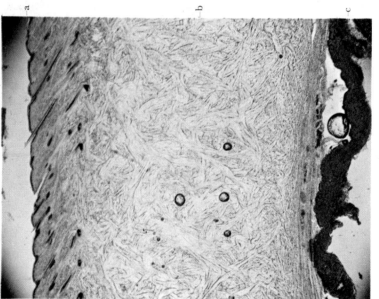

Plate 23.1. Section of oxhide, full thickness. Stained for fat with Scarlet R. (a) Epidermis, (b) corium, (c) adipose tissue (× 20)

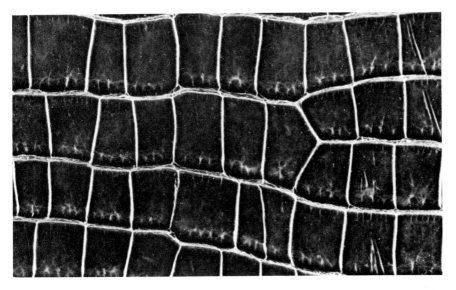

(a)

(b)

Figure 23.1. Genuine and simulated grains. (a) Genuine crocodile cut from the back of a skin approximately 15 in wide at its middle part. (b) Part of a cowhide embossed with a 'crocodile' grain from a heated, engraved metal plate; owing to the large area to be covered the relationship of the small-scaled 'belly' parts to the larger scaled 'backs' has been falsified, the latter being too narrow. Both photographs are actual size and taken by the same side lighting, both examples were stained brown, the genuine crocodile being highly polished, the hide having a semi-dull finish: the genuine crocodile has a beautiful variation of tone owing to the use of clear dye, the hide has a dull uniform colour due to the use of pigmented colouring. In the real crocodile, the horizontal channels that separate the rows of hard, polished scales, are dull, soft and lightly creased: in the simulated grain embossed on the flat firm hide, there is no actual difference of texture

beyond hope of recovery. Immediately the material is recovered it should be washed in several changes of pure water to which a small amount of formaldehyde or other disinfectant is added, then transferred to clean water to remain there until treatment can commence. If this is impossible the material can be kept in some of the liquid in which it was found, or placed, as it is, in polythene bags.

Treatment in the past has included attempts to work into the leather 'dubbin' (cod-oil and tallow) which rarely achieved full impregnation and left the material smelly, sticky and liable to harbour dust. Another method was to immerse the material in an emulsion of sulphonated castor oil and water, gradually increasing the proportion of oil until it alone constituted the bath. This was an improvement on the 'dubbin' treatment but generally penetration was incomplete, some water remaining in the inner parts which, when it evaporated, left the core dry and stiff.

The best results to date have been achieved by the following method. After washing, the wet leather is immersed in successive baths of acetone until the water content has been dissolved out. It is vitally important that this be done in a covered vessel in a well-ventilated room. Hydrometer readings of the acetone bath will indicate when all water has been extracted from the leather. The leather is then at once placed in a bath of British Museum Leather Dressing[1] (hereafter called BML Dressing) diluted with about 25% by volume of solvent (also in a covered vessel, in a well-ventilated room), the bath being agitated from time to time. The time taken for the leather to become thoroughly permeated with the Lanolin which is the essential ingredient of the dressing, will vary with its nature, thickness and condition. Its condition can be judged only by feel. When a measure of flexibility has been restored the material has probably reached a state when its preservation for a very long period is assured. It should be realised that for most museum objects flexibility has no particular merit for its own sake, but it is a guide to the effectiveness of the treatment. The time taken to reach a satisfactory state may vary from a few hours to several days.

The BML Dressing was introduced for the preservation of bookbindings under their normal storage conditions and contains small amounts of beeswax and cedar-wood oil, both of which are unnecessary in the above application and in some others may be a positive disadvantage. Several modified versions of the original formula are now available which have made possible a much wider use of this excellent dressing than was originally envisaged.[1]

23.4.2 DRY LEATHER

There are two recommended ways of dealing with leather recovered from relatively dry soil. Such leather will vary in its condition from rigid and brittle to slightly flexible and rather less brittle; it will also vary in colour from light brown to nearly black. Light-coloured leather will be darkened by any form of dressing but this is not very important as its existing colour probably bears no resemblance to the original hue. It is more important that the leather be treated so that it may resist future hazards, by protecting and lubricating the fibrous structure. Before treatment the surface of the leather should be cleaned as well as possible by very careful brushing with a moderately stiff brush.

The first method employs polyethylene glycol wax, a synthetic wax that comes like Vaseline in consistency and must be melted by heating to about 40°C in a suitable vessel in an electric oven or on an electric hot-plate.[2] The dry leather is immersed in the molten wax which must be kept at the same temperature until a satisfactory condition is achieved. It is then removed and laid aside until cold. 'Carbowax', as it is known, is hygroscopic and some have found this property objectionable in that it leaves a tacky surface. This can be prevented by placing the treated leather between blotting paper under glass or if that is not practicable by removing the preparation from the surfaces with a sponge moistened in hexane.[3]

For certain articles the hot wax bath might prove difficult to operate, but the second method may be found more practicable. The dry leather should first be soaked in distilled water until quite soft. The moisture is removed from the surface after which the material is submitted to the treatment described above for wet leather.

23.5   TREATMENT OF LEATHER OBJECTS— HISTORICAL MATERIAL

This heading includes specific objects which can be regarded, in general, as typical of a particular class of goods made by related methods and of the same kind of leather, classified under three main headings, vegetable tanned, mineral tanned and oil tanned leathers.

23.5.1   OBJECTS MADE OF VEGETABLE TANNED LEATHER

Vegetable tanned leathers, with a few exceptions, are subject to a destructive chemical decay known as red rot. This is brought about by the action of sulphuric acid, the presence of which can be due to a variety of cases. As early as 1843 Faraday demonstrated the destructive effect of gas lighting on bookbindings, but it was not until the end of the century that alarm spread and a committee was formed to examine the causes of the now widespread destruction of bookbindings. It was eventually found that in leather made approximately between 1850 and 1900, red rot was often caused by a residue of sulphuric acid, which was used in the processing and could not be entirely eliminated. It was not then realised that tanning agents are divisible into two chemical groups, the pyrogallols and the catechols, and that the latter produce leather that is particularly susceptible to sulphur dioxide. Sulphur dioxide was and is plentiful in the atmosphere of industrial areas, being added to, inside buildings, by the combustion products of coal and gas for heating and lighting. The matter was aggravated by certain changes in methods of leather manufacture by which substances known as 'non-tans' were removed. It was found that these substances, although they do not contribute to the action of the tannins, nevertheless afford protection against the action of sulphuric acid.

Today, although many of the old causes of air pollution are disappearing, their place is being taken by the products of the vast consumption of fuel oils. It is now possible to introduce, during leather manufacture, protective agents that counteract the effect of acid, but this is by no means always done and red rot still occurs. Unfortunately, museum objects, including bookbindings, made of vegetable tanned leather, are frequently found with red rot in some stage of development. In the early stages affected leather will exhibit a pinkish tone (this can best be seen on the flesh side or at a cut edge, but it may also be visible on the surface). The colour gets progressively darker as the decay develops until when it is dark red the leather is in an unmistakeable state of disintegration, and a decision then has to be made as to whether it is worth while spending any time on trying to save the object. The ravages of red rot cannot be reversed (Figures 23.2 (a) and (b)).

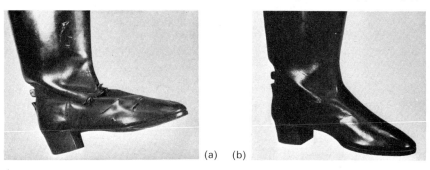

(a)   (b)

Figure 23.2. One of a pair of royal riding boots. (a) Before restoration the boot had evidently been stored in a place, where it was affected by sulphur dioxide, and was in an advanced stage of 'red rot' as demonstrated by the gashes. (b) After restoration. Restoration involved the application of new leather inside the boot to support the badly weakened leather and to fill the gap so far as possible. Patches of new leather were cut and fitted where the original had disappeared

The most that can be hoped for is that its progress can be arrested, if not permanently at least for a substantial period, but this is by no means certain.

The recommended treatment is to apply potassium lactate to every surface that is accessible, but the opinions of chemists are divided as to the efficacy of this remedy and no other has yet been developed. Potassium lactate is usually supplied as a 50% solution in water which for use is further diluted, using one part to nine parts of water.[4] The solution should be applied with a wrung-out sponge and left to dry. The application is usually made after washing but before application of other dressings. Even when there is no sign of red rot it is probably a wise precaution to apply it to those kinds of vegetable tanned leather known to be susceptible in the hope that development in the future will thereby be prevented.

Heavy Cattle-hide Leather

'*Sole leather*', a kind of heavy cattle-hide leather, is a dry dressed leather produced primarily for footwear soles, but also used for certain nineteenth century trunks, travel and other cases.

First the leather should be carefully washed, using potassium oleate soap as a 2% solution in white spirit, rinsed with the same solvent and dried, all at ordinary room temperature.[5] The material should then be examined for any sign of red rot. If any sign is present the treatment recommended above should be applied to all available surfaces, although it is better still to apply it anyway. Suitcases, trunks and the like, when quite dry, should have micro-crystalline wax applied to all exterior surfaces, well rubbed in and thoroughly polished.[6] Worn footwear soles can be treated with a mixture of equal quantities of refined neat's foot oil and hexane which may leave the colour a little darker.[7] The soles of women's footwear are sometimes beautiful and worth exhibiting, and where darkening of colour might be thought objectionable, micro-crystalline wax may be used provided the soles are only a little worn.

Curried leather is used for parts of harness, saddle seats and strapping, other kinds of straps, belts and certain items of military equipment. When grease has been used in the dressing it is usually self-evident. Objects in good condition and only slightly soiled require no special cleaning. Very dirty leather, if a natural light brown colour, should be carefully washed with a warm solution of good pure soap in water, but if black or coloured with a 2% solution of potassium oleate soap in white spirit. A small part in an inconspicuous place should always be tried out first. After washing, the leather should be rinsed with the same solvent. Commercial detergents should never be used. This kind of leather, if the currying has been well done and it remains flexible, is usually resistant to red rot; nevertheless a careful search should be made for any signs of it.

After drying at ordinary room temperature, BML Dressing should be applied sparingly to all surfaces with a small pad. The solvent (hexane) evaporates very quickly, so after thoroughly shaking the container, the solution should be decanted a little at a time into a small glass jar, the lid being returned to the main container. If, however, the dressing becomes too thick through evaporation it can be diluted with more hexane (warmed). In most cases the dressing should be absorbed within a few days, leaving a thin film of beeswax on the surface which can then be polished. If a polish is not required the beeswax can be removed with a sponge moistened with turpentine or hexane. Old leather that is generally in good condition but has lost its suppleness and even become brittle can also be successfully treated with BML Dressing. Absorption will take longer and may in places be incomplete, leaving some Lanolin (not to be confused with beeswax) on the surface, in which case it should be re-moistened with hexane. If, when absorption is complete, the result is not satisfactory, a second application may be made, first removing the beeswax (if any) with turpentine or hexane.

In most cases remarkable results will be achieved, but it is not to be expected that old leather will regain its original degree of suppleness. The important thing is to prevent it from deteriorating any further and improve its appearance.

Shaved or Split Cattle-hide Leather

Objects made from cattle hide, reduced (by hand shaving or machine splitting) to roughly one-third of its natural substance (that is to about 1·5 mm) include travelling and other bags, pouches, purses, suitcases, document cases and wallets, satchels, sheaths, some military equipment and upholstery leather. Most of this vegetable tanned, shaved or split cattle hide is dry dressed. In a few cases such leather may have been lightly fat-liquored or oiled to impart a degree of suppleness, but this will not be obvious and can be ignored in the present context.

Most of the leathers encountered under this heading, if very dirty, can be washed, although water should not be used because this might adversely affect some of the colouring agents employed. A 2% solution of potassium oleate soap in white spirit will probably be effective, but this should be carefully tested on an inconspicuous part. After washing, rinsing and drying at room temperature, the leather should be examined for any sign of red rot, or better still, treated, as a routine measure, with potassium lactate on all accessible su faces as already recommended.

All the leathers in this group will benefit from an application of BML Dressing applied sparingly, except some of the modern 'case' or 'folio' hides with a smooth, shiny surface and the modern upholstery hide which has a sur-face coating of pigmented nitrocellulose for which the cream form can be used. The leathers with a smooth finish which are used for suit- and attaché cases, document cases and the like, will have been given this finish under the pressure of heated metal plates, and washing will probably disturb it. The recommended micro-crystalline wax has excellent cleaning properties and after polishing provides a protective film. Occasionally, leathers in this class may have a matt or 'velvet' finish which are not amenable to BML Dressing but from which surface dust and dirt can be removed with a granular cleaner,[8] the beeswax left on the surface being removed with turpentine or hexane.

Saddle seats, skirts and flaps, which are the principal parts of a saddle, are not all made of the same kind of leather. In addition to various kinds of hide leather, pigskin is used. This is classified as a skin but as it is vegetable tanned it may be included here for convenience. In a riding saddle of hide the seat will have been moulded from fine-quality curried back, probably about 4·5 mm thick, the skirts will be of similar but thinner leather, about 3 mm thick whilst the flaps will also be of similar leather but 3·5–4 mm thick. All these, being made of curried leather, may therefore be dealt with as recommended in the previous section, especially if they are old, and the question of red rot does not arise.

In a so-called pigskin saddle, the seat will be of moulded pigskin, the skirts may be of unbacked pigskin and the flaps are usually of curried hide on which a pigskin grain has been imprinted. The pigskin parts if old, should be treated with BML Dressing applied sparingly. Stirrup leathers and girth straps will usually be of curried leather and also come under the previous section.

Many variations will be found amongst old saddles, notably seats made of doeskin which has a 'velvet' finish. This will usually not require any treatment (being oil dressed) apart from cleaning which can be done with the granular cleaner 'Facteka A'.[8]

Modern saddles in good condition can be treated with 'saddle soap', which is a mixture of beeswax and soap and both feeds and polishes the leather. It is applied sparingly with a damp sponge very evenly, gently rubbed in, left to dry and then polished. It will be found that surface dirt has been transferred to the rubber. At first the leather may look patchy but the blotches will disappear as the moisture dries out leaving a thin film of beeswax on the surface. Saddles showing signs of age and wear are better treated with BML Dressing.

Objects moulded in bovine leather *(cuir bouilli)* include 'bombards' (jugs), 'black jacks' (tankards), bottles, flasks and small containers of many kinds, buckets, fire and other helmets, shields and parts of armour. These are all made of vegetable tanned, dry-dressed cattle hide varying in thickness from about 4 mm down to 2 mm according to the nature and size of the object. They were made by steeping the leather in cold water until it reached a plastic condition, draining and then moulding it into shape over formers of various kinds including those made of wood, clay or sand, or in moulds of wood or plaster. The various parts were then sewn with waxed thread while still damp and the object then set in shape by drying out slowly in a warm place. They have continued to harden with age and through the influence of the pitch or resin with which those intended to hold liquid were lined. They generally appear to be in remarkably good condition, but may have become brittle and should always be treated with care in spite of their apparent robustness. There is little that can be done to such objects, but they should be given an initial application of BML Dressing (to the exterior only). Owing to the extreme hardness full absorption may not occur, but generally sufficient will have entered a little way to afford valuable protection. It is best to leave them for several weeks after which any Lanolin that may remain as a sticky deposit on the surface, should be removed with a sponge moistened with solvent. When quite dry the recommended micro-crystalline wax should be rubbed well in and polished. This should be repeated from time to time.

WARNING. Occasionally, sheaths, boxes and other smallish objects thought to be of *cuir bouilli* may, on examination, be found to have been made of raw hide. These can usually be detected by their exceptional rigidity and by the fact that the surface colouring has worn off at corners and edges, revealing the parchment-like material below. Provided they are not subjected to damp or humid conditions, these will require no attention beyond an occasional application of micro-crystalline wax.

In treating objects having a covering of shaved or split hide or calf leather, stuck to a foundation of wood, paste-board or other material, such as coffers, caskets, boxes and cases *(étuis)*, consideration must be given to the possible effect of water, chemicals, dressings and other restoratives on the foundation material, adhesives, metal components and linings. First, a careful search should be made for any signs of wood-worm. This pest does not normally attack leather but will bore through it in order to get at wood. Treatment can be by fumigation (a job that should be entrusted to specialists) or by injection of one of the proprietary fluids with a hypodermic syringe in every hole. The object must then be laid aside until the fluid is completely absorbed before further treatment can be applied. If the worming is very bad and the foundation in a fragile state it should be completely impregnated with 'Bedacryl' 122X, applied with a hypodermic syringe until no more can be absorbed.[9] If this treatment is used, de-worming is unnecessary as anything living will be irrevocably embedded, like bees in amber. In ancient objects the adhesives will be bone or skin glue or paste (very occasionally, perhaps, casein) which must not be wetted on any account. Cleaning can be done with potassium oleate soap in white spirit, and the objects should be rinsed afterwards with the latter. Paper or textile linings can be cleaned with micro-crystalline wax[6], textile linings with Genklene[10] but if colouring, painting or printing are present, the effect of the solvent must be tried out on an inconspicuous part.[10] If parts of the exterior covering or the lining have come away from the foundation, they should be replaced, before cleaning, using polyvinyl acetate emulsion adhesive ('internally plasticised'), both surfaces being first cleaned.[11] This adhesive requires to be under pressure during setting (say for half-an-hour) and an effective method of applying this should be worked out before the work commences. If this adhesive has been used, Genklene *must not* be used near it as it will have a harmful effect on the adhesive. Finally, the exterior covering, if of leather, should be treated with BML Dressing and then polished. From time to time the surface should be repolished with micro-crystalline wax.

NOTE: Leathers in this class which have a napped (suede) finish require different treatment. See below.

Vegetable Tanned Leather Made from Skins

This section includes leather made from goat, sheep, hair-sheep, pig, peccary and calf (other than 'box-calf' which is mineral tanned). Uses of these leathers are legion but they include pocket-books and wallets, handbags, boxes of many kinds, document cases, leather hangings ('Spanish' or 'Cordovan' leather), and bookbindings.

Probably the most lasting of all the vegetable tanned 'skin' leathers and the most resistant to decay, is *morocco* made from goat skin and traditionally tanned with sumach leaves. Unfortunately, in modern times leather sold as 'morocco' is sometimes tanned with other agents which are not resistant to red rot. The same applies to 'roan', an attractive leather with a long grain, much used in the eighteenth and nineteenth centuries for small leather goods but rarely made now, and Scotch 'basil', a full substance sheepskin, often used for aprons and linings of certain bags. Where red rot is found in 'skin' leathers, the treatment is, as usual, with potassium lactate. With the exception of pigskin which, if in good condition, is perhaps better dealt with by cleaning with saddle soap or micro-crystalline wax, so as not to disturb its attractive colour, all the leathers in this group can be protected with BML Dressing, after a very careful sponging with potassium oleate soap in white spirit, and rinsing. Light colours tend to be very slightly darkened by this dressing but not nearly so much as appears when it is first applied. It should always be applied sparingly and evenly, the object being placed, during the period of absorption, in such a position that all treated parts are free to circulating air. The treatment of 'handbags', the earliest of which (as distinct from the earlier pouches) date back to the beginning of the nineteenth century, presents many problems because of the variety of materials employed in their make-up. Many of the leathers employed can be freshened and protected with micro-crystalline wax. Some, showing signs of wear, can be protected with BML Dressing but particular care must be taken with white or gaily coloured leather which may be alum tawed. The so-called 'kid' gloves of Victorian times, although usually stained brown, were generally of tawed leather on which no water should be used.

For bookbindings the British Museum recommends washing with a barely damp sponge and a little good soap and then rinsing, also with a sponge barely damp with clean water, to remove all traces of soap. When thoroughly dry they should be sponged lightly with a 10% solution of potassium lactate 50/50 in water and the books stood on end until dry. The smallest possible quantity of BML Dressing should be rubbed well into the leather with a cloth, and after about 48 hours the binding should be polished. Elaborately gold tooled bindings must be washed and treated with great care if there is any sign of decay.

Skiver is the name given to the very thin leather (from 0·2 mm to 0·5 mm), nearly always vegetable tanned, formed of the top or grain split of sheepskin and occasionally goatskin. It is finished in an immense range of colours and grains, some of them simulating other leathers, others in more original designs, also with its natural smooth surface. It is used for a wide range of small leather goods and for linings of many kinds of cases and boxes, nearly always stuck to the foundation. Being so thin it is naturally somewhat delicate and because of this it has been the habit of leather workers to apply a coat or 'leather varnish' to the surfaces of objects covered with skiver. This is simply shellac dissolved in methylated spirit, with which it can also be removed if necessary, although great care must be taken not to disturb the surface finish of the leather.[12] Only a thin coat of varnish should be used. Otherwise micro-crystalline wax can be used for both cleaning and polishing.

Reptile leathers vary greatly in tannage, dressing and finishing. Crocodile leather has generally been vegetable tanned. Native-tanned skins brought to western countries are almost invariably re-tanned because the native tannage leaves the skins harsh and unevenly tanned, a prey to red rot, and generally they will not lend themselves to the 'plating' which provides the high polish so much esteemed. If red rot is present it is most difficult to deal with. Potassium lactate can be applied to the flesh side if it is accessible (most unlikely). If it is applied to the surface it will generally not penetrate the hard scales although a little will seep through the soft leather between them. BML Dressing will sometimes penetrate a little and its application can do no harm. A good coating of micro-crystalline wax, repeated from time to time, is advantageous.

Python, watersnake and lizard skins are usually tawed and require little treatment. Cleaning can be undertaken with potassium oleate soap in white spirit or with micro-crystalline wax.

Shagreen, in its best-known form, is made from the skin of a ray fish (*Hypolophus sephen*) that is covered with pearl-like papillae. Since the eighteenth century, these papillae have usually been ground flat leaving the charming mottle pattern, which is emphasised by applying dye to the flesh side of the skin. This does not affect the flattened papillae but seeps through between them. No treatment is necessary apart from occasional polishing with micro-crystalline wax.

23.5.2   OBJECTS MADE OF MINERAL TANNED LEATHER

Tawed with alum and salt

Leather which has been tawed may be used in this state or subjected to further 'dressing'. Leather that has not been dressed is used for tally bags, some gloves, small purses, etc. This leather appears to suffer no deterioration except through water, but in its natural white state it soils readily, especially when it is used flesh side out with the surface sueded. With warm water tawed leather can be reconstituted into the original elements, but it is otherwise long-lasting (tawed leather sandals 3500 years old, from Egypt, are still in perfect condition), not subject to 'red rot' and requires little or no treatment. Alumed leathers are, however, attractive to silver-fish, which are not generally interested in any other kind. If the leather has become stiff it can be softened by kneading if the nature of the object permits. Alternatively, it can be treated with BML Cream Dressing, used very sparingly. This treatment will impart a slightly creamy tint to the leather.

Tawed leather was dressed with grease, oil, flour, egg-yolk, etc. when it was required to have more 'body' and to be very soft and supple. Its uses include gloves, purses, pouches, women's footwear and many other things.

Fashion gloves from the sixteenth century to the eighteenth were, to a large extent, made of dressed tawed goatskin which was called 'cordwain', a corruption of the French *cordouan* that originally indicated the beautiful white leather made in Córdoba after the Moorish invasion of Spain. But, curiously, more often than not this leather was used flesh side outward with a suede finish and generally stained in shades of fawn and grey. This kind of leather is difficult to clean and varies considerably in its response to treatment according to its condition. In the sixteenth and seventeenth centuries both men's and women's fashion gloves often have embroidered cuffs which are very elaborate and embody, in their ornamentation, silk, seed pearls, silver-gilt wire and sequins, which complicate the problem of cleaning. The cleaning and restoration of these cuffs call for special skills and are outside the scope of this article. The leather can be dealt with after carefully covering the cuffs with polythene bags. Suede leather can be cleaned with the proprietary, granular cleaner, Facteka A, or dry carbonate of soda which is carefully rubbed in and then brushed out bringing much dust and dirt with it. It is sometimes possible to remove or reduce stains by dabbing them very carefully with a sponge dipped in potassium oleate soap in white spirit, but only after testing the effect upon colour and finish in an inconspicuous place. It is better to leave marks that are resistant to mild treatment than to risk damaging the leather. Gloves in which the smooth, grain side is outward may be more safely sponged with potassium oleate soap in white spirit, remembering that after the cleaning operation the surface should be equally carefully rinsed with white spirit.

Women's shoes or 'bottines' of tawed leather (sometimes dyed) are always made grain side outward and may be sponged as recommended above. The soles should be examined for any sign of red rot and if there is the least sign, treated with potassium lactate.

Modern White Leathers

Alum tawed leather, to all intents and purposes, is no longer made, its place having been taken by white leathers made by the zirconium or aldehyde processes. Such leathers can be washed with good soap and warm water.

Chrome Tannage

This important mineral process, introduced in 1885 and greatly developed since, has resulted in leather of a completely different character from anything that preceded it. Today, full chrome leather is pale duck-egg blue, highly water-resistant, extremely hard wearing, not subject to red rot, slightly 'empty' in character. It can be finished in various ways but it will not readily lend itself to imprinting or embossing. Its principal use is for footwear upper leather such as 'box' or 'willow' calf (which are used also for other purposes, notably handbags), and glazed kid or goat, with clothing and gloving leathers a close second.

The smooth finish footwear and bag leathers appear, so far, to require no treatment beyond an occasional cleaning and polishing with micro-crystalline wax. The clothing and gloving leathers are, however, different. Those finished to be used on the grain side are usually coloured with pigment 'bound' with cellulose or synthetic resins; they also contain a small amount of oil introduced by the fat-liquoring process, which is an important part of the dressing. The suede finish leathers have a fine nap raised on the flesh side and are dyed by immersion. In the ordinary way the cleaning of garments made of either kind of leather should be entrusted to firms who specialise in this work and have the necessary equipment. If necessary, however, it can be undertaken in the laboratory. The grain leather should be sponged very lightly with potassium oleate soap, 2% in white spirit, and rinsed with the latter. This will probably be all that is necessary but if the leather has lost some of its suppleness it can be sponged very lightly on both sides with a 10% solution of purified neat's-foot oil in Genklene. The suede leathers are more difficult. If only slightly soiled they can be cleaned with Facteka A rubbed well in and then brushed out. If this is not sufficient suede leathers can be washed with potassium oleate soap in white spirit. This will tend to lighten the colour through loss of the natural oil but the normal colour can be restored by a light application of neat's-foot oil, 10% in Genklene. This is best done by spraying but if this is not practicable the solution can be brushed in, care being taken that the application is even.

23.5.3   OBJECTS MADE OF OIL TANNED LEATHER

'Buff' Leather

This term is thought to date back to the time when oil tannage leather of heavy substance, used principally for defensive purposes, was made from the hide of the European buffalo, now extinct. In fact, for some centuries 'buff' leather has been made from cattle, horse and deer hides, the latter usually being called 'doeskin' and used for men's gloves, long boots and saddle seats. These leathers are very tough and lighter in weight than vegetable tanned leather of equivalent substance. As the natural 'grain' layer is 'frized' off to facilitate the entry of oil from both sides, it is not possible to ascertain the nature of the pelt except by microscopic examination.

The 'buff' colour of the leather results from oxidation of the fish or marine animal oil with which the pelts are impregnated and the products of which combine with the fibres, and subsequent washing with soda. It is not always possible to detect with ease which is the grain side and which the flesh, but usually the latter will display some vein or flay marks, and its surface will tend to be coarser than that of the frized grain side. Oil tanned leathers appear not to suffer from red rot, nor are they adversely affected by washing which can be done with either good soap or potassium oleate soap (2%) in water followed by rinsing. As with other leathers having an abraded surface, loose dust and dirt become ingrained, but can be largely removed by rubbing in the proprietary granular cleaner Facteka A and then brushing it out.

'Shammy' or 'Wash' Leather

This was at one time made from antelope skin (from which the ancient name—chamoising—of the process derives), but is today made from the under-splits of sheep and lamb skins, the grain layer of which has been removed, by splitting, to be made into 'skivers'. The process employed is, in principle, similar to that used in making 'buff' leather (see above), although it varies in some details. For example, proper penetration of oil would be brought about by tumbling in drums. These thinner chamoised leathers tend to stiffen up with age and after wetting. Washing should be done with potassium oleate soap in white spirit. They can be softened with a 10% solution of purified neat's-foot oil in Genklene, followed by a careful kneading if the nature of the object permits.

23.6 SUPPLEMENTARY INFORMATION

Fungus

As a general rule fungi affect only vegetable-tanned leathers. An effective treatment both for protection and cure, is to sponge all surfaces with a 10% solution of 'Topane' (orthophenylphenol) in industrial alcohol or methylated spirit. Paranitrophenol is not recommended because, although a good fungicide, it produces a yellow stain that will bleed into adjacent material.

Sunlight

Leather objects should never be allowed to remain in direct sunlight, or for that matter in any very strong light. Apart from the long-term harm this may cause, the colour of certain leathers, particularly those which have been vegetable-tanned and are light in colour, can be seriously affected within a few hours.

Colour

Attempts to restore faded or damaged colour can encounter so many pitfalls and occasion such disastrous results that the safest advice is 'do not try' There are so many kinds of stain and dye that to obtain a match that is satisfactory under all conditions is fraught with the utmost hazard. What may appear an excellent match under one form of lighting may look dreadful under another. The chemical composition of the restoring dye can react on that of the old one and perhaps turn it black.

Adhesive Labels

No form of adhesive label or tape should ever be attached to the surface of leather, particularly the self-adhesive kind which will almost certainly bring away the surface layer when removed, and the older the leather the worse will be the damage.

Varnish

As a general rule the surface of leather should never be varnished if this has not been done previously. Objects which have been varnished may need renewing but this must be done with the same kind of varnish. If over 25 years old they will almost certainly have been coated with shellac varnish; since then, nitrocellulose might have been used. Shellac varnish can be detected by moistening a small corner with methylated spirit. If this brings no reaction try other solvents such as acetone or hexane. Where there is a need for a protective coating where there has been none before, micro-crystalline wax is completely safe and in every way to be preferred to varnish. In special cases the use of a varnish may be essential in which case consideration should be given to the use of a synthetic resin varnish used in the restoration of paintings, such as MS 2A.[12]

NOTES

1. British Museum Leather Dressing: the original formula, intended for leather bookbindings, was:

Lanolin (anhydrous)	200 gr (7 oz)
Beeswax	15 gr ($\frac{1}{2}$ oz)
Cedarwood oil	30 ml (1 fl oz)
Hexane	330 ml (11 fl oz)

Owing to the extension of its use to other purposes, the dressing is now also available with the following modifications and choice should be made according to the circumstances.

(a) with beeswax omitted (for use, for example, on the flesh side of leather or where the grain surface is not to be polished).

(b) with the flammable hexane replaced by non-flammable 1.1.1. trichloroethane (Genklene) rendering it safe for use where other than very small quantities are concerned.

The above are marketed under the name Pliantine.

(c) in cream form emulsified with water instead of a hydrocarbon solvent. Marketed as Pliancreme.

All the above are obtainable from Arthur Rich & Partners Ltd., 42 Mount Pleasant Drive, Belper, Derbyshire, England

2. Carbowax 1500, obtainable from Union Carbide Limited, 8 Grafton Street, London, W.1

3. Hexane: an aromatic hydrocarbon, highly flammable, immiscible in water, toxic; the solvent originally used in British Museum Leather Dressing (see above) but in this and other applications it can be advantageously replaced by the non-flammable, low toxicity, Genklene (1.1.1. trichloroethane) made by Imperial Chemical Industries Ltd.

4. Potassium lactate, supplied as a 50% solution in water; for use dilute 1 part with 9 parts of water. Obtainable from Hopkin & Williams Limited, Chadwell Heath, Essex, England

5. Potassium oleate soap (liquid): marketed under the name Vulpex by Picreator Enterprises Ltd., 44 Park Gardens, London N.W.4

6. Micro-crystalline wax, National Gallery formula:

Cosmolloid wax 80.H	200 gr (7 oz)
BASF 'A' wax	50 gr ($1\frac{3}{4}$ oz)
White spirit	700 ml (24 fl oz)

Cut the waxes into small pieces. Melt the Cosmolloid to 120°C in a suitable vessel on an electric hotplate, then add the BASF and stir until well mixed. Pour into the white spirit and stir until cool.

Wax made to the above formula is marketed under the name Renaissance by Picreator Enterprises Ltd., 44 Park Gardens, London N.W.4. There is also a modified form which contains inhibitors of moulds and metal corrosion

7. Neat's-foot oil; 'low cold test'

8. Facteka A granular cleaner. Obtainable from Durham Raw Materials Limited, 1–4 Great Tower Street, London E.C.3

9. Bedacryl 122X. A clear, colourless, polymethacrylic ester sometimes used as a varnish but not recommended as such for leather. Supplied as a viscous fluid which, as a filler, can be used neat, or it can be diluted with xylene. Obtainable from Edward Gurr Limited, 42 Upper Richmond Road West, London S.W.14

10. Carbon tetrachloride should not be used on leather as it is harmful to some kinds. It is also highly toxic. For cleaning traditional textiles and some papers, some prefer Genklene (1.1.1. trichloroethane), which is also a solvent for oils, grease, rubber and bitumen but much less toxic than carbon tetrachloride. An ICI product obtainable from Frederick Allen & Sons (Chemicals) Limited, Upper North Street, London, E.14

11. Polvinyl-acetate emulsion adhesive for museum use must be 'internally plasticised' to ensure that it will remain stable. Recommended is No. WS 11 made by National Adhesives Ltd., and marketed by Williams Adhesives, 165 The Crescent, Chelvey, Slough, Buckinghamshire, England

12. MS 2A, from Laporte Industries, Ilford, Essex, England. For stock solution dissolve 50 gr of resin in 100 ml of white spirit; this dries with a bright finish. The film can be removed, if necessary, by friction or with white spirit; a matt finish can be obtained by the following formula: take 18 ml of the stock solution, dissolve 7 gr Cosmolloid Wax 80H (see note 6) in 150 ml white spirit by warming and add to the stock solution with vigorous stirring

Biographies and Contributors

Anne Buck
Gallery of English Costume, Manchester City Art Galleries, Platt Hall, Manchester, M 14. 5LL

Anne Buck, B.A., F.M.A. British. In 1947 she was appointed Keeper of the Gallery of English Costume, Platt Hall, Manchester. She is the author of *Handbook for Museum Curators: Costume*, published in 1958.

C. A. Burgers
Department of Sculpture and Applied Art, Rijksmuseum, Amsterdam.

Cornelis Adriaen Burgers. Dutch. Formerly director of a linen manufactory, he is now Assistant Keeper at the Department of Sculpture and Applied Art, Rijksmuseum, Amsterdam. Mr. Burgers is a specialist on white linen damasks.

Johanna M. Diehl
Workshop for Restoration of Ancient Textiles, Leidseplein 36zw, Haarlem (Netherlands).

Johanna Diehl. Dutch. Graduated in chemical engineering at the Delft University of Technology in 1935. She worked subsequently as scientific assistant at this University. From 1943 until 1 July 1971 she has been scientist on the staff of the Workshop for Restoration of Ancient Textiles at Haarlem.

   Johanna Diehl has published five papers on restoration of tapestries and flags.

G. Ekstrand
Kungliga Livrustkammaren (The Royal Armoury), Stockholm (Sweden).

Gudrun Ekstrand. Ph.L. Swedish. Miss Ekstrand is Keeper at the Kungliga Livrustkammaren in Stockholm, and has published several articles on costumes and textiles in the periodical of the Museum, *Livrustkammaren, Journal of the Royal Armoury* (1955–57, 1958–60, 1961–63, 1964–66, 1967–69) and in *Waffen- und Kostümkunde* (1968)

K. S. Finch
Private restorer of textiles. 7 Western Gardens, London, W.5.

Karen Finch (British) obtained her Diploma in textile design and weaving from the Kunst-haandvaerkerskolen in Copenhagen. She is a Fellow of I.I.C. While living in the museum of Applied Art in Copenhagen, she became interested in conservation and developed this interest on coming to England and being employed at the Royal School of Needlework (London). Later she was a member of the Conservation Department of the Victoria and Albert Museum. Since 1959 Karen Finch has had her own studio for the conservation of textiles.

H. J. Gowers
Department of Ethnography, British Museum, London.

Harold J. Gowers (British) commenced work at the British Museum in 1939 with a background training in Art. He studied conservation under the Research Laboratory at the British Museum and carried out conservation in the Department of Ethnography. At present he is Senior Conservation Officer, and specialises in organic materials.

   He has published articles in *Studies in Conservation* and *British Museum Quarterly*.

D. Heinz
Austrian Museum of Applied Art, Vienna.

Dora Heinz (born Bruck) (Austrian) obtained her Ph.D. at the University of Vienna in 1948. Since 1949 she has worked at the Oesterreichisches Museum für Angewandte Kunst in Vienna, first as Keeper and then as Head of its Textile Collections.

She is also Lecturer in History of the Art of Textiles at the Academy for Applied Art, and Consultant of the Oesterreichisches Bundesdenkmalamt in Vienna. Since 1950 Dr. Heinz has published many papers on textile art, textile history, tapestries and carpets.

Dr. H. J. Hueck
Department of Biology, Central Laboratory TNO, 97 Schoemakerstraat, P.O. Box 217, Delft.

Dr. H. J. Hueck (Dutch) is Head of the Department of Biology, Central Laboratory TNO, 97 Schoemakerstraat, Delft, The Netherlands. His main interest is in (applied) entomology and mycology. Since 1951 he has held a position in the Organisation for Applied Scientific Research (TNO) in The Netherlands where he is engaged in studies of the biodeterioration of materials. The protection of textiles against biotic influences initially constituted the main problem. In 1961, at the request of the Organisation for Economic Cooperation and Development in Paris, he organised an International Working Group of Experts, now continuing independent of the OECD as the International Biodegradation Research Group, of which he is president. Dr. Hueck has published several papers on biodeterioration of textiles and other materials.

H. Jedrzejewska
Research Laboratory at the Department of Antiquities in the National Museum in Warsaw (Poland).

Hanna Jedrzejewska (Polish) obtained her Ph.D. in physical chemistry at the University of Warsaw in 1930. From 1950 to 1958 she was lecturer in chemistry and theoretical technology for students of conservation at the Academy of Fine Arts. In 1956 she was nominated as assistant professor in matters of scientific conservation, and from 1957 to 1969 was Head of the Research Laboratory at the Department of Antiquities in the National Museum in Warsaw. She became a Fellow of I.I.C. in 1959.

Since 1958 Dr. Jedrzejewska has been interested in the conservation of textiles, especially of Coptic and archaeological textiles, and has published several papers in this field.

Her present address is Solec 109ª/39, Warsaw, Poland.

J. G. Kerkhoven
Nederlands Leger- en Wapenmuseum 'Generaal Hoefer', Leiden.

Jacob G. Kerkhoven (Dutch) graduated in history at the University of Utrecht. He is now conservator of the collections of uniforms, flags, colours, medals and documentation on military history at the Netherlands Army Museum.

Jacob Kerkhoven is author of a number of publications on mediaeval and military history, on the restoration of Spanish and French flags of the sixteenth and eighteenth centuries, and on the manufacture of Waterloo mannequins.

S. B. Landi
Conservation of Textiles Department of the Victoria and Albert Museum, London.

Mrs. Sheila B. Landi (British) obtained her National Diploma of Design in Painting in 1950, followed by a 3-year post-diploma course at the Royal Academy Schools. Member of the Conservation of Textiles Department of the Victoria and Albert Museum since 1963, she has found her practical painters' training has stood her in good stead for the handling of textiles.

Mrs Landi has published two papers in *Studies in Conservation* on textile conservation and lightfastness of natural dyes. She is co-author of a pamphlet to be issued by H.M. Stationery Office on *The Conservation of the State Bed from Erthig House.*

A. C. van der Leeden
The Indonesian Department, National Museum of Ethnology, Leiden.

A. C. van der Leeden (Dutch) obtained his Ph.D. at Leiden University. From 1960 to 1969 he was curator of the Indonesian Department, National Museum of Ethnology, Leiden. In December 1969 Dr van der Leeden was appointed lecturer on the staff of the Institute of Cultural Anthropology, Catholic University, Nijmegen.

Jentina E. Leene
Laboratory for Textile Technology, Mekelweg 2, Delft University of Technology.

Dr. Leene (Dutch) received her D.Sc. in 1938. She is Senior Reader in Fibre Technology at the Delft University of Technology.

A member of the Council of the Centre International d'Etude des Textiles Anciens and of the Council of I.I.C., and member of the Advisory Committee for the Central Research Laboratory for Objects of Art and Science (Amsterdam), Dr. Leene is also Adviser of the Board of the Restoration Workshop for Ancient Textiles (Haarlem) and President of the Textile Committee on behalf of Dutch Museums. In 1964 she presided over the 1964 I.I.C. Delft Conference on Textile Conservation.

Dr. Leene has published fourteen papers and reports on textile conservation, ageing of textiles, ageing of adhesives used in textile conservation, and archaeological textiles.

J. Lodewijks
Central Research Laboratory for Objects of Art and Science, Gabriel Metsustraat 8, Amsterdam.

Johan Lodewijks (Dutch) graduated in chemical engineering at the Delft University of Technology in 1956. He is now Director of the Central Research Laboratory for Objects of Art and Science in Amsterdam.

Mr Lodewijks is a member of the Directory Board of the ICOM Committee on Conservation, and Coordinator of the working group on textile conservation of the aforementioned ICOM Committee. He is also a Fellow of I.I.C. and a member of the Centre International d'Etude des Textiles Anciens, Arbeitsgemeinschaft des Deutschen Technischen Museums personals, the Netherlands Museums Association, and of the Directory Board of the Netherlands I.C.O.M.O.S.

Mr. Lodewijks has published seven papers on textile conservation and restoration.

P. M. Mäder
The Swiss National Museum, Zürich.

Peter Marcel Mäder (Swiss) is by profession an interior decorator. He followed courses at the School of Arts and Crafts in Zürich, and then undertook further training at the Textile Schools in St. Gallen and Zürich. He subsequently made extensive educational journeys to Sweden, Holland, France, Germany and the United States. Since 1964 he has been textile restorer and manager of the Department for Conservation of Military Textiles at the Swiss National Museum, Zürich.

J. W. Rice
Col. James W. Rice, Consultant in Textile Chemistry and Engineering, Textile Museum, Washington, D.C.

James W. Rice, U.S.A. Retired. Col. Rice obtained his B.S. degree from the University of Nevada, Reno, Nevada; and his M.S. degree from M.I.T., Cambridge, Mass. He started his career as an Officer in the Chemical Corps, U.S. Army, retiring as Colonel. He then took up an appointment as instructor in Textile Chemistry and Engineering, at the National Institute of Drycleaning, Silver Spring, Md., and later became Director of Research, of the National Institute of Rug Cleaning, Bethesda, Md. Col. Rice is at present Consultant in Textile Chemistry and Engineering, at the Textile Museum, Washington D.C., and for the Division of Museums, U.S. Park Service, Springfield, Virginia.

Col. Rice has published over sixteen papers on cleaning and textile conservation science in the *Textile Museum Journal*, and also some in *Studies in Conservation*, as well as a paper on 'How to Dry Rugs—Air Engineering for Rug Cleaners', for the National Institute of Rug Cleaning (1957).

M. J. Taxinha
Textile Department of the Instituto de José de Figueiredo, Lisbon.

Maria José Taxinha (Portuguese) was trained as a technical restorer in the Instituto de José de Figueiredo, Lisbon. She then received special training at the Restoration Workshop for Gobelins (Royal Palace) and at the Historiska Museet in Stockholm, followed by an advanced technical course in analysis of ancient textiles, organised by the Centre International d'Étude des Textiles Anciens. She is now chief restorer and an Associate of I.I.C. and a member of C.I.E.T.A., and belongs to the working group of the Portuguese version of the C.I.E.T.A.

Maria José Taxinha has published several papers on conservation of lace and tapestries.

Garry Thomson
The National Gallery, Trafalgar Square, London W.C.2.

Garry Thomson (British) obtained his M.A. from Cambridge. In 1951 he joined the editorial staff of the late Dr. Charles Singer to work on the production of the first two volumes of *A History of Technology*, to which he has contributed. He was Research Chemist at the National Gallery from 1955 to 1960 and was appointed Scientific Adviser in 1960. He was Editor of *Studies in Conservation* from 1959 to 1967, and is now Editor of *Technical Publications* and a council member of I.I.C. He has carried out missions for Unesco, mostly related to environment control, in Bulgaria, Romania, Jamaica and Egypt. He is Coordinator on Lighting to the ICOM Committee for Conservation, and author of *Control of the Museum Environment* (I.I.C.), and has contributed articles on lighting and air pollution to *Studies in Conservation*, and other journals. Mr. Thomson was also Editor of *Recent Advances in Conservation* (Butterworths, 1963), and *Museum Climatology* (I.I.C., 1968).

F. Visser
Workshop for Restoration of Ancient Textiles, Leidseplein, 36zw (Haarlem), Netherlands.

F. Visser (Dutch) was trained as a painter during World War II. After the war he was engaged at the Workshop for Restoration of Ancient Textiles at Haarlem as restorer, and since 1949 as chief restorer.

John W. Waterer
The Museum of Leathercraft, London.

John W. Waterer (British) is an R.D.I. (Royal Designer for Industry), F.S.A. (Fellow of the Society of Antiquaries of London) and A.I.I.C. (Association of the International Institute for the Conservation of Historic & Artistic Works). Publications include *Leather: in Life, Art & Industry* (1946), the article on leather in *A History of Technology* (1956), *Leather and Craftsmanship* (1968), and *Spanish Leather* (1971). One-time designer and producer of luggage and leather goods, he is Honorary Secretary and Conservator of the Museum of Leathercraft, London and Walsall.

Index